"Joe Robinson is a true inspiration."

—**Brian Grazer**, Producer *A Beautiful Mind*
and Co-Chair Imagine Entertainment

"We searched long and hard to find the right trainer
to help us with the uncertainties ahead. Joe Robinson
was the best choice we could have made."

—**Linda Sellan**, Nestle Global

"Joe Robinson hit a home run for our team."

—**Ron Moeller**, MedQuest

"Talk about speaking the truth. It was like being in church with
all the 'Amen's' and 'YESes.' Joe is an inspiration, and we have
all committed to making personal changes after his keynote!"

—**Robyn Garrett**, Georgia Assoc. of Community Service Boards

"Joe's keynote was fantastic! Our team raved about the
session—and folks are still talking about it days later. Joe
provided them with effective, tangible tools to combat stress.
We will be recommending Joe's work to everyone!

—**Michelle Smith**, Bliss Point Media

"Joe did a great job engaging the audience through different exercises
and breakout groups. It was a great session, and our group learned
a lot of useful tactics to bring to the company. Thank you, Joe!"

–**Adena Barber**, Ocean Spray

D0989021

Work Smarter Live Better

The Science-Based
Work-Life Balance and
Stress Management Toolkit

JOE ROBINSON

2022

Published by Joe Robinson
Roadworks Press
www.worktolive.info
joe@worktolive.info

First Edition 2022

Copyright © 2022 by Joe Robinson
Book Design: Pablo Capra
Cover Design: Susan Dworski | theblueone.com
Cover Photo: fsstock
Back Cover Photo: Michael Justice
All rights reserved. This book, or parts thereof, may not be
reproduced in any form without permission.

LIBRARY OF CONGRESS CATALOGING-IN-PUBLICATION DATA

Robinson, Joe
Work Smarter, Live Better/Joe Robinson
Includes bibliographical references and index. ISBN 978-0-578-89940-4
1. Work-life balance 2. Stress management 3. Burnout 4.
Resilience 5. Positive emotions 6. Life satisfaction
I. Title
Library of Congress Control Number: 2021915875

Printed in the United States of America

For Marcia, the heart of my life balance

Contents

Acknowledgments xi
Introduction 1

CHAPTER 1
You Are Not a Hard Drive with Hair 7
Exit Overwhelm and Triage, Enter Smarter Work

CHAPTER 2
What Is Work-Life Balance, Anyway? .15
Identify the Work-Life You Need

CHAPTER 3
You Can't Control the Wind, But You Can Adjust the Sails. 39
Set Boundaries on an Unbounded World

CHAPTER 4
Stay Calm in the Storm. 65
Reframe Reflex Stress & the Thoughts That Drive It

CHAPTER 5
The Hidden Blowback of Stress and Burnout 95
Fight Back with the Best Stress-Busting Strategies

CHAPTER 6
Be Quick, But Don't Hurry. 132
Opt Out of Time Urgency and Reflex Rushing

CHAPTER 7
Set the Terms of Engagement 150
Control Devices, Distractions, and Interruptions

CHAPTER 8
The Power of Possibility. 184
Build the Engine of Resilience: Optimism

CHAPTER 9
The Upside of Positive Emotions. 209
Multiply Performance, Success and Happiness

CHAPTER 10
The Refueling Principle. 225
Recharge, Renew, Reset

CHAPTER 11
Life's Out There, If You Are. 248
Activate Life Skills

Notes 277
Bibliography 289
Index. 300
About the Author 310

"This is the real secret of life—to be completely engaged with what you are doing in the here and now."

— ALAN WATTS

Acknowledgments

One of the things that comes across clearly in the science is the importance that others play in our seemingly solitary struggle on the road of making a living. Whether it's a friend, a friend of a friend, a colleague, a contact, their guidance, direction, good humor, or friendship is crucial along a path that doesn't always have a clear route but does have plenty of challenges.

I'd like to acknowledge those who made it possible for me to bring these pages to you. My parents, John and Helen Robinson, against their better judgment, encouraged me to follow my enthusiasms, gave me the freedom to do so, and taught me what really matters in a world of external goals. Many thanks to my wife and partner in adventure, Marcia, for the encouragement, love, and making sure life would never be dull. *Te amo.*

I'm very grateful to the multi-talented Susan Dworski, who designed the cover of the book, and David Dworski, who helped me light out for the speaking territories. Thanks to Pablo Capra for his superb work on the design and formatting of the book.

Great to team up again with *Escape* artist Jordan Rane—thanks for a clutch editing job on the manuscript. Thanks to Jeff Sievert for the quotes, brainstorms, and support on many a journey without maps; Ran Klarin for the mindful and musical balance; Marty Herman for his salsa tutelage and always stalwart support; and Chris McGowan for his encouragement to follow this path and for inducting me into the samba schools of Rio de Janeiro.

My special thanks go to the real heroes of this book, the scientists around the world whose research maps the way forward for all of us to a happier, more effective, and sustainable path to success. If you can, check out some of their amazing studies listed in the bibliography—fascinating work. They deserve our appreciation for the critical work they do.

I appreciate the early encouragement for my work from Shari Morwood, formerly with IBM Research, and Sue Baechler of Originaliti. com. Thanks to Linda Sellan of Nestle, Robyn Garrett of the Georgia Assoc. of Community Service Boards, and Adena Barber of Ocean Spray for their support and spreading the word.

I'd like to thank all the people who reached out from their organizations to connect with me and bring my work-life balance and stress management programs to their team, department or company, and, of course, all the participants in my trainings and keynotes who have welcomed me so warmly, laughed mostly at the right times, and made the proceedings so interactive and fun. I feel very fortunate to be able to do this work, to bring the good news from the science that can help us work and live more skillfully. It's very gratifying to be able to help. I love my job.

I write mostly with jazz in my ears. Music aids concentration, but it has to be instrumental music (lyrics distract). Not only does music order thought, as you will learn in the pages ahead, which makes it easier to focus, but it is also the greatest mood elevator. As I was writing this book, and especially the chapter on positive emotions, it was clear that the great artists I was listening to—Gerald Clayton, Edward Simon, Amina Figarova, Billy Childs, Aaron Parks, Brad Mehldau, Chick Corea, Herbie Hancock, Joey Calderazzo, John Coltrane, Snarky Puppy, Javier Santiago, Robert Glasper and Pat Metheny—were doing for me exactly what I was writing about in the chapter—increasing my positive emotion count—my positivity ratio—and with it my energy, clarity and vitality. Positive emotions broaden and build emotional resources, so I want to thank these musicians for powering me across the finish line. Please support the musical artists who lift up your life. They lead us in an instant out of the worry wilderness to the counterbalancing realms of joy, beauty, soul, and discovery.

And thank you too for coming along on this journey to a more gratifying experience of work and life.

Introduction

Now that you are sitting down, I would like you to stand up for a little pre-reading exercise. It's simple. Just stand alongside your chair or sofa, lift one foot off the ground and balance on the other foot. How did that go? Not too difficult, is it?

Well, we're going to step up the challenge. I want you to try to balance on one foot with your eyes closed. Make sure to open your eyes if you get too wobbly. We don't want any casualties before we even get to Chapter 1.

It's tricky, isn't it? It's difficult to be balanced when you have your eyes closed, but that is effectively what's happening when we are not paying attention to *how* we work—to our work style. What's a work style? That's something we never think about, is it?

No, we get the skills of our profession but are never taught how to work in the most productive way based on what the scientific data actually says. So, what do we do? Most of the time we just react to stuff all day long—other people, other people's crisis mentality, devices, interruptions, pressure, deadlines. That's our work style. It's all reflex, retaliatory, without awareness.

Acting before we think plays right into the hands of the autopilot of stress and burnout. Both are about reacting before we think, and they drive us down the road to the Burnout Model—just keep going until the paramedics arrive. Unfortunately, they are arriving, so we need a healthier, and obviously more effective, approach.

Any engineer can tell you that even the strongest materials pull apart subjected to the right amount of force and load. That is also true for people. We've always had a hard time knowing when to say when in a culture in which we define ourselves through labor more than anything else. This tendency has only been intensified by unbounded, always-on technology and the nonstop email and digital interruptions that come with it, which are driving cognitive overload, chronic stress, and the growing epidemic of burnout, the last stage of chronic stress.

The three-way shutdown of burnout—mentally, physically, and emotionally—is not a productivity strategy. Anything that drains energy, motivation, and the attention of a focused mind is counterproductive, all the research shows.

What's needed more than ever today is a style of work that is actually based on something, something proven in the research to be productive. I call it sustainable performance, a work style that allows you to manage demands, instead of having them manage you; set boundaries on an unbounded world; make adjustments to how you do your work that cut stress; and recharge regularly to keep brain and body sharp and life on the agenda.

The central skill of sustainable performance is attention, which is under siege from all sides these days. At its core is awareness, the ability to maintain presence of mind in the fray and not go off the reactive deep end. The research says that attention is your chief productivity tool, life tool, and happiness tool. The more of it you have the less stress you have, since that tends to be in the other two tenses you are not in.

And that's not all. The more attention you have the faster you get tasks done, the more you like what it is that you are doing, and the longer you remember it. When your skills meet a challenge while in full absorption in the task at hand, you can have an optimal experience, also known as flow, in which all worries and concerns drop away and you ride the moment of synchronicity. In other words, your thoughts and deeds are one, which makes you as happy as a husky gulping air out the window of a passing car.

You can't bring awareness and attention to the job, though, unless you are able to manage their commanders—the mind and the thoughts in it. Most of the time in a time-urgent, overloaded world, the mind is not in charge. Reflex reactions and the certifiable thoughts and false beliefs they stir up are.

An old folk tale illustrates what happens to two different trees when snowfall weighs on their branches. If too much snow stacks up on the branch of a pine tree, the weight can snap it right off. Pine branches are rigid and don't have any give. However, the branches of the willow tree can't be defeated by snow because they bend and spring back. They are agile. Our minds need to be like the willow tree branches and bend with the pressures bearing down on us—or we break.

Emotional reactions make minds rigid, stuck with false explanations served up by a host of counterproductive beliefs we don't even know we have. There are surface beliefs, such as taking everything personally or its opposite, always blaming someone else. There are thinking traps and "icebergs," beliefs buried within us (*I shouldn't need any help*) that self-inflict stress and prevent solutions.

As Nobel Prize-winning psychologist Daniel Kahneman has put it, "We are very influenced by completely automatic things that we have no control over, and we don't know we're doing it."

To manage the reflex mind that undermines attention and leads to stress, burnout, and lives missing in action, you need an agile mind, one that is open, flexible, and able to deal with pressure and demands through problem-solving, not emotional reactions. A mindful work style allows you to bend with the demands and stay focused on solutions. The chapters ahead will show you how to do that.

This book brings you the tools of sustainable performance that I teach in my work-life balance and stress management employee trainings and keynotes for organizations around the country and world, from IBM to Pfizer, Amazon and Ocean Spray, to Truman Medical Center in Kansas City, New York City Public Health, and the Reserve Bank of India. You will get strategies from the science to increase attention, reduce disruptions, work smarter, improve mental health, boost wellness, and build better work-life balance.

Work-life balance is often thought of as a perk. As you will learn, it's no less than who you are, built into your very physiology. You are designed to have the mind and systems of the body functioning in effective alignment with one another. The activation system of the autonomic nervous system, for instance, is counterbalanced by the rest-and-digest functions of the parasympathetic nervous system. Positive emotions are the offset for negative emotions and help us bounce back from difficulties.

The struggle is to be the balanced characters we are supposed to be by nature. What can help are strategies that allow you to end the work-life conflict that comes from trying to be in two different places at the same time—feeling guilty when you are working and not taking care of home issues and at home feeling like you should be getting work done.

The solution is more concentrated attention wherever you are. When you are at work, you can be 100% there, and when you're at home, you can have 100% of your mind on that. That's the kind of balance we are aiming for in these pages.

This way you don't have the guilt nag bearing down when you get a spare moment to relax. You can devote all your energies to the project at work when you are there. You don't have to rack your brain for the last time you had fun or a great vacation. You actually have a bathing suit.

Sustainable performance helps you manage your most precious commodity—time, inside and outside the office, and not burn it up on the false alarms of overreaction, busyness, overwhelm, and hurry-worry. When we work and live on autopilot, time is something to be filled, by to-dos, meetings, email, texts, errands. There is little thought given to why we're doing the task or where it's going. We plow ahead in mechanical momentum without using our time on this planet wisely.

It's easy to lose touch with the skills and goals outside the frenzy of the workweek—curiosity, play, exploration. These realms we rush past are crucial for core needs and life satisfaction and are the engine of the positive outlook and vitality that fuel productivity. Life satisfaction and job satisfaction are a team.

The goal is to shift out of the filling time routine to fulfilling time—at work and life beyond work. The answer to stress, distractions, and life postponement is a work style focused, not on trying to do three things at once (since multitasking is a myth, as you will learn) but on informed, conscious performance of the matter in front of you.

Carving out work-life balance is a matter of proactive self-management—a series of adjustments to tasks, schedules, and time after the workday ends. You are the entrepreneur of your life, and only you can make it happen by initiating changes that help you feel more in control of your schedule at work and at home.

Activating a gratifying life takes a skillset most adults don't have, something beyond the work mindset. It's a different goal structure—intrinsic, meaning you act for no payoff, very different from the output metric. The reward is internal, and that makes it something essential to self-worth and happiness, which is a function of populating memories with a steady stream of positive experiences. A fabulous study by Kennon Sheldon of the University of Missouri and Sonja Lyubomirsky of the University of California Riverside found that "the more positive and novel the recent experiences you can remember, the higher one will rate one's happiness."

During the Covid-19 pandemic we all got a very intense lesson in what happens when the stream of positive experiences supplied by the world beyond the office stops. Suddenly all the things that brought joy, fun, and connection—social activities with family and friends, eating out, going to concerts, travel—were gone, replaced by isolation and seclusion. The experience hammered home how important those things are and that we should never take them for granted again, since they constitute the living we are making for ourselves. We were also reminded just how precious this realm of life is. There are a lot more minds focused on that and the necessity of work-life balance to help us get there.

You will learn in these pages how a more effective work style offers the path forward. When you make adjustments to tasks that push coping systems and hours to the limit, you can cut stress and open up more time and inclination for life opportunities.

All you need to do to get there is follow the science. Scientists are hard at work at universities and labs across the nation and the world finding practices that increase performance and health, boost motivation, build the attention we need to counter the barrage of distractions and intrusions, activate recharging and life skills, and help us get out of our own way.

In the pages ahead, you will learn from their research how to reframe stress, challenge false beliefs, keep messaging from running amok, get time urgency under control, and increase your focus. One of my favorite parts is our journey through the science of optimism, which is crucial to bouncing back from tough events and building resilience and positive emotions. You will learn how something you may never have heard of before, explanatory style—how you explain why bad things happen to you—is one of the most critical things you can know.

As I think back to all the people I've led work-life trainings for, from offices high above the Big Apple in New York City to church halls in small towns in rural Michigan, to medical classrooms in Texas, to hotel conference halls in Bend, Oregon, Mumbai, India, Bogota, Colombia, Cabo San Lucas, Baja California and Phoenix, to hospital auditoriums in Laporte, Indiana and Pittsburgh, to federal agency conference rooms in Washington, D. C., to dental offices in Honolulu, what I'm struck by is how hard folks work everywhere. The work ethic is alive and very well.

The vast majority of us go to the mat every day to get the work done right, but the lack of boundaries, ceaseless messaging, and overload are taking a huge toll.

People tell me they think there's something wrong with them, because they can't keep up. But it's not them, it's the wall of physiological limits, as real as the one that hits marathon runners at the 18- to 20-mile marks. You want to do a great job, because it's part of your identity in the land of a ferocious work ethic. Yet there's more to do than can be done in a given day and increasingly less space to carve out for nonwork and recharging. It's harder and harder to leave work at work, so it comes home in the form of endless email and the mental replay of the day's events.

These pages will help with that. You'll get some great strategies from the science of work recovery, which says that you have to detach yourself from work—and thoughts of work—when the workday is done. If you don't switch off after work, recovery from the day's stress doesn't happen, and it comes back to work with you the next day, along with negative affect, better known as bad mood. Stress suppresses the play equipment in your brain, so it's very hard to activate life and fun without unplugging from the strained brain.

The stats say you spend about 30% of your life at work (and another 30% sleeping). That's a big chunk of your time on this planet, so it's crucial to be smart in how you spend your workday, so you have the energy and desire to utilize the remaining 40% for something other than passing out on the recliner.

Work is an epic journey that tests wits, patience, resilience, and resourcefulness in the face of constant technological change, economic volatility, and digital velocity. You need all the resources and strategies you can muster to take that on. These pages will give you tools to work more sustainably, pull less hair out along the way, and put that thing we're all working for, life, on the calendar. Remember that?

CHAPTER 1

You Are Not a Hard Drive with Hair

Exit Overwhelm and Triage, Enter Smarter Work

Since he lacks the android capabilities needed to answer the 250-plus emails he gets each day in business hours, Brian, a VP for a large tech firm in San Diego, gets up at 5 a.m. every morning and spends two hours plowing through messages at home before he goes to work. "It just seems futile some days," he says, "like I can never dig out."

In Denver, Susan, a financial advisor, has been at wits' end from 10- to 12-hour days that have left her so exhausted when she comes home at night, all she can do is pull out a frozen dinner and shove it in the micro.

Once able to outwork anyone, she's now running on empty. "I can't work any harder, but I still can't meet my financial goals," she says. She doesn't know what to do, since working harder and longer, her instinctive option, isn't working, and she can't go down that track any longer. "I don't eat right, don't exercise, don't do stuff with friends."

It's a pattern easy to fall into these days. In a nonstop digital world, reflexes are not your best friend. They lead to reacting to the incoming, instead of managing the practices that drive the overload. The default is to go at it harder and harder without real thought.

It reminds me of an old Monty Python Flying Circus comedy sketch, "Argument Clinic," an absurd bit in which a guy goes to a clinic specializing in verbal brawls, but he enters the wrong room and is immediately hit on the head. He shrieks and says, "But I've come to have an argument." He is informed that the room he's in is "Being Hit on the Head Lessons." It's an apt analogy for what can happen to our noggins—and the thoughts and attention in them—when we work without awareness.

The problem with the harder metric is that it quickly gets to a point where it's not viable, since it leads to inevitable blowback from stress and the fatigue and negative emotions it generates. Studies show that increased stress leads to reduced productivity and job satisfaction, as work overlaps with personal life, increasing burdens and fanning resentment.

Stress increases the more strain we feel from the workload, one of the reasons longer hours multiply the risk of major health problems, which undercut performance and run up medical costs. Working more than 55 hours a week increases the risk of stroke by 33% and coronary heart disease, which we all know as heart disease, by 13%, stress researcher Mika Kivimaki and colleagues reported in one study.

We don't have to go down this path, though, because we can work smarter and carve out a better quality of life when we set boundaries to keep overload at bay and bring more attention to what we do.

The Constrained Brain

Unfortunately, work-life balance is not the default in an always-on world. Instead, the reflex is to go at it as if we came equipped with four arms and heads. No doubt we could get a lot more done that way, but we remain strapped with a single preoccupied brain, two arms, and a lot of limitations we don't know we have that make it even more apparent why we need work-life balance.

Like, for instance, how long your brain can stay on task. fMRI scans of fatigued brains look exactly like ones that are sound asleep. After two to three hours of continuous time on task, studies show we need to get off task, because mental fatigue has taken over. We need to step back to reboot, or the brain spaces out, self-distracts, or wanders in circles.

The reality is humans don't have silicon chips, only Red Bull and Starbucks. It may seem like we can go all day and night, because most of us are just sitting on our butts all day, but scientists say the brain goes down well before the body.

This is because of the many mental limits we have compared with digital hardware. It takes a tremendous amount of energetic resources for you to stay on task, remain disciplined, and hold thoughts in mind without deviating to something easier. Yet the attention you need to get the job done is a highly constrained resource.

Let's start with working memory, also known as short-term memory, which is what you use to get anything done in your day. You can only hang on to three or four thought "chunks," or associations, at one time and only for a few seconds. It's very tenuous.

Interruptions and intrusions from email, texts, and notifications blow up working memory, and it takes time to retrieve those germinal thought chunks, which slows performance more than 40%, according to University of Michigan multitasking expert David Meyer.

You also have self-regulation limits that affect very key parts of performance: self-control and willpower. Staying on task takes discipline to override emotions, impulses, and desires. Some researchers say that every act of discipline makes the next one harder, since we use up self-regulation resources in the process, namely, blood glucose.

And, of course, you have demand limits—stress. When demands outstrip perceived control over them, an ancient part of the brain hijacks modern faculties and initiates the stress response. That undermines intellect, impulse control, and decision-making, which sabotages performance and drives mistakes and conflict.

When we ignore the limits of attention, we get caught up in the habits of unsustainable performance and wind up throwing our bodies at a 24/7 world. Sustainable performance recognizes mortal limits and curbs excesses. Productivity comes from brains and bodies that aren't maxed out. Recharging and refueling are central to bring alertness and attention to the task at hand.

That's the idea of work-life balance, which provides opportunities to access the parts of life that restore energy and vitality, infuse positive emotions, and gratify core needs. People who feel they have good work-life balance work 21% harder than those who don't, reports the Corporate Executive Board, which represents about 80% of the *Fortune* 500.

One study documented that shares of publicly traded companies increased $60 million per firm after the companies initiated work-life balance policies. Companies attract better talent and more engaged employees with good work-life policies, and employees have more job satisfaction.

Contrast that with the negative impact studies say work-life conflict has on employee performance and the bottom line—reduced work effort, increased absenteeism and turnover, poor health and energy, increased stress and burnout, and higher medical costs. Employees with high strain and stress make 26% more doctor visits and see 27% more medical specialists. All that makes work-life conflict a very effective self-destruct button for any organization.

Get the Job Done Without Finishing Yourself Off

All roads to better work-life lead to an exit from the prevailing work style of overwhelm to a new performance model, one that is based on what the research says is more effective than terminal distraction and exhaustion. It's a work style rooted in ongoing vitality and attention, where the thinking comes before the action, where we manage demands instead of having them manage us.

It's an approach that lets us catch ourselves before we go off the counterproductive cliff and marshal strategies to take on an unbounded world. These are the upsides of sustainable performance. It helps you get control over, not just work, but also the mind that runs the whole show. How you think about the job and react to its challenges and personalities is crucial to mental health and a sustainable path.

Change how you think, and you can turn overwhelm around, solve bottlenecks that drive aggravation, and open up space for your life. Let's start our journey with a look at five principles key to sustainable performance and work-life balance that we will be exploring ahead.

The Five Principles of Smarter Work

1. Bring Full Attention to Everything You Do

The answer to distractions, disruptions, and emotional reactions to them is attention. You need to shield your executive attention function from as much of the bedlam as possible and deploy strategies to reverse fractured concentration.

The more attention you have, the more control you have, and the more perceived control you feel you have over events, the less stress. When you race through tasks with one eye on the next item on the list, it self-inflicts intrusions, interruptions, and anxiety. As you will learn, it's relaxing to pay attention. The mind is not split into warring factions by competing concerns and noise, not trying to do more than it can do at one time.

We all have the power to pay full attention. It's how we are designed. Your higher form of attention, called top-down attention, lets you select one thing out of the universe and focus on it like a laser. The problem is that digital distractions and interruptions blow up top-down attention and saddle you with what's known as bottom-up attention, a survival response that erodes a key piece of your executive attention function, effortful control, which regulates your impulse control.

You lose the ability to regulate impulsivity without the ability to stay disciplined. Not only that, but your attention span shrinks. You can keep your brain from short-circuiting by controlling distractions and building practices that train the mind to focus.

2. Think Before You React

Another very big plus of attention is that it makes you more likely to think before you go into action—or reaction. This is a very handy behavior, since it ensures that you give the matter before you the service of your higher brain that can analyze and weigh pro and con, instead of turning things over to the low road of the limbic system and raw, irrational emotions.

It's smarter when you don't immediately send an explosive email to a colleague because something set you off. It's smarter when you can sleep on a big decision to let emotions cool. It's smarter when you don't let hurry-worry drive you into System 1 thinking—shallow, rash, knee-jerk, instead of taking the time to talk to a colleague or do the legwork that will prevent a major mistake. It's definitely smarter when you don't chew the heads off family members or significant others because you are still steaming from what happened hours earlier at work.

Unfortunately, humans are designed to react to stimuli in the world, not think about them beforehand. We are stuck with reflex mode unless we can build the awareness to control it.

Managing the reflex mind comes down to managing the thoughts in it. There are great tools ahead to help you do that, such as a strategy from the University of Nevada's Steven Hayes called cognitive defusion that lets you separate yourself from your thoughts, so they can't trigger you. You can build the mind like a muscle to be resilient to nonsensical, automatic thoughts and reactions.

3. Set Boundaries on an Unbounded World

Boundaries are the most basic management tool—and something that has vanished in the onslaught of technology. Without them, our offices are like city streets without traffic lights—anarchy. As a report from Harvard Business School's Laura Nash and Howard Stevenson details, boundaries are a success tool. Those who have them are able to find sensible perimeters that let them work more effectively and enjoy more life satisfaction as a result.

There used to be bright lines that could keep us from doing more than we can do well. Technology erased them. It's critical that we rediscover them. Just because it's possible to be online or email at three in the morning doesn't mean it makes any sense to do it. Do you have to be checking work email at home at 7 p.m.? Do you have to even be thinking about work after dinner? Not according to the science of work recovery, which says you need to be able to separate yourself from the work mind when the workday is done.

You don't have to feel guilty about setting boundaries. Every time management strategy is a system of bringing perimeters and order to unbounded chaos. Boundaries manage time, cut stress, and make you healthier and more effective.

4. Act as If You Are a Smartphone and Recharge Daily

It would be easier if we all had a battery bar on our wrist that we could check to see when we need a recharge. Unfortunately, though, few of us give our physiology as much attention as our digital significant others. That's a problem, since our energetic resources, which give us the ability to concentrate, regulate impulsivity and stay on task, need to be resupplied, or we can't get the signals in the brain to perform effectively.

Working in a sustainable way means you are respecting the limits and needs of your physiology. It's easy to get one-tracked, and before you know it, you've spent a day inhaling junk food, with no exercise and not enough sleep.

The science of work recovery says you need to recharge on a regular basis like a smartphone. It's what I call the Refueling Principle. Energy spent must be replaced. The brain expends 20% of the body's energy.

It burns through its fuel quickly and needs to be resupplied. It's called the time-on-task effect—too much time concentrating on a task, and attention and performance plummet, until you step back and allow the brain to reboot. Strategic pauses to refuel during the day and recreation and relaxation strategies after work and on vacations keep you charged and focused.

5. Ask for what you need to do your job *and* your life.

The number one thing people say in surveys that they want when it comes to work-life balance is more control over their schedules. That means more flexibility in how and where they work. After the largest unofficial telework study in history, the coronavirus pandemic, proved the viability of remote work, this is an ask that is no longer a pipedream.

But you do have to ask. Speaking the words and having the conversations about what it is you need for a better work-life fit are crucial. Broaching the topic of flex schedules and options may seem nerve-wracking, but it is being done by a host of your counterparts across the nation. For instance, three-quarters of Americans favor a hybrid work schedule, a couple days in the office and the rest at home.

Flex arrangements are popular for many practical reasons—managing kids and school issues, not burning up time on long commutes, and the freedom to make a doctor visit or a child's play. There's something else too: autonomy, one of our most important psychological needs, which pays off in life gratification. Ask and it's something you just may receive.

When you adjust your work style to reflect these smarter-work principles, you begin to feel more flexibility and a sense of control over the work environment and your life.

Susan, the overwhelmed financial advisor in Denver and a coaching client of mine, did just that. She was able to transform her work style with checks and balancing measures, turning 10- to 12-hour days into eight on a schedule redesigned to take advantage of her peak hours of alertness and concentration through focus zones. "I'm getting 20% more done than before easily," she told me, while working less.

Instead of being too tired and grumpy for a social life, she found the energy to put her personal life on the calendar. By changing false beliefs about performance that locked her into head-down, auto-overload and adjusting work practices that kept the pattern entrenched, she escaped a burnout trap that seemed to have no way out. "I'm not freaked out about things that need to be done anymore," she said. "Things are just flowing."

Sustainable performance shifts the emphasis from the job as a triathlon in pants to informed performance, how well your brain is functioning throughout the day. The goal is to do less of what gets in the way of the mind performing skillfully and more of what keeps the cognitive end in tip-top shape. In other words, fewer being-hit-on-the-head lessons.

CHAPTER 2

What Is Work-Life Balance, Anyway?

Identify the Work-Life You Need

When your car is out of alignment, you know it. It drifts into the other lane when you take your hand off the wheel, and you wind up fighting your own vehicle to stay on the path. You have to take the car to the shop and get the wheels balanced, or you shave life off your tires. When you are misaligned by stress, overwhelm, or five hours of sleep a night, you know it too.

That's because your physiology was designed to function with all systems operating in tandem at a level the brain can manage most efficiently, known as homeostasis. It's another way of saying you are born to be balanced. When you are not, you drift out of your physical and mental lanes into the repercussions of what is known as allostatic load, the cost of adaptation to stress and pressures that over time can lead to serious illnesses and diseases that burn up health and performance like unbalanced wheels burn rubber.

Part of the body is tasked with activation. The autonomic nervous system that manages your automatic behaviors also responds to the threat of a stressful event. It does this by rousing the physiology to scarf up fats, sugars, and energetic resources in your cells, which then need to be replaced.

Afterwards, the internal counterbalance squad, the parasympathetic nervous system, then steps in to put a brake on the hyper-arousal and fuel-burning with its mandate—rest and digest. It makes you hungry for foods that help you replace the lost nutrients you just used up and calms you down after the threat is gone. It is part of the natural balancing system that resupplies resources and vitality again.

You need not fear stepping back or resting as if they were starter drugs for slackerdom. They are the forces of your own internal recovery process, part of your built-in anti-zombie mechanism. They bring you back to a balance of internal systems that promotes the best functioning, health, and vitality.

The Mandate of Equilibrium

You wouldn't know it from the state of the world or the sales of Tums but staying aligned is a favorite topic inside your head and body. In one study, researchers measured why humans aren't crazy about dissonant music with no discernible melody. The study found that our ears search for "consonance," or harmonistic sounds.

Other researchers measured what people like about good dancers. Judging by the number of dance shows on the air, we do love to watch great dancing. We admire people deft on their feet, from Fred Astaire to the *Soul Train* line dancers and *Dancing with the Stars*. Researchers digitized the figures of the dancers, so the study's participants wouldn't be distracted by looks or clothes to go for the coolest or most attractive person's moves. It turned out that what they were attracted to in the best dancers was their symmetry, the flow of body movements with musical rhythms—harmony once again.

Balance is an aspiration and a mandate, from balanced music to bodies to nervous systems, to positive versus negative emotions, to meals, to work-life balance. And others seem to prefer us when we are in that state. Those who are unbalanced we tend to give a wide berth to.

You can see that maintaining equilibrium, then, is an essential part of the physiology and not a frill by virtue of the body's own balancing acts. Work-life balance is home base. When you leave it, you get out of whack, and you know it by the familiar signals—anxiety, headaches, high blood pressure, insomnia, and parts of your life that are missing in action—family, fun, friends.

Unfortunately, we have been trained to ignore those signs and grind on in the overperformance direction. In the process we miss our appointment with life—an urgent meeting that gets shoved aside without the awareness and commitment to make it happen. It doesn't seem like a priority. Yet it's no less than why we are working, to live, right?

Are You Unbalanced?

In the blur of the career speedway, it's hard to pause long enough to reflect on where you are and where you would like your life to go. Let's take a moment right now for a break away from the fray to assess the state of your work-life and where you would like it to be. I'll start with a bold question: Are you an unbalanced character? Over the edge? Don't worry. It's okay if you are. I have this book between you and me, so I have nothing to worry about.

But seriously, if you are unbalanced, the question is what does balance look like, and how can you get there? I'd like you to reflect on what work-life balance means for you. Here are some of the responses I get to this question from my training participants.

- Able to do fun things outside of work
- More time for family
- Having a hobby I can practice regularly
- I can stop thinking about work after work
- More time for health and self-care
- Time for quality conversations with family, minus devices
- I'm not checking work email at home and on vacation
- Time for exercise
- I feel like I have permission to have a life
- More time for friends
- More sleep
- Able to enjoy time off without guilt

Taking Your Life and Health Seriously

So, what is work-life balance? One logical description is the lack of interference and spillover of work into the home and family domain. To make that happen, though, we need another definition. Work-life balance is the act of taking control over the conflict between professional and family/personal responsibilities caused by role overload and carving out a manageable fit between the two. The crunch is huge in an era of long hours and 24/7 technology that doesn't recognize office hours and is happy to put you on night and weekend keyboard statue duty.

The basic proposition behind work-life balance is that having a job shouldn't foreclose family and personal life. That's common sense. No one would argue with that but turning it into reality takes uncommon diligence and persistence.

One thing work-life balance isn't is a 50-50 deal, which is why some prefer the term "work-life fit," instead of "balance." There isn't a magical ratio, though you can certainly feel it when it's overly tilted to one side. Work-life balance comes in many shades and varieties depending on the individual's needs and goals. A number I like, though, is one that is a determining factor in quality work-life—how much attention you can bring to the things that are of value in your world.

When I ask my training participants what work-life balance means for them, one of the best answers I get is this: When I'm at work, I can be 100% there, and when I'm home I can be 100% at home. I'm sure you know what they mean. You feel guilty when you're on the job thinking you need more time for family or significant other and when you're at home feeling like you should be getting work done. Being torn between the two creates pressure, strain, and work-life conflict—stress, which the research shows leads to fatigue, burnout, high blood pressure, insomnia, and decreased satisfaction at work and at home.

What if you could be completely where you are? That's the plan here. The 100% solution underscores our central theme of leaving unconscious drift and bringing attention to everything you do. You avoid work-life conflict by paying attention to the needs of your private life, your health, and who and what you love and valuing them enough so that they help you shape a more balanced work style through changes in work practices, flexibility, expectations, and schedules. I see it as an alignment of the work ethic with a *worth* ethic, in which the value of your life is felt through the fullest expression of the fruits of your labor.

Work-life balance is at its practical root proactive self-management—making a concerted, daily effort to take time for the things that sustain well-being and give life meaning. You are the entrepreneur of your life. It's about taking your life as seriously as your work and committing to fit it in to your day and week, whether it's pausing for a reset with a walk, a workout at the gym, playing with your kids, getting together with a friend, doing a hobby that fuels you, participating in civic events, or volunteering to help others.

Finding the time for all that is the mission. Normally, whatever scrap of time there is left in the day or week, well, that's your life. Yet my experience on the frontlines of overloaded America is that you can make the changes needed to improve your work-life. As you will see ahead, you can have the conversations, make the proposals, and organize personal and family schedules to get the quality time you need.

There's another key part of work-life balance—taking your health seriously. Working in an unsustainable way drives health problems, most of which stem from the strain on your brain that leads to stress. This makes work-life balance an essential piece of mental health and wellness.

Multiple studies show the connection between job stress and heart disease, diabetes, stroke, and many other conditions. Work-health balance has been shown to be as important to job satisfaction as work-family balance. A concerted work-life effort should include ongoing stress management, exercise, and healthy eating habits as crucial checks on an unbalanced world.

The big shift is moving from life and health as an afterthought to an intentional front-end approach. You'll have to schedule, prioritize, and set boundaries at work and at home. When you do, you know, wherever you are, the other side is being taken care of. Your mind isn't wandering to other places because you are fully present to whatever you do.

Tweaking the Homefront

Although most challenges to work-life balance come from the work side, there are also actions on the home front that can make that realm less chaotic and more balanced. For instance, a supportive spouse or partner can provide help with the household and childcare demands to reduce stress that can intrude into the workplace, known as family-to-work conflict.

A more even split of household duties can improve balance at home. You probably know where I am going with this. In a Pew Research Center survey 59% of women said they do more household chores than men, while 46% of men say the duties are about even and 20% say they do more. On caring for children, 74% of mothers say they do most of the work while men say they are as involved as a parent as their spouse. When it comes to preparing meals and grocery excursions, women say they do 80% of the work, while men say they do about 20%.

It's important to have a conversation with your partner and all your family members about an equitable distribution of duties. Older children can lend a hand, make their bed, take care of the dishes. You're all in it together.

While you are meeting, it's also a chance to get feedback on your own work habits and how they are affecting your attention at home. Kids will let you know if they feel an imbalance of attention. If you model good work-life balance for your children, they can learn that when they are older, they can have a job and a life.

Take some time to jot down the things you and your family have to do and want to do. Who needs to do what when? Show that getting organized and helping out frees up time for fun activities and family outings—and spell out which kind—and that there is a payoff for doing the work.

Identify how many hours a week you would like to set aside for time with your kids, your partner, and yourself. What do you have to do to free that time up? Are there others who could help—friends, babysitters, neighbors?

Many of us have skills that we use in our professional life, such as time management, that we can use to upgrade family balance. They can help you organize and prioritize to create a more relaxing environment where you can put your feet up without the nags of to-dos and guilt assailing your brain.

Set Work-Life Targets

Jot down on a piece of paper or type onto a screen what you need from better work-life balance. If you don't have targets, there's no direction and little motivation to realize them. Open your mind wide and imagine a life that has work *and* life satisfaction. What do you see?

Flesh out the possibilities. What does the work-life you want look like? What would be different? What are the key elements of that picture missing right now? What would you have more of with a better work-life fit? More family time? What kind? More exercise? More time for hobbies? Answer the questions below to chart your work-life path forward.

- What does work-life balance mean for you?
- What are your top targets for improving work-life balance?
- Identify the next step to reach your WLB targets.

What Are Your Life Deficits?

It can sometimes be hard to visualize parts of life that have been a blank for a while, so let's try to jog the old memory by breaking down key life components and how you are doing with each of them on a balance sheet as important as your financial ledger: the Life Balance Sheet, something you don't want to be in a negative position on.

Check off for each category below whether you have a deficit of attention in that department right now, whether you are satisfied with it, or have a surplus:

The Life Balance Sheet

	Deficit	Satisfied	Surplus
Family Time			
Significant Other			
Friends			
Me-Time			
Health/Wellness			
Exercise			
Recreation/Hobbies			
Social Outlets			
Learning			
Entertainment			
Travel			
Growth			

What was this exercise like for you? More deficits than you would like? Doing well in some categories but not in others?

Identify the categories that you want to bring more attention to and experience more often. Write them down on a list you can call Work-Life Targets. What can you do to get started in each of those deficit categories you most want to change? If you would like to put your health on the agenda, how can you get going? Join a gym? Do a daily walk? Choose a weekly schedule and time slots for exercise? See a nutritionist? Which friend do you want to get together with? When? Jot down some ideas.

Think back to some of your best times. Where were you? What were you doing? How could you get more of that into your life? Is there an activity you used to do but put aside because you got busy? How could you set aside an hour a week to get that going again?

Imagine you are working to live. What does that feel like? What does it look like? You may think you don't have a right to indulge in things that make you happy when there's so much to do. It feels selfish, but that is a false belief, not to mention unreal guilt—you haven't punched someone in the face or committed real harm. It's just a thought manipulated by the scolds in your head.

The mild-mannered realms of the life side play a critical role in health, happiness, and the gratification of needs such as novelty and challenge. Take friends, for instance. Studies show that one of the things that goes missing when people get consumed by their professional lives is friends. Social support and friendship have been found to be key to happiness and connection to others. One of our core psychological needs is known as relatedness, having close relationships.

I found it very revealing that among the top regrets people have in their final years, according to Bronnie Ware, a hospice nurse who spent years caring for folks in their last days and author of *The Top Five Regrets of the Dying*, is, "I wish I had stayed in touch with my friends." Who could you get back in touch with? How?

And while we are at it, let's take a look at the other four regrets Ware detailed, since these can help give us the perspective now on what really matters while we still have a chance for a course correction.

- I wish I'd had the courage to live a life true to myself, not the life others expected of me.
- I wish I hadn't worked so hard.

- I wish I'd had the courage to express my feelings.
- I wish that I had let myself be happier.

The last bullet point directs us to an obstacle and enabler of a life without regret. We have the power to let ourselves be happier by the thoughts we choose to engage with and the choices we make. We can do that more skillfully if we consider how we would like to look back on our life, as one fully lived, instead of one squelched by busyness or fear.

How We Get Out of Whack

There's a reason, or more likely a few of them, why you may be an unbalanced character. Tracking them down gives you a chance to identify the mostly unconscious causes for work-life imbalance and make adjustments, so they can't drive you or your work-life over the edge.

In an always-on world, there's no shortage of culprits—email overload, too many meetings, the mentality of busyness fed by time urgency, not enough boundaries, lack of support, ambition, Type-A personality, perfectionism, workaholism, and, of course, stress, which makes your brain fixate on problems and ignore the very thing it needs for solutions, the positive emotions and mental reset that come from the life side of the equation.

What are the bottlenecks and balance blockers bogging down your life? They can seem like overwhelming obstacles, but they are not. I have found that most of the blockers tend to be barriers we can overcome with boundaries, better communication, changing how we think about work, and planning. Other structural or organizational issues driving work-life conflict can also be tackled through dialogue and proposals for more productive processes.

Email and texting, for instance, are a major balance blocker at almost any organization I work with. There are rarely any rules of the road or etiquette guidelines, so unbounded messaging eats up work hours, seeps into the home, and leaves precious little time for anything else. As you will learn, a few strategic best practices to manage the deluge can unearth many more hours of living time.

Oftentimes, we have assumptions about doing work at night or on the weekend or when to leave the office that are not required. One federal government employee told me about how she worked every day, including weekends, for three months straight. It didn't make sense why she would be doing this or what the need was, so I asked her to speak to her supervisor about the situation. It turned out that the manager didn't want her working every day. My client had just assumed she had to do it to stay on top of everything.

Likewise, a woman in Pennsylvania told me in a training that she was taking about two hours of work home each night. I asked if her boss required that. He didn't. It turned out she had taken it upon herself to do it. That might work for a few days, but when it's every day, you eventually pay in stress-related health issues and resentment about the life that's squeezed out. The work you can't finish today can be done tomorrow. Your health might not be as predictable when you push beyond the capacity of your physiology.

How about obstacles on the home front? What could clear space for more relaxing or engaging nights and weekends? Would you like to read more books? Listen to more music? Do you need more quality time with your kids? Do you need a chore chart, so everyone is pitching in? How could you start a new hobby? What would you like to try? What about less screen time for everyone, so there is more time for conversation and activities together? Do you need to get a new child-sitter?

Is there a belief in the way of your life preventing you from participating in activities outside the job? *I'm too busy. Two left feet. No play partners. I have kids.* Write it down on a piece of paper and then rip it up. Think about how hard you work. You deserve to have a rewarding life as well as a career.

Uncovering Balance Blockers

Now it's time to zero in on the barriers that block you from the work and life you want. Pinpoint three chief obstacles that drive stress and squeeze out space for life. Write down how the blocker impacts your work-life balance and a step you can take to reduce its effects or eliminate it like this.

Balance Blocker

- How it impacts your WLB
- Next step to get around blocker

Try to notice every day the things that drive stress, drain time, and make it hard to balance your life. You are steering the boat. As the captain, you can make the course corrections needed to navigate to your work-life targets.

Proactive Self-Management

Though most people struggle to find work-life balance, not everyone falls into this category even at companies where the majority are in the clearly unbalanced to wits'-end column. At just about any company I visit I find people who have managed through boundary-setting and clarity of communication to carve out a better schedule at work and a more satisfying relationship between work and life outside the job. They are seen by colleagues as a role model for work-life balance.

What this tells us is that some people are finding ways to manage overwhelm and create a better work-life fit. They tend to be folks who have been to a few workplace rodeos, and typically by their late-30s and into their forties, they have learned that they need to speak up and communicate regularly on issues such as expectations and availability. Usually, family responsibilities help them take the initiative needed to lobby for boundaries.

But there's no age limit to improve work-life. Family helped Sophie Parker, a mother of two who manages health and wellness at Dayton, Ohio-based Inboard Skate, reach out for a better way to navigate work and young kids. "I thought it was impossible for me to achieve a good work-life balance, but I found that it's possible once you have the courage to communicate," she reported. "The Monday-to-Friday, 9 to 5 setup just didn't work for me, so I talked to my manager about a compressed workweek and flex hours. My manager agreed to let me work flexible hours, and that allowed me more time for myself and my family."

Some people are bold enough to ask for what they want in their job interview. Jose Sanchez was candid in his interview with Shipbots, an ecommerce fulfillment firm in Los Angeles, explaining "what I wanted in a career as well as what I was striving for in my personal life. It set expectations between us that were realistic, and we both knew what we were agreeing to from the start. I work harder now that I feel valued and respected. My social life is healthier, and it has made me a happier person."

Jose's increased engagement and job and life satisfaction illustrates what makes work-life balance such a winner for employee and employer. As one study put it, "family-supportive interventions can be expected to increase employee perceptions of control" over competing demands. That is appreciated and makes you want to reciprocate.

There is a path to better work-life. Like Sophie and Jose, you have to take the initiative. You are the only one who can make your work-life a better fit. You know your obstacles, needs, and affinities. You just need to translate them into goals for your life, health, and family—and communicate them.

The Work-Life Makeover

Better work-life balance requires a series of adjustments on both the work and life sides. Making improvements to how you do your work practices, not only makes things more efficient, but it also has a major impact on your state of mind. The more you can increase flexibility and tweak practices, the less stress you have.

Beyond that, two of your core needs are autonomy and competence. We all have a need to feel as if we are writing our own script. Changes that make work style more sustainable feed the need of choice, which is how autonomy lives in the workplace, and that makes you feel more competent to boot.

Here are the key tweaks needed on the work side:

WORK ADJUSTMENTS

Effective Task Practices

You don't have to reinvent the wheel. The best practices and science point the way to a more effective work style. The goal is to change the way you do tasks, so they create less strain, stress, and overwork, and make you more productive.

The focus is on eliminating the bottlenecks that drain attention through strategies such as interruption and information management, better time management, prioritizing, realistic deadlines, and utilizing peak alertness, when we have the most focus to do our most demanding and creative tasks.

Manage Demands, Instead of Having Them Manage You

Yes, there are a lot of pressures, but you don't have to let the demands call your tune. You can change the way you react to them and think about them, so that you are in charge of the demands and the false alarms of your fight-or-flight equipment.

Two hundred emails are a hassle, but they are not life-or-death. What the colleague said to you is aggravating, but you're not going to die from it. Your out-of-time brain, though, treats it all as threats to your physical survival on the planet.

This means your brain responds to pressure with rigid, emotional, and bogus explanations that only make matters worse. You can catch the autopilot, knee-jerk response and shut it down.

Communicate Needs

Silence is not golden when it comes to your health and life satisfaction. If you are doing more than you can do well, and it's affecting your health or squeezing out family and life, it's crucial to say something. Failure to speak up about an untenable workload can lead to heart disease, burnout, or worse—a nervous breakdown in the case of a woman in Pittsburgh I spoke with who was taking hours of work home for a long period. She wound up in a hospital for a week.

Leaders are not mind-readers, and most of them don't want to drive out good people. You need to let them know what's going on. If you are having health issues and/or major work-life conflict, it's critical to have a conversation about it.

Limit Overwork

The research shows that the number of hours we work per week can make a big difference in productivity and health outcomes, and there is a connection between the two. Stress and health problems increase dramatically with long hours.

Overload reduces performance because of the fatigue and lack of focus that come with elevated stress levels. Yes, there are crunch times and periods that require extra time. The goal is to keep hours from drifting into the chronically excessive column. It's the duration of stress that's hazardous to health. Of course, extremely long workweeks also reduce the amount of time you have for family, friends, and pastimes off-the-clock.

Clear Boundaries Between Work and Home

Nothing insures a void on the life side like a lack of bright lines between work and home. The overflow from excessively long workweeks will show up at home unless you have a plan for it not to. We all need to flip the work switch at the end of the workday to the off position.

Setting a stop time, for instance, an alarm on your phone to go off when the day is over, puts a clear end to the workday and signals the start of your life activities and family responsibilities. It puts you on a schedule that gives you the confidence you are allowed to be fully in the life domain in the hours after 5 p.m., 6 p.m. or whatever time works for you.

LIFE ADJUSTMENTS

Work Recovery and Recharging

After a full day of work many of us continue to be at work, at least in our minds. Leaving work at work is an essential part of work-life balance and stress recovery. The proactive move needed here, say researchers, is having strategies to detach yourself from work and thoughts of work. You need to be able to wind down the activation in the body from strain and tension and transition to other responsibilities and interests.

The science of work recovery says you need recharging after work—relaxation, recreation, and mastery experiences that can shift mood, connect us with others, and replace strain with enjoyment and engagement. Mastery activities, such as hobbies that build skills, are the most effective at reducing stress, since they build self-esteem and infuse positive emotions. Whether you go for a bike ride, meditate, listen to music, or take a walk, these actions recharge vitality and crowd out worries, negative emotions, and thoughts that keep you at work long after the workday is over.

Put Family, Friends, and Yourself on the Calendar

Appointments are a very useful tool in the working world. They also work splendidly for life opportunities outside the workday to make sure you don't bail on those close to you or yourself and put dedicated time for all of you on the agenda.

Planning seems to go against the concept of kicking back. Yet, if you want to make more memories, you need to do more of it. There's just too much going on that can bury goals that haven't been etched in pen on a reminder list or typed on a screen. The other great thing about this is that it helps you stick to the plan when saboteurs in the form of funky moods or fatigue get in the way.

Activate Life Skills

As a kid, you had no problem hurling yourself into the middle of activities you had never done before. You tried things for no other reason than to try them, to see what it felt like, or learn how to do it. Over the years, though, the innate talent for tapping into the experience of living goes missing. You worry about what others will think if you try salsa dancing, even though you haven't done it before. Are you supposed to be a dance pro on your first day?

As an adult, the reason for doing something new shifts from *I want to do it* and *do it no matter what happens*, to *what will others think* and *what am I going to get out of it?* The intrinsic goal of fun is replaced by the external goals of instrumental gain and the approval of others, which can shut down new life activities out of fear of the gaze of complete strangers.

It turns out that to activate your life, you have to use a different skill-set than the performance metric of external rewards. Unlike work skills, which are about results and outcomes, the magic of life is participating in activities just for the experience, something we all knew in grade school before the killjoy of adulthood. In other words, what do you do for fun? Just for the pure enjoyment? Is that a hard question? It's one key to grat-ified lives.

Bring the Changes To Life

Now it's time to translate the adjustments into specific work-life solutions. Which tweaks to work style and practices could make a difference for you? Which smaller changes could you make quickly to get things going? What are the most important modifications? Which of the adjustments below would you like to put into action to upgrade your work-life?

- Unplug from work email and turn off notifications after work.
- Spend less of the day in meetings.
- Set a stop time at the end of office hours. No work or thoughts of work after that time.
- Remove yourself from reply-all lists you shouldn't be on.
- Listen to music to increase positive mood on breaks.
- Take a real lunch break, and don't do any work on it.
- Talk to your manager about flexible start and stop times to help with kids or elder care.
- Create a calendar for personal and family activities. Set aside one night a week for a shared family experience.
- Have an understanding with coworkers about respecting home time by not sending email after work hours.
- Find a hobby you or your household can learn and enjoy regularly.
- Speak up about work hours that are chronically late into the night.
- Plan meals for the week, breakfasts, school stuff the night before.
- Make an appointment with a fitness instructor to get started on a regular exercise routine.
- Put time with your partner on the calendar.
- Get more support if you have too much on your plate at the office.
- Be more available and present for family and friends.
- Prioritize time to do what you enjoy.
- Get kids to help with household chores.
- Hire a tutor to help kids with homework.
- Put a weekend getaway and your next vacation on the calendar.
- Get in touch with a friend you haven't seen in ages.
- Let others know you will respond to email as swiftly as you can but not instantly.

Do a Work-Life Audit

A major obstacle to work-life balance is the swarm of tasks that overwhelm the best intentions for a more sustainable path. We need regular reminding, or we fall back to our default—more stuff to do.

This is where a weekly Work-Life Balance Audit comes in. I would like you to pull out your phone and set an alarm for your audit to go off on, say, Friday afternoons at 3 p.m. When it rings, you rate your work-life balance for the week on a scale of 1-10, 10 being best. If you are in the 1-6 range, then ask yourself:

- What do I need to do to bring my week more in balance? What's causing the imbalance?
- Is there something I need to say to someone to rein in strain and stress?
- How can I get some life on the calendar?

Use this reflective moment to plan an activity for the weekend or a weekday night the following week when you can get together with a friend. Brainstorm ways to improve your quality of life. Stop, so you can go again with more intention.

Honk If You Need Balance

My taxi came to a sudden halt about one-quarter of an inch from the truck in front of us. A sign on the back of the ancient vehicle said, "Blow Horn," and my driver and the scrum pressed up against us on all sides—three-wheel auto-rickshaws, motorcycles, bicycles, sedans, and seemingly every conceivable type of moving vehicle in Mumbai—obliged.

Lanes are a theoretical concept in India's teeming financial hub. Two lanes can easily contain parts of four vehicles. You see a lot of trucks in India with signs and bumper stickers telling drivers to honk if they're passing, perhaps since many truckers tend to operate without side mirrors on streets so tight there's not enough space for them and to avoid collisions with smaller vehicles darting in and out.

I had been invited to Mumbai to lead a work-life balance training for the Reserve Bank of India. I took it as a honked horn for another overloaded realm, the Indian office. An enlightened general manager and human resources leader wanted me to speak to a group of executives who were about to disappear from all but official duties. They were taking on the role of directors in addition to their current duties.

India has one of the most overworked populations in the world, averaging 48-hour workweeks. With so many people competing for the best-paying jobs, most feel they can't rock the boat and have to go along with very long work hours. Yet even in this capital of overload there are people trying to make a difference and moderate unproductive overperformance.

I explained to the group how excessive hours are driven by habit and appearances, not productivity research and data. We discussed how attention, the key productivity tool, is a temporary resource that must be managed and resupplied on a regular basis, and that marathon workweeks guarantee those depleted supplies are not replaced. It's why boundaries are attention's best friend. I mentioned the regrets we have when we miss our lives, such as losing track of friends. One man came up to me afterwards to share a universal sentiment. We don't regret in our later years that we didn't work enough, only that we didn't live enough.

It's something we all know, but we get caught up in the whirlwind. It struck me that, as different as Indian and American cultures are, we are very similar when it comes to the challenge of getting life on the agenda. Each in their own way is hemmed in by false beliefs about performance and the appearance of hard work, as opposed to the scientific reality of what's productive in the knowledge economy.

I looked at the group and wondered if they would be able to resist the social pressures and ironman expectations. They now had the scientific evidence on more effective practices. They could see from their colleagues that they were not alone in the need for boundaries. And they had the fact that the Reserve Bank's own human resources department had sponsored my program. Their own organization was giving them permission to work healthier, which is the case at every training I do, a clear sign employers know that poor work-life balance is a liability for the organization. If you are in bad shape physically and mentally from overload, so is your work, health, and home life, and that can lead to leaving the company.

To a great extent, this is what work-life and a sustainable path is all about—permission, permission to do what the data and everyone knows in their bones makes a whole lot more sense. This team was trying to change the mentality. If they could take that on here, with a much steeper climb, so can we, by working more effectively, speaking up, finding allies, and identifying leaders who can move the sustainable performance ball forward.

Payoffs for Bottom Lines and Happier Lives

As you can see, work-life balance is not just important to you. It's important to employers as well, or certainly any of them who are concerned about performance and keeping their best people around. This is because work-life conflict has been shown to hurt job and life satisfaction, a key metric for engagement, and cause disengagement—a checked-out staff.

Work-life balance programs have such a potent effect, signaling that the company cares about its workforce, that for employees, just the awareness that their organization has work-life balance policies in place, without even using them, increases their loyalty and engagement, studies show. They reciprocate and then some when they perceive concern about their well-being.

No doubt that dynamic plays a role in how work-life balance policies improve productivity and the bottom line, as detailed in studies like these:

- A survey of more than 64,000 federal workers, the first-ever Federal Work-Life Survey Governmentwide Report, conducted by the Office of Personnel Management, found that employees who utilized telework and wellness programs were 76% and 74% more likely to get performance ratings that exceeded their last rating. Those who participated in work-life balance programs were also 75% - 80% more likely to be satisfied with their jobs.
- An analysis of 36 pharmaceutical companies in the U.S. found that the use of flexible work hours can boost performance, increasing productivity 10%.

- Researchers who looked at 527 U.S. companies found that firms that have a wider range of work-life practices had greater performance, profit, and sales growth.

One study documented that work-life balance programs "increased organizational profitability when their use was high," which means these practices also boost the bottom line. Work-life balance pays.

Employee morale and engagement were tanking at a nonprofit school, when management decided it had to revamp with a comprehensive work-life balance initiative. A researcher who looked at the school's metamorphosis described the shift: "The employees were expressing severe anxiety over the amount of work and the pressure that accompanied those workloads. The implementation of the WLB programs was the first step that illustrated that the employer cared about personnel lives inside and outside the workplace," reported the study's author, George Sheppard of Walden University.

After adding flexible schedules and health and wellness programs, job performance, commitment, motivation, and satisfaction soared. One participant in the study said, "I am grateful to have more control over my job and work schedule because this has helped to improve my job performance as well as reduce the anxiety that I was feeling for months that was affecting my health."

I typically hear from clients after they have done a work-life balance survey of employees, and the scores come back lackluster. This is evidence of strain, stress, and work-life conflict, which reduces job satisfaction.

Clearly, many employers know the connection between job satisfaction and engagement and can change things up when the numbers call for it. We tend to think about the job as a place where everything is set in stone. The reality is that the main business of every company is ad-libbing, making it up along the way to deal with ever-changing markets and convulsive change. We evolve, too, in our career skills and responsibilities and from single to parent, to caring for children or elderly family members—so adjusting to changing roles at home and within our professions is the way of the world. Work-life balance recognizes those stages, and now more companies are recognizing it.

Melanie Musson, a mother of five who works for USInsuranceAgents.com, told me she has good work-life balance now that she is working remotely. "When flexibility wasn't optional, I felt like I had to hide my family, and I couldn't take care of their needs," she said. "Communication is the key to figuring out how to achieve balance. Voicing your struggles to your boss may help the two of you work out a better arrangement."

The Covid-19 pandemic revealed that organizations could work just as productively when employees are working at home as when they are in the office. There was no drop in productivity. Data from surveys by both the National Bureau of Economic Research and productivity software company Prodoscore showed that productivity increased 5% during the pandemic year of 2020. In fact, studies have shown for years that performance increases when people are working remotely. There is more focus, additional time minus the commute, and people feel less stress when they have more control over their schedules. A Harvard Business School online survey reported that 81% of respondents prefer a hybrid work schedule, with some days in the office and some remote each week. This is clearly the future of work.

The remote office success has accelerated growing acceptance of a more flexible workplace. There is a wider recognition of the realities of the full spectrum of life and the need to bring the work and life sides into a better alignment. This makes it an auspicious time to improve work-life balance.

A design firm in New York, Smart Design, responded to the increased stress loads from the pandemic by starting midday mental breaks. Could that be something to broach with your team or firm? People have permission to block off time for nonwork breaks, from running to biking to family lunches for parents working remotely. Employees at Versus Systems, an advertising company, switched to having every other Friday off.

The list of companies that have shifted to work-from-home permanently include Dropbox, Indeed, Facebook, Quora, Reddit, Square, Slack and Shopify, with many others—from Salesforce to Siemens—offering hybrid setups, from one to three days at the office and the rest at home.

You are in good company as you make your pitch. Start by clarifying your goals and priorities. What do you need? More quality time with your kids or partner? Time for health maintenance? Time for socializing? Time for thinking? Time for a hobby?

Then figure out the adjustments you need to make to tasks, schedules, boundaries, and mindset to make those things part of a better work-life mix. Start by identifying your objectives.

- What do you want to prioritize in your life?
- What work-life arrangement do you want?
- How will it improve your life and your family's?
- What's the benefit for the company? Improved productivity and job satisfaction are good answers here.
- How would the new arrangement work?

The Work-Life Policy Menu

There are two routes to getting support for work-life balance changes—more informally through family-supportive supervisors and globally through new work-life-friendly policies for the firm. You may be able to work out a simple individual agreement with your manager, as you see some in this chapter have done. Think about what could make the biggest difference for you—working remote several days per week, a no-email zone at home after work, options for childcare resources, the ability to leave early two nights a week or start later to help with commutes or getting kids to school. Find an opportune moment and put the ideas out there.

If your proposal needs to follow a more formal route, here are the standard categories to explore for flexible work arrangements:

- *Remote working.* We all know how productive this is now. You have control of more of your schedule and the freedom to step away for a child's event.
- *Flextime.* Arranging different start and stop times.
- *Childcare and elder care.* Having childcare options onsite or supported by your company, plus the flexibility to take care of the needs of seniors in the household.
- *Family leave.* Paid leave for new mothers and fathers as well as time for family health issues.
- *Reduced hours.* A less than full-time schedule.
- *Compressed workweek.* Completing your allotted time in a shorter time span.
- *Annual paid time off.* Getting sufficient vacation time to recover and recuperate and spend time with loved ones—at least two

weeks—is crucial to health, the research shows. A growing number of companies, mostly in the tech world, are offering unlimited vacation policies. As long as it's cleared with a supervisor and the work is done, you can take time off.

Keep in mind that these options are being used successfully by thousands of companies around the U.S. and the world. Some 70% of companies surveyed by the Society for Human Resource Management said they offered some form of remote work, either full-time or part-time. These practices can be done and are being done.

Having and Surviving the Conversation

The key to a better work-life is you have to propose something. Unless your employer knows what you want, you can't get it. Your negotiation strategy should be simply that what you are proposing is going to make you more productive by making it easier to handle your life and family obligations, take care of your health, and be more energized and recharged as a result.

When Francesca Nicasio, a content marketer at Payment Depot, realized she was "spending all my time earning the money and none of the time enjoying the fruits of my labor," she decided she had to find a way to speak with her boss about being able to make her off-hours more reliable life opportunities. She decided to bet on herself and a productivity test.

"I've worked long enough to know that smart businesspeople don't care about the time you put in as much as the results you achieve, so that was the angle I took," she explained. "I presented my case for what I needed and how granting my request would actually make me a more valuable employee (less stress, less burnout, more creativity, more energy). To make it even easier for them to say Yes, I asked for it on a trial basis. If after six months my productivity went down, I'd go back to the way things were. If, however, my performance stayed level or went up, the new arrangement would stay in place. I'm happy to say that what I proposed turned out as I expected and both me and my employer are better off and happier for the change."

The test-case idea was a savvy stroke and one that I've seen others use to great success, including even with extra vacation time. One salesman told me he got an extra week's vacation by proposing that it would result in increased productivity. It did, and he was able to lock in that additional vacation time. You'll learn later how one work-life researcher was able to solve a burnout and productivity problem at an insurance company that had cut staff by bringing in temporary workers as a trial, who increased sales dramatically and then were hired full-time.

Schedule a meeting or send a written proposal. Conduct the pitch in a way that demonstrates that you've done your homework and thought about the impact of what you are asking for. Remind yourself that you've done your job well and that you can do it better and take care of your personal responsibilities with adjustments to work practices and schedules that make you more effective.

Make sure the timing is right—for the manager and the company. Have these conversations late in the week, which is usually less harried. Friday is best.

Get Started on Better Work-Life

The data tells us what we all know—that brains, bodies, families, and lives function better when they are not fried, when there is space to recharge and take care of responsibilities we have as spouses, parents, friends, and citizens. Being able to have more choice in how we do our tasks, where we do them, and when we do them has a dramatically positive effect on performance, job satisfaction, and well-being.

You can start mapping out your path to work-life balance by answering the following questions:

- Which work changes, from task practices to schedules, do you need to improve your work-life?
- Which parts of your life do you need to have more time for?
- Which conversations do you need to have for work-life balance? With whom?
- Which health and wellness actions can you take to improve your well-being?
- Which life opportunities do you want to pursue? Hobbies? Enthusiasms?

CHAPTER 3

You Can't Control the Wind, But You Can Adjust the Sails

Set Boundaries on an Unbounded World

I wouldn't want to live in Los Angeles, Houston, Boston, or any other major city without traffic lights. The roads are crazy enough as it is, but without rules of the road, you've got anarchy, which is what things are verging on in the workplace today.

The anarchic flow of messaging and interruptions pour in without any kind of traffic management, causing massive tie-ups that lead to always-on availability and distractions that torpedo productivity and drive overwhelm and unbalanced characters.

The flood operates unchallenged, devices calling the tune, with the humans caught up in a kind of learned helplessness, as if nothing could be any different. The unbounded approach remains the status quo because of the disappearance of one of the most basic management tools—boundaries. We need to launch a worldwide search for their whereabouts before something else disappears, the sanity of those who need them, which is all of us.

Researchers say that having no perimeters doesn't make sense, because it results in shredded working memory and attention, soaring stress, and leaves you disengaged and jumpy, bracing for the next intrusion. We give kids boundaries. We need them too.

It turns out there is hope, though. We don't have to throw up our hands and surrender. There are many things we can do to control the chaos with effective boundaries. We can start by not pretending we can do good work without them.

The Default to Yes

I led a work-life balance program for a global German organization facing the challenges of overwhelm and overload. The group of managers, from China to the U.S., England, and Germany, were highly committed to their work, but prompted to focus on hurdles, turned out to be hungry to talk about ways to manage competing demands and time zones and carve out better boundaries.

My experience is that it's not lack of interest in reining in the excess that keeps the cycle going. It's habit, fear, and will. During our session, the consensus was that in the scramble of information overload and exploding to-do lists, there was a default to take on more than they could handle. Too many of us are in the same boat. Trying to keep all the balls in the air, we don't pause long enough to reflect if we can really take on one more thing to juggle right now.

This was perfectly illustrated when an employee of the company who was based in Hong Kong talked about the difficulty of being able to turn around difficult deadlines and get any respite from a schedule that had him taking meetings at 11 p.m. in Asia.

The executive in charge of the event took the floor and said something that surprised everyone in the room. "When I give deadlines on projects, I expect to get some pushback, but I never do. You have to let me know if you can't do it. If you have too much on your plate, tell me, so we can make adjustments."

I have heard many variations on this story. The default to an immediate Yes whenever a task is proposed, regardless of time and resources, inflicts excess when there can be other options available.

Granted, there are workaholic bosses who don't care if you are overwhelmed, but most don't want zombies working for them. Too many people work extreme hours because they assume that is what they are expected to do without an explicit demand for it.

It's an assumption based on missing communication that can push health and job to the brink. The more burned out you are, the more performance suffers. One woman at a federal agency told me her burnout had gotten so bad, that her performance had slipped to the point that she was told she had to do better work, or she would be let go. Not addressing an overwhelming amount of work can wind up sabotaging the job you think you are saving by taking on too much.

It makes more sense to discuss scheduling conflicts and workload jams and offer possible alternatives instead of undermining your ability to do your assignments. Speaking up about a challenging workload, though, brings dread and fear. It seems to be an admission that you aren't up to the job.

No, the problem is: You are not a bot. You are a human, one saddled with physiological limitations and constrained mental bandwidth.

Which Boundaries Do You Need?

Boundaries are the most basic management tool. They keep you from doing more than you can do well, and they keep you healthy. Take some time to think about the tasks and bottlenecks that cause the most strain, the most overwhelm and overload in your day. Which need boundaries? What type of boundaries?

• Identify three boundaries that would make your work more effective and your life less difficult. Then list a next step for each.

You Can Adjust the Sails

It may seem like there's not much you can do about the barrage of messaging and tasks coming your way, but that is not the case. There are many ways to alter the way you work to moderate the incoming and organize workflow better.

There is an expression in the sailing world: "You can't control the wind, but you can adjust the sails." What that means for us in the workplace is that we all have a job we *have* to do—the wind. Nothing we can do about that. But we can change *how* we do the work, our work style, to build in the flexibility—the sails—that increases perception of control and choice, which lowers stress, boosts attention, and puts us on a sustainable path.

Adjustments to work style are largely none other than boundaries, a concept that today seems as quaintly outmoded as a record turntable. The false belief that we can do it all without consequences has led some to see boundaries as tools for wimps.

Wrong. They are the indispensable mechanism of smarter work and the gateway to work-life balance.

Boundaries aren't so scary. Every single management strategy, from time management to information management and prioritization, is a system of boundaries, ways to organize and stage workflow to achieve the maximum focus and efficiency. Not having boundaries makes no sense. It's triage, anarchy, highly stressful, and completely counterproductive for attention, productivity, and excellence.

When you leave the office at the end of the workday, that's a boundary. When you ignore a notification on your computer screen and stay on task, that's a boundary. When you tell a colleague you can't take on another task right now, that's a boundary. When you make the time for exercise to cut stress, that's a boundary. When you refuse the hurry-worry of time urgency and stay laser-focused on what you're doing, that's a boundary.

We all work more productively when we have perimeters in place that give us a chance to think, plan, and organize. So why is it so hard to set boundaries? Here are three of the main reasons:

1. Technology and information overload have swamped the brain's capacity to deal with it, leading to overwhelm, crisis mentality, "want-it-yesterday" timelines, and a belief there isn't a minute to stop and find ways to control it. Little to nothing is being done to moderate the flood.
2. Performance is still measured by the wrong metrics: quantity of hours and stamina, which sabotage the chief productivity tool, attention, in the knowledge economy.
3. Employees don't quite know how to broach the topic of boundaries, seeing it as forbidden territory.

Despite all this, people are setting boundaries every day and not winding up out of a job. We will be taking on boundary obstacles in the pages ahead, as we learn how the science and empirical evidence blazes trails to perimeters.

Work Expands to Fill the Available Time

There is an adage in the management business that spells out the problem in all its mounting glory: Work expands to fill the available time.

In a world of 24/7 technology, that is all the time unless we make some of that time unavailable. That's what boundaries do—and what you can do when you set them.

It's the very nature of work to pile up unless a human steps in to keep the office's version of kudzu from overgrowing all in its path. The default is to let the work swamp in and not manage it.

One of the reasons is that we put such a premium on output that we ignore the input needed to plan, organize, prioritize, reflect, and step back from the fray for perspective. Boundaries show us the need for input. When we lift our heads from nonstop performance mode, we can see that there are better ways to do things.

Some heads lifted at the Boston Consulting Group and realized that unbridled hours were not working. Alarmed that marathon workweeks were driving out too many talented people, the Boston Consulting Group created a program to head off the problem. Called the Red Zone, it flags employees who log more than 60 hours a week for five weeks, citing their exploits on reports seen by partners and managers.

"A hero is not someone whose light is on at 10 at night," Kermit King, a senior partner and managing director at Boston Consulting, told me in an interview.

A Red Zone event triggers a meeting with a Career Development Committee sponsor to find out what's causing the pattern. The manager reviews the project to see where adjustments can be made to prevent an expensive burnout.

Solutions range from reprioritizing duties, to adding more resources, to changing the timeline and better time management. The program makes it clear that pushing to the brink isn't a smart way to work. The Red Zone has increased the number of consultants who feel their job is manageable and, as a result, boosted the number of people who say they want to stay at the company and that the program improved their work-life balance.

I'd like to see the Red Zone initiative spread far and wide. The failure to rein in excessive overperformance can have very tragic consequences. When I did a program for a major federal agency in Washington, D.C., I was told that pressure was sky-high and that there had been two suicides over the last year.

At an employee training I did for a large consulting firm, I learned that one of their colleagues, a man in his 40s, had recently had a heart attack and died in a hotel room on a business trip. This particular consultant was known for his long work hours and ironman endurance. This was one of the reasons I was brought in, to help change the mentality of quantity of hours over quality. What if we could prevent excessive hours and the stress and health havoc that comes from them on the front end and keep these senseless incidents from happening? Boundaries can literally be lifesavers.

A report from the World Health Organization documented that working long hours, more than 55 per week, results in 745,000 deaths per year. Those who work 55 hours a week and more have a 35% increased risk of heart disease compared to people who work 40 hours per week. The deaths come from stroke and fatal heart conditions—heart attacks to coronary artery disease. This is all avoidable when we choose the lessons of science and what's actually productive, instead of the fallacy of brute hours.

Why More Is Less

Sometimes policies are not well thought-out and don't make any sense. I had an encounter with such a policy in Enfield, Connecticut, where I had come to lead a training for LEGO, the international toy company beloved by kids everywhere. I had gotten to my hotel late because of a cancelled flight and resulting bus trip from Newark, and I had one thing on my mind: grub. The hotel didn't serve any, but I spied the glow of Golden Arches across the street. Fast food, make that super-fast food, was looking like gourmet fare at this point.

Yet when I got there, stomach growling like an angry Doberman, the door was locked. They said they had stopped serving. Yet their drive-thru window was still operating. Cars were pulling up to the window and people were getting their food. I guess I had to be a car to score some dinner.

I got into line with the cars, moving up slightly as each auto in front of me moved forward, as if I was a motor vehicle. Yes, I felt a little deranged doing this, but I was in need. After a couple more cars, then it was my turn. I got up to the window and was told that only people in cars were allowed to get their meals. I thought it was an attempt at a joke, so I laughed and tried to order. "No, sir, our policy is that we can only serve people in cars for the drive-thru window." You've got to be kidding. I tried to reason with the window agent, but he was firm. Conversation over. I had to make do with a vending machine in the hotel.

Many of the policies and norms that drive overperformance behaviors make about as much sense and fly in the face of the research. A meta-analysis of 52 studies, titled *Overtime and Extended Work Shifts*, conducted by the Department of Health and Human Services and the National Institute for Occupational Safety and Health, found that people who work long hours regularly are less productive than ones who work 40-hour weeks, and are a lot less healthy.

Stanford economist John Pencavel analyzed data from a British munitions factory and discovered that, as the hours beyond 40 per week go up, productivity slides. After 50 hours, productivity drops and by 55 hours there's a productivity cliff, with so little getting done that you might as well be in suspended animation.

"When hours get too long, hourly productivity suffers and eventually total productivity suffers," Boston College economist Juliet Schor told me.

Overtime shrank productivity across multiple industries in a study by Edward Shepard and Thomas Clifton. Research in the construction trade found that people who worked seven 50-hour weeks in a row got no more done than if they had worked seven 40-hour weeks.

I'm sure you can see a trend here. Working more than the physiology can maintain focus or physical energy for produces diminishing returns. The main reasons are stress and fatigue, which operate in that order. Strain causes stress and stress burns up energetic resources in the body to cause fatigue.

Stress and fatigue mount dramatically after 50 hours a week. When we ignore fatigue and press on into chronic overtime, the blowback comes in the form of mistakes, low-value output and an assortment of health problems. One of the most serious is hypertension, or high blood pressure, whose risks include heart attack and stroke. People who work chronically long hours increase their chance of developing stress-related hypertension. University of California Irvine researchers found that people working 41 to 50 hours a week were 17% more like to develop hypertension than those working under 40 hours, and 29% more likely for those working more than 51 hours.

And that's not all. Long working hours can increase the risk of coronary heart disease by 40%, a meta-study from stress researchers Marianna Virtanen and Mika Kivimaki found. Studies also show long workweeks can lead to depression.

A report by the Business Roundtable found that chronic overtime can substantially reduce productivity, not just during the extra hours but also during the rest of the workweek. This is because the fatigue is cumulative. It comes out of your hide the next day and the next when there is no time to recover.

Meanwhile, multiple studies going back to the 1920s show that productivity increases with more time to recover—from breaks to vacations. A program instigated by Microsoft Japan in 2018 demonstrated this principle still reigns. The company gave their staff five consecutive three-day weekends to see what impact it might have on output in this famed overwork culture. The result: a 40% increase in sales from the prior year.

The nation of Iceland found the same outcomes when it conducted large-scale trials of a shorter workweek. Spearheaded by social groups and labor unions, the Reykjavik City Council and the Icelandic government each initiated studies to weigh the impact of shorter working hours on productivity and work-life balance. The city tracked 2,500 people in more than 100 workplaces across a wide range of industries over a four-year period from 2015 to 2019. Those who got shorter hours shifted to 35 or 36 hours per week without reduced pay. Icelanders had been working an average of 44 hours a week, third highest in Europe. The second trial, sponsored by the national government, involved 440 participants.

To make up for the reduced hours, meeting volume and time were cut, prioritization of tasks improved, more services were moved to digital delivery, there was less time on coffee breaks, and start and finish times were shifted. The results: Productivity and service levels increased or remained the same, stress was cut, and happiness and work-life balance improved. People had less stress at home, more time for themselves, more exercise opportunities, and more energy to engage in life outside work, from getting together with friends to hobbies.

Well-being also improved in the office but not for people in the control groups in the studies who maintained their old hours. Likewise, stress at work dropped for those in the studies but not for those in the control workplaces that made no changes. The clear improvement in well-being and stress reduction in the groups with shorter hours, in addition to better or no loss of productivity, underscores that smarter work slam dunks the quantity metric of rote overwork.

The trials were such a success that 86% of Icelandic workers are now either working the shorter workweek or in the process of getting there. The report's authors noted that "the key to achieving shorter hours was often flexibility in how tasks were completed (the kinds of things we are talking about in this book), how hours of work and shifts were constructed, combined with interest and engagement in the process of shortening hours in the workplace."

Effective Workload Inventory

Work responsibilities have a way of constantly expanding, like a snowball rolling downhill, sucking up an array of tasks and duties unrelated to the job description along the way. Doing an inventory of the disparate parts of your workload can help you discover things you shouldn't be doing and perhaps some you should. Finding the most effective balance of tasks plays a key role in reducing overload and stress.

Let's start with two simple questions that helped one of my clients, IBM Research, save hundreds of thousands of dollars and improve the team's work-life balance.

- What should I be doing less of?
- What should I be doing more of?

What you discover in this exercise is that there are a variety of assignments and responsibilities that have attached themselves to you that don't make sense. How could the work be allocated better? Get the whole team or department to try this, and it can lighten overload and transform productivity.

Boundaries Are a Success Tool

Contrary to the conventional wisdom that boundaries are a constraint on performance, it turns out they are just the opposite, a success tool, and not just for financial bottom lines but also for psychological ones. Harvard Business School's Laura Nash and Howard Stevenson found in their research that the key component for successful business executives that led to true satisfaction in their lives was "the deliberate imposition of limits."

Satisfaction is the ultimate success, and the ability to bring proactive self-management to the table through boundaries delivers it. "It allows them to say I don't need to work at this particular thing until I'm satiated and hate the very sight of it," said Nash and Stevenson, authors of *Just Enough*, in the *Harvard Business Review*.

That's what Susan, the Denver financial advisor we met earlier, discovered when she got to the end of her rope with 70-hour weeks. "I was hating work that I love and, by driving myself harder and harder, I had started to hate myself and my life," she said. "My productivity was at a standstill, and I was always angry at myself for not accomplishing more."

The problem, she came to see, was that she was trying to *be* the best, an external goal without any tangible marker for what that was except raw hours, instead of focusing on *doing* her best, which is where the more important internal rewards come from. After shifting her outlook and revamping her schedule, she was able to set boundaries and improve her performance at the same time. Raw hours, she came to see, were the wrong metric in the knowledge economy.

When a client asked her to do another loan report after she'd just finished one for this customer, she did something she never did before. She said No. "I knew I had done enough," she said. The client was initially unhappy but called back the next day and apologized for being out of line.

"It feels great to know you can say you've done enough," she added.

Research by Mark Cullen, former associate dean of research at Stanford's School of Medicine, uncovered something very revealing about the impact of overperformance on job satisfaction. Even if you love your job, if you do too much of it, you'll hate it. Overly tasked people, says Cullen, don't like what they have done at the end of the day. It turns out that too much work strips all the accomplishment, and fun, from what you're doing.

Overboard Instincts

There's another piece to the boundary equation: psychology. We grow up in a culture that defines identity and self-worth through labor going back to the Protestant work ethic of Max Weber. Our jobs are so much a part of who we are that it's very difficult to find anything other than what is on the job description as self-definition.

When you draw most of your self-worth from what I call the performance identity, that becomes the go-to place for validation. This can lead to more and more performance and going beyond a healthy amount of work to unconscious overperformance. It also makes it hard to shift over to relaxation or fun since those don't supply the validation the performance identity wants.

Healthy performance is great but overperformance not so much. Performance is an external metric, based on the approval of others. The bump in satisfaction is ephemeral since you don't really buy it internally. You need to keep overdoing it to feel good about yourself.

This makes us our own worst enemy. Type-A personalities are particularly prone to this marathon route, needing to feel they can work more than the average mortal and seeing the term "workaholism" as a positive description. Scientists had to create a new word for workaholism that wasn't regarded as a badge—"overperformance."

You can get so far on-task that you can't get off task or stop thinking about work. You lose track of your own health and don't do any self-care, become unavailable to those close to you, view anything but work as trivial and valueless, and can't see the years whizzing by while in this state of unawareness.

The job is, in actuality, your social face, what psychologists call a "persona." The term comes from the masks actors wore in ancient theatrical performances to indicate roles in the play. When you think of yourself as your persona—an accountant, a scientist, a teacher—you have only part of the identity equation.

A resilient identity is the sum of a much bigger equation of personal attributes—competence, intelligence, kindness, humor, integrity, creativity, friend, family member, cyclist, or barbeque chef. You need to expand identity to your personal life, or you won't have one. Your true identity is deeper and guides you to the life you are working for.

Why Workaholism Doesn't Work

Researchers have found no positive correlation between workaholic behavior—long hours, feeling you should be working every waking minute, overwork—and productivity. Melissa Clark of the University of Georgia documented in a meta-study on workaholism research that "even though workaholics may spend more time thinking about and physically engaging in work than the average worker, this may not be of any benefit to their employer."

Clark discovered that "workaholism was related to the experience of negative discrete emotions (i.e., guilt, anxiety, anger and disappointment) at work and home, whereas work engagement was related to the experience of positive discrete emotions (i.e., joviality, attentiveness and self-assurance) at work and home."

People driven by negative emotions and pessimism have been shown to have reduced productivity, sales, and rapport with others on the job. In other words, healthy work is generated from within and satisfies core psychological needs as a result, while workaholism is a chase for external approval that can never be attained, since there is always the next item on the to-do perfectly list. Engagement fuels positive emotions. Workaholic behavior is rife with negative emotions.

And, of course, there are other consequences to workaholism in the form of health repercussions, including fatal heart attacks, like the one that happened to the executive at the consulting firm I mentioned earlier, and burnout. I spoke with one woman who had a heart attack at the age of 29 from her nonstop workaholic ways. The cocktail of long hours, high stress, and anger and hostility, which is a huge factor in heart attacks, is a ticking time bomb with a very short fuse.

Workaholics put themselves and their families at risk for a behavior that has zero upside—for work, friendships, or parenting, and it leads to a big void in the life department. If you have this habit, please step back while you can and consider the people who want you to be around for a while.

6 Autopilot Routes to Overdoing It

Many mechanical habits can drive an unbounded work style. Let's take a look at some of the patterns that can make us the kind of person we would never want to work for.

Over-Optimism

Many of us wildly overestimate how quickly we can get a job done. Then we find ourselves behind schedule because there was more to it than we thought. It makes a lot more sense to under-promise and over-deliver, instead of the other way around. Repeat after me: *I need to check time, resources and get back to you.*

"Just one more thing."

This habit makes you do one more email, then another, and before you know it, you have just added another hour to the workday. The way out: Use a stop time. Set an alarm for when you want to finish up for the day. When it goes off, stop there and pick up where you left off tomorrow.

Peer pressure

It's human nature to take our behavioral cues from what the majority is doing. It's also true that workaholics often set the tone for that majority and drive everyone overboard with them. The most important job is results, not mirroring the lack of discipline of others.

Rote busyness

It's very easy to flit from one thing to another in sprint mode without noticing that you have gone too far. The unconscious speed trap doesn't allow pausing for planning or reflection. It's not the speed with which you work but the focus that creates effective performance.

Center of the universe

Many of us like to think we are indispensable and that the company will fall apart without us. Confidence is good. Yet a belief that you are existential to the operations of the business can saddle you with a burden that can make work-life balance very difficult. It can make you work longer than you have to and skip or abbreviate vacations. I have met people who didn't take a vacation for years out of a fear that everything would collapse at the office without them. Then they finally took one and realized it was all a false belief. The company is still there, the job is still there, when they return. They never make this mistake again.

The cause is greater than me

Some of the most overworked people work for nonprofits, aid groups, and religious organizations. Their cause is so great, they feel they are not worthy to step back. They put in long hours and feel very guilty if they don't, since their mission is so important. Burnout is rampant in these organizations, which are also usually underfunded and understaffed, which adds to the stress load and the belief you have to go to heroic lengths to keep things going. No job, whatever the higher purpose, should jeopardize your health. What good are you to the organization, the people you serve, and your family and friends if you can't do your job because your health is deteriorating?

Home of the Brave

For all the logic of boundary-setting, putting it into action is a challenge. The boss-employee relationship is not one where we expect to have a say in anything. The lopsided leverage can make it seem that it's a no-go zone, but it's not.

A report in the *Harvard Business Review* by James Detert of the University of Virginia and Harvard's Amy Edmondson on speaking up in the workplace found that it is happening, and people aren't winding up having to send out resumes afterwards. They say the fear of speaking up is real but that the consequences of saying something are overestimated.

They found that people with better communication skills were more inclined to not keep silent. The conversations tend to be done by extroverts, which tells us something. Those who lean to verbalizing and interpersonal activity are doing what they tend to do.

Detert and Edmondson said that "self-preservation" was the culprit in preventing many people at one firm from speaking up. They urge managers to make it easier for more people to be candid and offer viewpoints about what is not working. Speaking up is how management learns what isn't working. The authors have a great description of the word No— which they dub "the improvement-oriented voice system."

I do an activity in my training workshops that illustrates the fear and potential success that comes from the topic of boundaries. I ask the group how many people in the room are good at setting boundaries. In a room of 30 people, two brave souls may raise their hands. In a crowd of 100, maybe five will volunteer. Boundaries are not the strong suit of most of us.

Next, I ask each of these intrepid folks what happens when they speak up about something, say, not enough time or resources for a particular deliverable, more urgent priorities, shutting off work email at home. Fire and brimstone? Nope. Usually no untoward reaction. One woman at a health organization said that sometimes the supervisor is not happy about it and she may get some static. But other times the boundary is accepted. I ask, "And they still employ you?" Everyone laughs.

Oftentimes, managers don't know how many things you're working on. Clarify with them the tasks you're doing. Your duties and schedules can help him or her see that it doesn't make sense to have you do an excessive number of things poorly that don't reflect the real priorities. Ask questions and offer more productive solutions than mechanically taking on more than the bandwidth can handle.

Boundaries give everyone a clear picture of where things stand, which is what you want to be able to do at the end of the day.

Finding Boundaries

Potential perimeters are all around us. You can get started on them on an individual or team level. Identify the pain points and practices that make the job difficult, drain time, drive stress, and are ineffective.

Here are some questions to ask:

- What are the time sinks, tasks, or processes that are keeping you from high-value projects and output?
- What is causing excessive workload and hours?
- What can you do to cut back, eliminate, or delegate some work?
- What could make your workweek less time-urgent, pressured, and more under control?
- How can you control distractions and interruptions?
- Are your turnaround times too optimistic?
- Which deadlines are the biggest drivers of stress? What could be done to make deadlines more realistic?

Perimeters, Calling

Identify from the list of potential boundaries below which you could implement to keep a 24/7 world in check:

Check email at designated times

Unbounded messaging is one of the biggest drains on productivity and often follows you home. Researchers have found that one of the best ways to get control and reduce distractions is to create a schedule for email and phone checking. Turn email and phones off (or on silent) and turn them on three to four times a day at your command.

Restrict reply-all

Everyone hates reply-all. We are on too many lists. It's crucial to cull them and remove yourself from lists you don't have to be on.

Use noise-silencing headphones to focus

A background of cacophony and distraction disrupts attention and productivity and drives stress. Headphones shut chaos out so you can concentrate.

Identify meetings you don't have to attend

The ability to opt out of meetings where your presence is not crucial is a critical tool to gaining precious time back in your day to get things done. How urgent or important is the meeting? Can someone else update you? Do you have a conflict? Find a way.

Establish a work-home perimeter

Set a time after work when you will be 100% at home in thought and deed. When will you stop checking work email? 6 p.m.?

Stop multitasking

Multitasking is self-inflicted interruption. All interruptions blow up working memory, which causes a disruption to productivity and to brain neurons. You can't do two thinking tasks at one time, something you will learn ahead.

Don't condition others to instant email response

If you respond immediately to email, you set expectations for others that their message will always get an instant response. This puts the pressure on you to drop everything as soon as an email comes in. Answer during a scheduled email-checking session.

Check time and resources before saying Yes

Don't say Yes automatically to an assignment until you have checked time, resources, and the urgency of the task compared to the other priorities you have. Speak up if you can't meet a particular turn-around time.

Clear rules on availability

One of the fallacies of the unbounded world is that you have to be available around the clock for management or clients. This leads to burnout, resentment, and poor productivity. Speak to your manager and get a clear picture on hours of availability. When availability rules are vague, boundaries are missing.

Turn off email alerts and notifications

Visual notifications and email noisemakers play to a survival instinct that hijacks attention and hands over control to an ancient part of your brain concerned with threats to life and limb. They make you feel out of control, which drives stress. Turn them off and check them on your schedule.

Push back on fear

Speak up about problematic parts of workflow, deadlines, or other bottlenecks that continually drive overload and stress. Analyze the problem, suggest an alternative solution, and propose it to your team or manager.

The Proximity Factor: Remote Office Boundaries

You can't drive away from the office at the end of the day when it's in your house. The three priorities you didn't get to today are feet away from handling. Why not go back to the desk and polish off one more task?

Remote workers need to resist going overboard in a less structured environment in which there is added pressure to make it known you are getting the job done even though no one can physically see you. I led a work-life balance training for a remote team at a medical laboratory firm. The company was happy to retain top talent by giving them the option to work from their homes across the U.S. As much as they liked the autonomy that virtual work provided, the group was finding it difficult to shut off the workday, get the mental detachment necessary at the end of office hours, and were too accessible to technology, which followed some of them straight into bed at night.

We zeroed in on the importance of time management, traffic lights, and setting the terms of engagement with technology. Companies that allow employees to work remotely are providing a vote of confidence in the ability of their virtual staff to self-manage their day. The responsibility is on the individual to structure the day in an effective way and utilize technology so that it enhances, not overwhelms, the chief productivity tool—attention.

Here are some habits that can turn remote work into what it was designed to be—a flexible route to a better work-life fit:

Remote Boundaries

Keep office hours.
It's the same work, just in a different space. Turn your unstructured home office into a structured schedule for yourself and family members to respect. Working at home gives you the ability to go off schedule to take care of personal or family issues. Just make sure you don't get sidetracked for too long and that you come back to where you left off. Stop work at the same time you would at the physical office, even if leaving means you wander a couple of feet to your living room.

Make your workspace all work.
It's easier to separate work and home if all the working emanates from one dedicated space. Set up a desk in a space removed from the eating and entertaining areas and potential distractions. Don't do anything else there but work. This area tells you when you are at work and when you aren't. That goes for work thoughts as well. We'll learn how to do that ahead.

Plan and prioritize.
Avoid falling into a pattern of random reaction, just responding to things coming your way all day. Be proactive with planning and prioritizing. Take 10 minutes at the start of the day to identify your main to-dos. Qualify tasks by their urgency. Does it have to be done today? If so, do it. If it can wait, identify a time when you will get to it. Create a next physical action for items on the to-do list.

Cut distractions.
Clutter, intrusions and procrastination pile up at home. We normally don't have the discipline that we have at the office, and we let stuff

go. You are the boss of your virtual domain, and only you can create the conditions that promote attention and focus. Make the effort to clean up your desk and workspace and remove distractions from view.

Take breaks and get exercise.

This is an area that is tailor-made for remote work, so it's important to utilize it. You have been left to make your own schedule. That means you can create one that allows your brain and body to get the daily recharging they need.

Researchers say we need to give the brain a break every 90 minutes to two hours. Step back for 10- or 15-minute reboots a few times a day. Use your breaks to build in exercise, take a walk, do some stretching, or make your lunch break an exercise break.

Do a simulated commute.

During the Covid-19 pandemic some former commuters began to think something they never thought possible: They missed their commutes! They missed their National Public Radio news en route to work. They missed their bike rides to work. They missed the decompression that the space between work and home provided.

So, some began to reconstruct their old routines at home, listening to National Public Radio in the morning when they would have before. A woman in one of my work-life balance trainings said she gets on her bike at the end of the workday and rides around the block a few times, as if she just rode back from work. It's just enough to provide a transition from the workspace. Give it a try. Even if it's symbolic, you are creating starting and finishing rituals needed to enforce self-boundaries.

Start a hobby.

When we don't have an identity outside work, we default to what we know. It's important to find an interest or affinity that can help develop another side of your identity, one that play scholars call the central life interest. What have you always wanted to learn? Try a new hobby that will help you learn a skill. This pays off your mastery need, which is one of the most effective ways to reduce stress and build esteem. The times of your life await.

Set your life alarm.

Everything on your plate is not going to get done by the end of the day, so it's wise to choose a time to stop before midnight. What is a reasonable ending time for you? You are not always going to be able to stop on a dime, but aim for consistent, regular closing hours. Set an alarm on your phone as a reminder—your Life Alarm. You're going home now. Wait a second, you're already there.

Going from the corporate office to the home office can pay powerful dividends for those who get organized and prioritized—more control over your schedule, more opportunity to take care of personal and family issues, easier access to refueling breaks, more concentration, and best of all, gratification of one of our core psychological needs. We all have a need to feel autonomous and to chart our course. All we have to do is resist the digital, self-interruptive, and caloric temptations.

Installing Traffic Lights

You may not be a fan of setting boundaries, but there is no alternative in an unbounded world. With the right approach, you can exercise a perimeter defense that reins in excessive demands, unbounded interruptions, or clients who want you to be available at all hours.

The famed workaholic and ex-head of General Electric, Jack Welch, used to tell his managers to demand 110% from their staff. He said he knew that wasn't feasible, but that it was up to employees to push back. We have to push back when necessary—when workweeks are regularly 50, 60 and 70 hours, when there is routine expectation of availability at night and on the weekend, when unrealistic deadlines drive heroic measures and you're still well behind in your work, and certainly when conditions are driving health blowback from chronic stress and burnout. No job is worth the risk of permanently damaging your health.

One of my clients, Christina, was shifted from her main job to a big project management role to ride herd on a huge assignment whose unrealistic deadline was burning out her and her staff. She was just coming back from a prior burnout episode and was concerned she was headed into that abyss again. Management was adamant that the deadline had to be met. Christina felt the pressure rising higher and higher as the deadline got closer, but it became clear the target date wasn't physically doable. She had to say something, or her health was in jeopardy. She did, showing her manager in detail why there was no possibility to make the deadline. The result: the deadline that couldn't move did, pushed back by an extra seven weeks, preventing serious health blowback.

Reining in the unbounded world can start in any department and organization with a conversation about unviable due dates, messaging, and the work-life challenges that come from letting devices and blind frenzy call the shots. The humans can install traffic lights.

Without a clear signal of what's out of bounds everything is considered inside the foul lines in an always-on world. What this means is that you have to say No sometimes. You can't get it all done on that timetable. You need more resources or time. The client can wait another day. Or maybe the task doesn't add up or is at odds with what you know is a better way to go.

This is where one of the keys to sustainable performance comes in: clear communication that frames the boundary not as a rebellion, but as a proposal for a more productive approach. Present a solution. You want to make a case for how the job could be done better with certain adjustments, making the manager look good in the process.

There are other solutions than Yes, whether it's an extended deadline, delegating, or reassessing how you do the task. The way forward is getting behind the abstract fear of speaking up by considering the real impact of an unbounded schedule on your work, the company, personal and family responsibilities, health, and sanity.

Boundaries are simply self-management tools to help you perform better in all the categories of life. My experience is that speaking up for healthy boundaries, far from causing disaster, usually results in the opposite, more respect, even if the boundary may not go through the first time. The only way for someone to know the problem is to communicate it to them.

Align Expectations

Vagueness is the enemy of work-life balance, and it reigns supreme in unsustainable workplaces. With everyone flying on time urgency, we don't take the time needed to give or get all the details on an assignment or determine if the deadline is realistic or not. Availability is assumed to be always and email response times to be immediate. The way out of assumed always-on mode is, of course, boundaries, and a critical way to do that is setting expectations.

Letting others know when you are available and when you are not and realistic response times can save heaps of stress and prevent overwhelm. When coworkers, supervisors, and clients aren't made aware of a realistic turnaround time, the default is to an unrealistic one. When they know not to expect an instant response to a message or availability after hours, that makes your day much more sustainable. We all need to train others to have realistic expectations.

For messaging and email, for instance, you can let everyone know they shouldn't expect an immediate response. You will get back to them swiftly—if it's urgent, by the end of the day. Let them know you have embarked on a new information management program, and that response times are part of it. They will be jealous.

For clients, the message can be: We pride ourselves on the quality of our work. I'm sure you don't want a drive-thru service. To give your project the attention it needs, we require another day or two (pick your time frame). On big projects that won't meet a deadline, let clients know as early as possible in the process, and why, to save worse stress later.

For supervisors and coworkers, set expectations on work hours. Have conversations about messaging after the workday. Establish that you don't have to respond at night and on weekends. If people want to send messages then, fine, but get agreement that you don't need to deal with them until the next workday, unless it's an emergency. Then define what counts as an emergency and that it will be handled with a phone call, not email. The same applies to vacation time. Now it's your turn.

- What expectations do you need to set for messaging? With whom?
- What expectations do you need to set for turnaround times? For which tasks and projects? With whom?
- What expectations do you need to set for availability beyond work hours? With whom?

Getting to Clarification

Most boundary conversations are about clarifying goals and priorities, so that the manager can see what you already have on the schedule, and you can get a sense for how urgent the task is compared to your other projects. Many items wind up on your list without them being clearly thought through or the manager knowing all you are doing. The boundary conversation is part reconnaissance, part proposal for a route that's more effective.

You want to set the right tone. Be controlled, logical, non-defensive, and non-blaming. Ask questions that can highlight problems with the timeline, support, the volume of what's on your agenda and allow the manager to be guided to the vicinity of your conclusions. What kind of outcomes are you looking for? Have you thought about this route? What kind of support do you think we need for this?

Productivity guru Bill Jensen, author of *The Simplicity Survival Handbook*, makes the point that "the Number One behavior in business today is moving to-dos onto someone else's plate. In most cases, this isn't mean-spirited or dodging. It's merely an effective way of coping with too many to-dos, too little time, and too little resources.

"Once begun, work follows the path of least resistance. Most of us manage our daily workload through triage: We avoid or postpone all but the most pressing decisions and tasks. And when everyone is in triage mode, the path of least resistance is to just keep moving, passing work on to others as quickly as possible."

This is the essence of the unconscious work style of mechanical momentum. You wind up with work that hasn't been carefully thought out in time or resources available. That's what boundary conversations are here to rectify.

What If You Have a Workaholic Boss?

While it's the job of managers to support, lead, and protect their teams, as I'm sure you know, not all are going to embrace work-life in practice. Some are workaholics, who will expect the same mentality from everyone who works for them and dismiss work-life boundaries and vacations as signs of weakness. This is how they see the world—performance measured by bravado physical stamina, when it's smarter work—mental toughness— that is the critical ingredient of success and keeping good people around in an unbounded world.

If you work for a leader or company like that, it's still worth it to speak up, and you have to if it's affecting your health and family.

Go to human resources and detail the impact on health and productivity. Offer suggestions that could lower the stress levels and overtime. If there is no help there, try to find sympathetic leaders and colleagues and get their suggestions.

Ultimately, have a conversation with the boss. Be clear that the prevailing work style is not sustainable and that it's affecting productivity. Propose something that would make the work more productive and less hazardous to health and life such as a more effective/realistic schedule or deadline. Ask to do what you propose as a trial. If nothing changes, come back a month later and ask again. If the response is dismissive or worse, it's time to consider working somewhere else. Your health is too important.

Direct and Indirect Ways to Say "No"

To keep the tide of to-dos from overwhelming your cranium, you have to get more comfortable talking about obstacles to getting the work done right. Jensen provides a useful delineation, breaking down the action into two lines of communication: the direct and indirect No.

The direct No is for colleagues and friends as well as people you don't know well. The language needed is simple and basic. You dispense with it quickly and without a racing pulse rate, Jensen says.

No.

No, thank you, though.

Too busy, I'll pass.

You use the more artful Indirect No's with bosses, customers and leaders, those who direct your actions, and networked teammates in the same company, group, or team. This audience requires a more nuanced route, with phrases such as:

Help me understand what you're trying to achieve.

What's connected to this project that's driving the deadline?

Let's talk about this.

What tools, resources, and support are available?

What if I presented two solutions that stayed within the budget?

Looking at what's already on my plate, what can I put on hold?

The most important thing to clarify is tools and support, says Jensen. Those are what set you up for success or, lacking them, failure and burnout.

Boundary Language

It might be a little nerve-racking, but you can deliver your message with confidence by recognizing that your suggestions are all about making you and the team more effective. Using the improved productivity angle, show how your idea of focusing on critical tasks or making an adjustment to a project is going to:

- do the job better
- get it done faster with more resources
- have less risk of errors
- save time, money
- have a more accurate deliverable date
- improve time management

The goal of the conversation is to draw out information that helps uncover additional details behind the matter that needs perimeters. In the process, you have more to work with to build in the flexibility you are looking for.

Focus on the "how" of doing the task in question, instead of the task itself, which creates resistance.

Keys to Boundary Conversations

Hit the right tone. Keep it positive and non-complaining. Instead of saying *I can't handle this project on top of everything else*, keep it about the impact the task could have on clients, important projects, or your ability to do the job right, which is compromised by poor health.

I wanted to let you know that this could bring several other projects to a halt and not give us proper time to do this or the other projects well.

Ask clarifying questions. Here are some phrases that can open up the clarification process, so you can learn where the boss is coming from, get details on goals and timelines, and she or he can learn what you are up against. The mission is insight that can lead to adjustments in the plan, leading to fewer tasks, delegation, or delay:

Can I get your advice on which of these tasks is most urgent? Why?
How important is this task? Is it time-sensitive?
This is a good idea, but can we also consider…

Be a good listener. It's important to listen to the leader's points and to let her or him know that.

I understand this is important, but we are too stretched to do this right.
I get your perspective on this. Here's another way we could get to the same outcome.

Use facts, not feelings. Sometimes it's best to just put the facts out there. Provide the evidence of why you need a different solution.

My estimates are that we will need more time. Here's how much time each of these pieces will take. How could we delegate or redesign the schedule?

Be Persistent

The meeting may hit a dead-end or hard head. It may not produce a standing ovation. But if you make your case enthusiastically with supporting data, you may win support, and you can lay the groundwork for future issues.

Successful boundary-setters I have met, from tech to government, finance, and healthcare, have several traits that help them follow their convictions to effective outcomes. They tend to be confident in their talents and work ethic, willing to go the extra mile in a crunch, know when their bandwidth is maxed, are concerned about the right thing, and they are persistent. They pick their spots judiciously and don't become malcontents. And they are motivated to make a change. Reflect on what motivates you, and you will have what you need to make your case.

CHAPTER 4

Stay Calm in the Storm

Reframe Reflex Stress & the Thoughts That Drive It

You don't see a lot of dogs running corporations or doing brain surgery, but in some ways, they are a lot smarter than humans. Take, for instance, how they respond to a stressful event, say, a neighbor and his dog entering the sniffing space of your yard. Your dog gets a whiff of the intruder dog, and bam! Let the barking begin.

This makes dogs great security guards and sometimes the bane of neighbors. When the dog reacts, its ancient defense sentinel, the amygdala—the same mechanism that sets off the human fight-or-flight reaction—goes off with the timeless trigger built to insure survival through instantaneous recognition of danger and immediate response.

Now what happens after the stranger dog has gone on to sniff the tree trunks, grass, and hydrants blocks away, or heads home for some Kibbles 'n' Bits? Does your dog keep barking for another two hours? Two days? Two weeks? Two months? Two years? No way.

That's what humans do. We keep barking. The dog drops the event like an old chew toy. It's like it never happened. He goes back to resting mode, plopping his chin on the floor. What other dog? What barking?

That's why dogs are smarter than humans. We hang on to the stressful event, clinging to the undertow of emotions. But we don't have to.

It's the Reaction

We have the power to shut off stressful events right after they happen and avoid buying false beliefs that we ruminate about for months on end.

It all depends on how good we are at managing the culprit behind stress, which isn't an external event—what somebody said, the deadline, or the setback.

Stress is the result of something much closer to home: your reaction to the stressful event or stressor—in other words, what you think about the event. It's your thoughts in the moment that turn on the stress response. I hate to tell you this, but you're stressing yourself out.

The culprit is faulty brain architecture that leaves humans prone to false emergencies. What do you expect from survival equipment built for use on the savannas of Africa 150,000 years ago? The factory warranty was up on our noggins a long time ago. The outmoded brain treats monthly sales quotas or an encounter with a difficult client as if they were charging rhinos, blowing things out of proportion before you have a chance to interject a rational thought.

Back before the modern brain evolved for rational thinking, all our ancient ancestors had to guide them upstairs was the primitive emotional center of the limbic system, the original brain, including its main threat detector, the amygdala (or amygdalae; we have two). The amygdala plays a major role in your life, since it's the hub of emotional responses, such as fear and anxiety. It stores and processes emotional events and thought associations connected to them. An overactive amygdala can lead to more anxiety and aggression, while a calmer one is inclined toward more curiosity and exploratory behavior.

Back in early human days, raw emotions determined whether you ran away, fought your way out of danger, or in some cases froze, also known as attentive immobility, a stillness that allows you to hide or prepare yourself for the next move.

The problem is that the stressors that set off fight-or-flight (or freeze) today aren't life-or-death but, instead, social stressors, where clarity of thought is needed to solve problems. It doesn't make sense today to run a mile and hide in some bushes when you have too many to-dos, or to deck the first person you see after a tough phone call.

Yet the ancient brain still reigns supreme in a moment of perceived danger, difficulty, or pressure, even if the threat is only an overstuffed inbox. Decision-making usually gets vetted in the higher brain of the neocortex, which subjects the data to rational analysis and directs an appropriate response. But when demands overload coping capacity, the threat information bypasses the modern brain and the danger signal streams straight to the amygdala, touching off a stew of unfiltered, irrational emotions. You are no longer in control of your modern faculties.

Irrational emotions triggered by your ancient survival equipment feed your brain with primal fear and catastrophic thoughts. A part of your brain thinks you're going to die that second, which is pretty catastrophic. Those thoughts then form into a false story that drives the stress reaction, such as *I'm going to lose my job,* or *I'm going to fail on that project.*

The default programming of the amygdala is wired to go off even before you are conscious of the threat. This worked well back in the early days of Homo sapiens, but the mechanism is as good at interpreting threats in the modern world as a divining rod is at finding water. You wind up yanked by the amygdala chain into a cycle of false alarms that leads to unnecessary anxiety and major health disorders.

Sometimes the result is a fight-or-flight meltdown that can cost you friends, jobs, and worse. Steven Slater was a flight attendant for Jet Blue Airlines when on a routine flight that was taxiing to the gate at John F. Kennedy International in New York, he was involved in an incident that became news all over the world. He said that a woman got up to pull her bag out of the overhead bin while the plane was still moving, so he told the woman she had to wait. She ignored him, pulled it out anyway, and it hit him in the head.

Investigators said later that no passengers could corroborate his account. What they could verify is that Slater got on the intercom, said he'd been badly treated by a passenger, he'd been doing this for 20 years, and he was done, the outburst laced with profanities. Something sent him over the edge into a fight-or-flight meltdown known as an amygdala hijack, a complete break with rational thinking.

The fight part came with the intercom rant. Then came flight. He went back to the galley, grabbed a couple beers, and as soon as the plane came to a complete stop, he pushed the emergency slide button, slid down the inflatable evacuation exit with his beer, hit the tarmac, caught a shuttle bus to his car and made his way home. He was arrested later that afternoon.

For a couple of weeks, Slater was a global newsmaker and working man's hero. But the thrill was gone fast. He lost his job and life got difficult because he couldn't manage the stress of that moment. Millions of reflex reactions triggered by stress-induced anger play out every day across the globe, with much more dire results to life and limb.

Managing stress is the art of non-reaction, defusing extreme fight-or-flight reactions as quickly as possible after they go off. One way you can do this is to see the fight-or-flight reflex as a con job unless it is a real life-or-death moment. Your ancient brain baits you into emotional reactions that make it even harder to deal with the issue at hand.

The mission before you is: Don't take the bait. Life is, in essence, a battle to keep the fear default under control so you can function in the world, assess concerns accurately, and find rational solutions. Not falling for the calamitous alarms of the overwrought security equipment keeps dramas you don't need down and life manageable.

Demands vs. Perceived Control

The workplace is a hive of deadlines, pressures, and challenging workloads, so there are many buttons that can activate stress. The cause, though, is the same. Job stress is triggered when a demand, or stressor, threatens to overwhelm your *perceived* ability to handle it. I have italicized "perceived," because this is the operative instigator or defanger of stress.

Stress is very relative. What stresses you out doesn't stress someone else, and vice-versa. What used to stress you out may not do so anymore. It all depends on your perception of a demand or pressure. Change the perception, the thought that you can't handle something, to a belief you can, and stress can't bite. It's easy to see from this the role we play in creating stress—and can play in eliminating it.

Work stress triggers range from excessive workload to time constraints, to conflicts with coworkers, constant email and messaging, big assignments, change, rude customers, draining emotional work (for those in social work, health care, customer service), job insecurity, poor communication, and lack of support.

Stress, of course, is part of life and work and not all of it is bad. It can be motivating when it's controllable. When demands are high and there are also high levels of personal control, or as it's known in the research, decision "latitude," the pressures of the job can be seen as exciting—so-called "challenge stress" that can lead to a sense of achievement in handling it. But "when demands are high and the individual has little control over them, the negative consequences of strain and stress develop," the University of Massachusetts's Robert Karasek explained to me. This is what some dub "hindrance stress" for its legion of negative effects.

Workplaces with high job demands and little control or resources with which to manage them are at a higher risk for chronic stress that can lead to burnout and its telltale symptoms—exhaustion and cynicism, studies show.

Karasek's Demand-Control Model is one of the most influential in occupational stress research. Mental strain that leads to stress "results from the interaction of job demands and job decision latitude," Karasek wrote in one study. He pointed out that this is the same nexus where job dissatisfaction comes from. "Redesigning work processes to allow increases in decision latitude for a broad range of workers could reduce mental strain," he noted.

Making these kinds of adjustments is one of the goals of sustainable performance and the ground-breaking management model known as autonomy support, pioneered by Edward Deci of the University of Rochester. It's a work style based on the science of motivation and gratifying core psychological needs such as autonomy, competence, and connection with others. It spreads decision-making (latitude) through teams and increases perceived choice (and control along with it) and self-responsibility. It's the future of work—and present, if we can make it so. I've found in leading autonomy support programs for employee engagement that the increased latitude and better communication that result from them serve as potent stress management tools.

Use Your Levers of Control

When stress overloads coping capacity, the amygdala is quicker on the draw than your conscious ability to discern what the danger is. It can trigger the stress response in .02 one-hundredths of a second. That's great for real life-and-death issues, but not so great when it comes to social stressors, which it doesn't have a clue about, so you are subject to a lot of overreactions you don't need.

The main weapon in the battle against stress is cognitive appraisal, or your perception of control—how you size up the danger and your capacity to meet it. Do you feel you have the ability, time, coping skills, energy, motivation, support? Can you handle it?

Another leading workplace stress model, Job Demands-Resources, holds that physical, psychological, social, and occupational factors can increase perceived control and moderate stress. Strong self-efficacy, self-control, and optimism can help you cope with demands. More support from co-workers and supervisors, more role clarity, leaders who offer more participation in decision-making and autonomy can help you see the work as doable, manageable, and reduce stress. If demands outstrip resources, it can lead to stress, exhaustion, and burnout.

Most job stressors at the personal level come down to asserting control over demands, your mind and the false beliefs that come from it. You will be glad to know you have more levers of control than you might think.

You can increase control over your work environment by changing how you do your tasks and the conditions that drive stress, something detailed in these pages. For instance, using best practices to control email overload and messaging, one of the biggest sources of stress and overwhelm, can put you in charge of nonstop interruptions.

You control the story of stress. You can change how you think about the demands by disputing false beliefs that drive fight-or-flight. It's how you adapt, shift, and respond to demands that leads to the perception that challenges are manageable.

You control how long you hang on to that story and the stressful event. Drop it like a schnauzer right after the event is over, and there is no stress hangover orbiting the brain for weeks and months.

And you control your choice of a host of stress management techniques and recharging activities—progressive relaxation, breathing exercises, physical exercise, meditation, hobbies—that relieve stress and shut off its false danger signal.

What's Pushing Your Buttons?

Stress is such an autopilot behavior that most of the time its causes are lost in the intensity of emotions and the knee-jerk responses they set off. The event that precipitated the stress might have happened a week, a month, or many months before. Or it might be plainly visible from something that occurred today.

Also, you are not encouraged to acknowledge stress. You're supposed to suck it up. Yet what happens when you do that? You think about the stress over and over in a pattern called rumination, which is actually what causes your stress. Researchers say that acknowledging stress is key to getting rid of it, since identifying and describing the source of the worry gets it out of the fear gear in your brain and into the rational regions where you can solve the problem.

You can start getting control over stress triggers by getting them out of your head, where they do their damage, and onto paper or a screen, where they can be unmasked. What are your biggest stressors? Who or what is a frequent button-pusher? Why is the event or person making an ancient part of your brain think you're going to die—in other words, you can't handle something? What is it you can't handle? The better you get at recognizing stress triggers, the easier it will be to manage them.

The physical symptoms that show up when you are stressed—churning stomach, headache, backache, insomnia, tightening in the jaw, and racing heart—can tip you off to stressors. Be on the lookout for what's going on when you feel those symptoms.

Flush Out Stress Triggers

The first step is to identify the scenarios at work driving stress. What are the tasks, processes, bottlenecks, operations, and situations that make you and things feel out of control? Write them down.

Now go deeper into that list and identify the top pressures, triggers, and demands within those situations that are causing stress for you. Identify each major stress trigger and then break them down like this:

TRIGGER: Your Stressor

- How and when does it activate?
- What is the thought behind the stressor that is making your ancient brain think you're going to die, a belief you can't handle this situation?

- What behavior does it set off?
- What adjustments could you make in how the task is done or your thinking that could make you feel more control over this stressor. Is it life-or-death? If not, tell your brain and turn off the false survival alarm.

The Anxiety Spiral

When the stress response is triggered, it sets off a wave of intense emotions and extreme thoughts, since the ancient brain thinks your demise is imminent. The longer these thoughts are allowed to spiral and remain unchallenged, the more the false story gets locked in as true for days, weeks, and months. The mission is to stop the cycle as soon as the stress reaction goes off to avoid buying the false belief and hanging on to the stress.

This was confirmed in research by Penn State's Thomas Borkovec, Michelle Newman, and Aaron Pincus, along with Richard Lytle, who showed that nipping anxiety in the bud works. "Because the anxiety spiral is weaker at its initiation, coping responses have a greater chance of reducing the anxiety and of preventing its continued intensification," they reported in a study on treating anxiety.

"It's the accelerating spiral of anxiety, in which worry begets more worry—the rumination process—that leads the initial irrational thought to gain credence and power," they noted.

Rumination is the hidden engine of stress and pessimism, and it plays a major role in depression as well. You have to catch this menace when you go into rehash mode after a stressful event or fixate on a future fear and, instead, divert your thoughts and physiology from the false alarm of the ancient brain. The technique below will help you quickly calm the mind and body and wake up your rational brain.

Cool the Fire with Deliberate Breathing

When the stress alarm triggers emotions and panic, you have

to quickly extinguish the fire. That's made harder by the way stress acts on your breathing. It makes breathing shallow, which keeps you from getting the deep lungfuls of air you need to prevent the brain from adding more adrenaline to counter the lack of oxygen in your blood.

Deep breathing makes sure you get the oxygen you need in a moment of duress. Studies with mice have found that some breathing neurons appear to be able to calm the arousal system that turns on the panic button.

Deliberate breathing is a great tool to help you calm down quickly. Then you can use your analytical brain to deactivate the false danger signal. This exercise slows the heart rate, blood pressure, and raging emotions, so the modern brain can resume command. Make sure to do this exercise slowly to counteract the frenzy set off by anxiety.

Step 1

Put your hand on your abdomen and feel your stomach rise and fall as you breathe deeply through your nostrils from your belly. Feel the air swell the stomach and then chest as it moves up the body.

Step 2

Slowly inhale through your nostrils and count to five as you do so.

Step 3

Now exhale slowly and count to five as you do so.

Step 4

Repeat inhaling and exhaling to a count of five for two minutes.

The Call to Hormonal Arms

When you are faced with a demand you don't think you can handle, your brain reacts as it was programmed, sending the autonomic nervous system into fight-or-flight mode and preparing the body to escape or battle the threat. The process starts with a stress trigger or negative event—a deadline, overwhelm, a client's unreasonable demands, unnecessary criticism, traffic. The amygdala quickly calculates whether you perceive you can manage the demand.

If not, it sets off the survival equipment to help you fend off the threat, but that just makes things worse in the social-threat world. To solve a nonlife-threatening demand, you need your mind to be flexible, resourceful, the very thing fight-or-flight eliminates.

After the trigger has gone off, emotions quickly conjure up the most catastrophic scenarios. Because the dire thoughts are in your head, you think they must be true. But they're not. They are hare-brained fantasies concocted under the altered state of the stress response. It's a problem that has been around for a while. As the Roman philosopher Epictetus put it two millennia ago, "Man is not worried by real problems so much as by imagined anxieties about real problems."

The explosion of emotions and fearful thoughts after your buttons are pushed is the signal that you are headed for a stint of overreaction to an event that doesn't require it. You have to bring your modern brain back into the picture, or you go down the rabbit holes of anxiety and rumination that can last for days or months.

This means you must do something we are never taught—fight back against stress instead of, as we are always told, just gut it out. You need to contest, challenge, and dispute the stressful event right away before your brain buys the false beliefs and exaggerations of the stress response—and before long-term stress compromises your health.

Stress alters and suppresses systems in the body that aren't needed in a survival moment. It shuts down your digestion and processes that manage the production of acid, which leads to many stomach issues. The stress response suppresses the immune and tissue repair systems. To help you fight or sprint from danger, the velocity of blood moving through your body is supercharged by a jacked-up blood pressure and heart rate. Stress increases the bad cholesterol and reduces the good cholesterol, among many other things you can do without.

Then it's just a matter of time before physical symptoms start showing up. As you hang on to the stressful event, and the event turns into chronic stress, physical repercussions multiply. It might be bowel issues, back pain, or insomnia to start out with, but the longer the stress lasts, along with the effects of the alterations to key systems in the body, major illnesses from hypertension to heart disease and diabetes can develop. The last stage of the chronic stress cycle is burnout, total depletion of your energetic resources and a state of chronic exhaustion.

There are two basic phases of the stress response. In the first phase, activation, the threat signal rockets from the amygdala to the next-door hypothalamus, which plays a key role in hormone production. It dispatches a chemical known as CRH (corticoid-releasing hormone), which triggers the release of ACTH (adrenocorticotropic hormone) from the pituitary, which initiates, among other things, the release of glucocorticoids from the adrenal glands way down atop your kidneys. It happens in seconds.

The adrenal medulla unleashes stress hormones such as adrenaline and noradrenaline, while the adrenal cortex releases steroid hormones—cortisol and cortisone, known as glucocorticoids.

A typical minor stressor may have a period of minutes for the activation phase, followed by several hours of recovery. As the CRH component fades, it leaves glucocorticoids in charge. Their goal is to get the parasympathetic nervous system to step in and replace lost resources, namely, sugars and fat burned up during activation. Studies show that after a stressful event we reach for junk food to replace the lost resources. And, yes, this is how stress makes us fat.

Brain, You're Wrong

The thoughts triggered by stress live outside the world of reality. So, one of the first things to do to kill panic and restore order and sanity is to introduce the brain to reality—challenge the thoughts that feed you false beliefs. *Brain, I'm not buying it.* One of the most effective ways to do this is with an exercise I like to call the reality response, which comes from the cognitive behavioral toolkit. It vets crazy thoughts and puts them to the test of evidence.

You start by identifying the extreme, worst-case story being fed to you by panicked emotions. The first thought that goes off with a negative event is an exaggeration that sets off a false belief. You need to challenge it quickly before it convinces you it's real.

Take one of your stressors and identify in the exercise below the extreme, worst-case story behind it that is making your ancient brain think you are about to die. Usually, it's some kind of hit to the ego. The culprit can be a feeling that you're not capable of doing the job or will never make it in the world. Or maybe someone said something that you interpreted as a lack of respect, and that set off a hidden belief, known as an iceberg, that can't be tolerated.

After that, list the most likely story (or stories) for what happened. These are just the facts and evidence of what took place. Then finish by creating a new story going forward, utilizing the facts from the most likely story to describe how you will react the next time this stress scenario appears.

Counter Stress with the Reality-Response

What is the FALSE STORY behind the trigger that set off the stress response, a belief you can't cope? What is the worst-case scenario that your ancient brain is interpreting as imminent demise?

False Story: (Describe worst-case story)

Secondly, what's the MOST LIKELY story for the situation? Write down just the facts and evidence of what happened. No emotional characterizations.

Most Likely Story: (Describe most likely story)

What's your NEW STORY? What can you tell yourself to counter the false story and turn off the danger signal? Example: "Yes, I have a tough conversation ahead, but I've done it before. Here's how I can handle it."

Your New Story: (Describe new story)

Don't Believe Everything You Think

Managing stress is a function of managing your mind, not buying stressful thoughts, and, instead, contesting them. If the thought is in your head, you think it must be valid. Yet we have plenty of nonsense passing through our brains on the hour. Every year hundreds of people who get that email from the Nigerian prince saying he's found $10 million he wants to share with a complete stranger fall for it. The FBI says millions of dollars are lost on these scams.

Or maybe you are at the store, and you see a nice pair of pre-ripped jeans. The thought occurs, "Those holes would look really good on me. Should I go for the big holes or the more discreet ones?"

We are capable of a lot of wacky thoughts, particularly when the stress equipment is turned on. We need to take our thoughts with multiple grains of salt. Thinking is habitual, a livestream of unmoored fears, worries, and random associations nonstop. Just because it's in your head doesn't make it true. Just because you believe something doesn't make it true.

Harvard researchers Matthew Killingworth (now at Wharton) and Daniel Gilbert made the point in a fascinating study that the human mind is not like that of other animals, who don't spend their day thinking about where they aren't. They are laser-focused on where they are at any moment. Their study, "A Wandering Mind Is an Unhappy Mind," found that people are "thinking about what's not happening almost as much as what is," and that sabotages happiness.

The minds of the participants in their study were wandering 47% percent of the time when they were asked to check in through an app. They were less happy when they were off in other tenses. Mind wandering was "generally the cause, not the consequence of unhappiness." Having a flexible thinking style, the ability to choose which thoughts to pay attention to, instead of being at the mercy of random negative sidetracks, is critical to avoid the slide to unproductive worrying.

Ruminating about future dreads is especially a big stressor. "Anxiety is always anticipatory. It has to do with the possibility of future bad things happening," said Borkovec, Newman and colleagues in the Penn State study we touched on earlier. It keeps you responding to "mentally constructed realities as if those were actually happening."

That last sentence makes a very important point. As much as it might seem like it, thoughts are not real. They are more like theories and imaginings. Only experience is real. To manage thoughts that drive stress, you have to become skillful at not believing everything you think. That means being able to observe thoughts without having to grab them or engage with them. You have to see projected worries and worst-case scenarios as unreal neuron burps and let them pass.

It's like standing in front of a mirror. The mirror grabs your image, but when you step away, the image is gone. You can do the same with thoughts by simply noticing them without having to hang on to them and then letting them go, as any terrier could tell you.

The Mastery of Awareness

The mind has a mind of its own, so it's crucial to keep a regular and skeptical check on its uninvited intrusions, delusions, and knee-jerk reactions. That can't be done when you are on unconscious autopilot, which is the case with stress.

We live in a world of stimuli, some of which push us beyond our coping ability. If it's more than you think you can handle, off goes reflex stress, emotional reactions, and a beeline to anxiety, fear, and unwanted negative rumination.

The way out is self-awareness. Most of the time we are so caught up in pressure, deadlines, and racing through the day, we are oblivious to emotional reactions, moods, and counterproductive thoughts that drive our behavior. We even miss the signals from our bodies or ignore aches and pains trying to tell us we are pushing too hard. Working without awareness is hazardous to mental and physical health, not to mention working and living effectively.

When you have awareness, you are cognizant of where you are in the moment. You are not trying to get somewhere else. You have full attention on the task you're doing as well as the macro picture of how what you're doing is affecting your emotions, goals, and attitude.

Self-mastery is being aware of the stress reaction when you are in the middle of it and being aware of the mood when you are in the middle of it. Awareness is the prerequisite for stress management and work-life balance. It brings us back to our senses — and keeps us from losing them. It's also key to the two options we have at our disposal to manage stress:

1. Either catch stress in the act immediately after it's gone off and turn it off, or
2. Be calm and patient enough, so you don't get triggered in the first place.

We are going to learn how to use each of those strategies.

Change the Story of Stress with Attitude Breathing

A great way to change the bogus story fueling the stress response and catch yourself immediately after your button has been pushed is Attitude Breathing, developed by the HeartMath company. The goal is to substitute a story of calm for panic to wake up the modern brain, so it can take back the wheel from the primitive ancient brain. It's both a physical exercise and a thinking exercise, which makes it doubly effective at not just calming you down, but also reframing the thought behind the stress.

When stress is triggered, and you feel a wave of intense emotions and dire thoughts, step away from the location of the stressful event and find a private place to do this exercise. Go outside, to the rest room, sit in your car or some other quiet place, and do this very quick and potent process.

Step 1

Put your hand on your stomach and take a deep breath through your nostrils. Breathe from your belly. Feel your hand rise and fall on your stomach with each breath.

Step 2

Ask yourself: What would be a better attitude to have in this situation? Now, with each breath, think, or say out loud, if you are in a place where you can do that, a phrase that shifts the story from catastrophe to one that neutralizes emotions and wakes up the modern brain.

You can use the phrase "stay neutral." With each breath, you're thinking, or saying it if you are alone, "stay neutral." You can also use two phrases I made up for myself: "I don't react" or "stay objective." You can think, "don't judge before you get the facts" to avoid jumping to worst-case conclusions, or "make peace with this" when you have to accept something you may not want to. You can make up your own phrase, as long as it's something that takes your emotions out of the picture.

Step 3

Do the exercise for two to five minutes, until you actually believe the phrase, and you have just cut stress off at the pass before it has time to develop into a long-term hazard.

It's kind of like smelling salts for the brain. When you say the phrase over and over, your modern brain will start to think, why are you saying "stay neutral" again and again? The analytical brain wakes up, realizes it has been hijacked by a stress episode, and can then take back control of the ship. At the same time, the breathing is helping to un-tense muscles, which also shuts down stress, which can't coexist with full physical relaxation.

© 2001, Heartmath LLC

Bad Brain Architecture Feeds You False Alarms

Unfortunately, our brains aren't built for things like reply-all lists or congested parking structures, whose non-lethality they are clueless to compute. Lost in time, the mind conflates non-life-threatening issues with life-or-death emergencies.

Feel overwhelmed because you have too much to do? That's enough for the stress response to go off, because excess volume is by definition beyond your perceived ability to handle the load. Does that deadline seem impossible? Before you can even think that or verbalize it, the amygdala already knows and switches on the alarm if it senses you can't hack it.

Are you going to die if you don't meet the deadline? Hardly. Will you live to see another day when you have to start over again on a project because you made a mistake? No doubt.

Message overload is very good at setting off the fight-or-flight button, which is why we need strategies to manage it. Email overload makes you feel out of control, overwhelmed. You think *I can't handle it,* which equals *I'm going to die* for the caveman/cavewoman brain.

How many times have you thought or felt you couldn't handle something? It would not be a short list if you are a normal human. Now think about what happened every time you thought you couldn't handle something. You wound up handling it. You *always* handle it. So, the next time that thought appears tell yourself this out loud: I CAN handle it, because I ALWAYS do.

We burn up the best years of our lives responding to bogus alarms set off by malfunctioning mental hardware. Have you ever lived next to someone whose car alarm is on the blink, going off at all hours and particularly on Saturday morning when you're trying to sleep in? You have the same problem in your head—false alarms chronically sounding battle stations. The answer to both is to adjust the equipment and switch off the errant signal.

This is quite a bit easier to do with a car alarm, but with training and repeated practice, you can switch off perceptions that drive your survival equipment into repeated overreactions. You can reappraise the story of stress to one you can manage, because you are the commander of your ship. You control the story of stress.

Active vs. Passive Coping

There are two basic ways we react to stress. One is quite familiar, known as passive coping. You try to ignore the stress instead of taking it head on. Since the issue isn't resolved, it continues to nag away, triggering your body's survival equipment and its health blowback. Passive coping can result in chronic stress, alcohol and substance abuse, and anger that expresses itself at home and may be taken out on others, since the stress response aggravates the aggression part of the brain.

The research shows that passive coping is a dead-end. You need to eliminate the stress by fixing the problem. That's how the second style, active coping, works. You go after the root of the issue. You make adjustments to task practices driving stress, have conversations with supervisors about unviable schedules, change how you think about stressors, modify how you interact with others, improve skills of adaptability. Active coping is problem-solving. You see that the stress isn't tenable and are proactive about changing the situation.

What is your coping style? Passive or active? What could you do to be more active?

Stress Is a Thought

It's the stories you tell yourself through self-talk and beliefs under pressure or in response to negative events that determine whether you go off or not and how much control you can exert over the demands you face. When it comes to stress, that story is a false one, supplied by a panicked brain.

Stress is a physical-emotional reaction to demands driven by can't-cope thoughts. As Mark Twain said, "Drag your thoughts away from your troubles...by the ears, by the heels, or any other way you can manage."

The nexus of emotions, thoughts, and the words they like to hang out with are at the core of the problem. We are very verbal creatures. There's a steady stream of judgments, observations, beliefs, evaluations, and opinions streaming verbiage through our minds. Words and catch-phrases easily attach themselves to emotions, moods, and feelings, fusing in a way that saddles us with false labels about what's really happening and fuels beliefs that drive anxiety.

The University of Nevada's Steven Hayes, author of the fabulous book *Get Out of Your Mind and into Your Life*, has done some great work in getting under the hood of the scalp and managing the thought pistons. He says we get caught up in mental self-infliction and loops that drive anxiety because we mistake our thoughts as descriptions of ourselves when they are just thoughts.

He says that you have to look *at* your thoughts, instead of *from* them, which is the default mode. It makes all the difference in whether words that have attached to emotions in your head have the power to drive your pulse rate or not.

It's easy to be trapped in emotion-word framing that gins up false self-definitions and illusory catastrophic beliefs when you have no space between your thoughts and yourself. To keep the word machine that runs stress at bay, you have to find separation from your thoughts and learn how to reframe them as the harmless neuron ramblings they are.

Hayes calls the technique he developed to do this cognitive defusion. Counterproductive and extreme words fuse to emotions and feelings that then drive fearful and anxious thoughts—and self-definition. The idea is to decouple those words from the emotion and person thinking them. When you say, "I'm stressed," it's as if 'stressed' is your first name. It becomes your identity. Change that to "*I'm having the thought* I'm stressed," and the judgment and emergency are gone.

When your self-talk says, "This job/situation is too difficult for me," you set yourself up for anxiety. You can defuse that by thinking, "*I'm having the feeling* this job/situation is too difficult." A phrase that describes what's really going on—you looking at a thought—provides the proper labeling for what's taking place. It's only a thought.

"The point is to break through the illusion of language, so that you can notice the process of thinking as it happens rather than only noticing the products of that process—your thoughts," explains Hayes. "When you think a thought, it structures your world. When you see a thought, you can still see how it structures your world (you understand what it means), but you also see that you are doing the structuring. That awareness gives you a little more room for flexibility, explains Hayes in *Get Out of Your Mind and Into Your Life*.

"When you learn how to defuse language, it becomes easier to be willing, to be present, to be conscious, and to live the life you value, even with the normal chatter going on inside your head."

Hayes, whose work has been cited in studies about burnout, has zeroed in on one of humankind's biggest foes, our own thoughts. He has developed a host of exercises and tools to help us navigate pitfalls of the mind and create a more accurate thinking style. Let's take a closer look at his process for defanging thoughts by utilizing his cognitive defusion technique, thought labeling.

Look *At* Your Thoughts, Not *From* Them

Labeling your thoughts breaks through the reflex word blizzard and lets you catch yourself before the unchallenged thought sets off stress. When you have anxious thoughts, and the mind keeps ruminating about them, use some of these great cognitive fusion-busting phrases from Steven Hayes to label the thought for what it is.

- I am having the thought that…(describe anxious thought)
- I am having the feeling of…(describe anxious thought)
- I am having the memory of…(describe worrisome memory)
- I am having the bodily sensation of…(describe sensation)
- I am noticing the tendency to…(describe behavioral urge or predisposition)

Labeling breaks up the knee-jerk pattern of buying any old

stressful thought. You are not a hostage to uninvited, dire word fusions in your head.

Catastrophic Thoughts: The Worst-Case Default

You turn your wallet or purse upside down but can't find it. Your credit card is AWOL. Immediately, the heart rate quickens and thoughts race to catastrophe. Someone is running up a huge tab at the local jewelry store. Your identity has been stolen.

Or maybe you just lost a sale you had told your boss was in the bag. The self-talk goes to crazyland. *I'm going to look like a fool. Maybe I can't do this job. I'll have to look for another one.* If you want proof that everyone has a creative side, just look at the worst-case scenarios we concoct under the influence of fear and stress. Who needs Stephen King when we can tap into the wildest horror movies inside our head?

You can go from zero to 100 on the panic scale instantly, thanks to the automatic features of your survival equipment, which don't need your conscious participation to spring into action. And just like that, the modern, rational brain has been sidelined and you are a bystander on the unhinged ride of fight-or-flight.

The first thought after a stressful event is a catastrophic one, since part of your ancient brain thinks you are about to be an ex-living person. This sets off the pattern known as catastrophizing, a loop of worst-case scenario thinking that exaggerates what happened over and over.

You don't get a specific death message. It comes out in the form of an extreme thought or false belief that is equivalent ego-wise, a psychic fatality, such as *I'm going to be fired,* or *I didn't get that sale, maybe I'll never get another one.* Fused with the emotional charge of a seeming life-or-death moment, these thoughts are hard to pull away from. We cling to the false belief as truth unless we can catch ourselves, wake up modern faculties, and vet the situation with the facts.

Catastrophizing is an attempt to forecast the future effects of a stressful event. Studies show, though, we are terrible at predicting the future. We vastly overestimate the outcomes of future negative scenarios, from how long the negative consequences will last to the intensity of the experience. If you're in a negative mood, which you always are when stressed, the predictions get even more unreliable. One fascinating study by Eric Johnson and Amos Tversky that had subjects read a story of a tragic death found that it led to a 75% overestimation of negative future events happening to the participants.

How often have the imagined catastrophes in your life come true? Almost never, if ever. To manage stressful thoughts, you have to get out of the prediction business and understand how thinking traps like catastrophizing set you up for counterproductive behavior.

Catastrophic thoughts can come as a single worst-case notion or, more insidiously, as a spiraling cascade that ratchets up the disaster, with each false belief topping the prior one in exaggeration. Karen Reivich of the University of Pennsylvania and co-author of *The Resilience Factor*, reports that there are three styles of catastrophic thinking: Downward Spiral, Scattershot, and Circling. Some people are more prone to one or several. All of them keep you ruminating about doomsday fantasies, blocking any purposeful action to solve the issue.

Downward Spiral

No doubt you are familiar with this albatross, since it's easily unleashed by fight-or-flight episodes. It's a chain of increasingly dire thoughts, each one multiplying the scale of the disaster.

You've just been given a major project to manage at work. It's not due for a year, but already you are experiencing insomnia from a catastrophic projection. *This is the biggest job I've ever had. There are so many pieces to it. How am I going to get it all done? Can I do it? If I don't do it, I'll lose my job. Without my job, I won't have money. I'll wind up on the street. My marriage will fall apart.*

Scattershot

This style of catastrophizing flits from one doom to the other. The stress response leads you to see dreads and impossibilities everywhere. It's a stew of bad outcomes.

I put so much work into that proposal, but the client wants me to start over again and redo it! How can I do that with everything else on my plate? I have to go to that parent-teacher meeting. My son will be upset if I can't make it.

Circling

Since the ancient brain thinks you're going to die from the stressor, it's adept at keeping your thoughts locked on the threat like a spotlight. This makes circling, thinking about the anxious thought over and over again, a very frequent pain in the brain and a major cause of rumination, which cements the false beliefs into a credible story.

Circling comes from the research of Susan Nolen-Hoeksema, author of *Women Who Think Too Much*. She taught at Yale and investigated the thinking style of rumination, found to be a key piece of depression. She discovered that men and women tend to have different responses to the beginnings of anxiety or sadness. Men typically distract themselves—go to the gym or play a video game—while women ruminate, the anxious or sad thoughts circling around and around, giving the false beliefs life by doing so.

Here's how circling plays out for someone who has to speak in front of a big group:

How am I going to get up in front of a hundred people to give that pre-sentation? The first two speakers were incredible. How can I go on after them? I'm already hyperventilating. I'll be the worst speaker there. I know I'm going to blow it.

Worst-Case Triggers

Besides stressful events, there are several other triggers that set off catastrophizing. By understanding how they increase the odds for negative projections, you can keep them from driving your thoughts over the cliff.

Ambiguity. Uncertainty is a major engine of stress and predicting behavior. The known is safe, the unpredictable prone to make us worry about exaggerated things that might befall us.

Something you highly value. Threats to things that are very important to you are quick triggers. The very late-night call from an aging parent. The cancelled flight that prevents you from getting to an important business meeting. This has happened to me a few times. Once, my flight was cancelled due to mechanical problems after I had boarded a plane in Charlotte, North Carolina scheduled to go to Myrtle Beach, South Carolina, where I was leading a training the following morning. It was the last flight to the area that night. After I got the "flight cancelled" message with a rebooking for the following morning on my phone, I could feel a catastrophic geyser ready to blow like Old Faithful.

Instead, I went into action mode to shut it up. I Googled the drive time from Charlotte to Myrtle Beach: three-and-half hours. I could pull it off. All I had to do was stay awake all night. Easier said than done. I rented a car at the airport and was on the road by 11:30 p.m. I drove in a torrential downpour that slowed things to a crawl multiple times, but I got to the hotel after 5 a.m. I was in the conference room leading the four-hour training by 7:30 a.m. and as the morning wore on, I imagined a grand finale of being hauled out of the room on a stretcher. Somehow, I stayed on my feet until the end.

You already fear the situation. Things that are already on your radar as a fear are primed for catastrophizing when a threat in that realm occurs. These can range from having to get on a plane when you fear flying to worrying about a party you have to go to if you are an introvert.

Get Out of the Prediction Business

Catastrophic thoughts trigger future threats that stir up fear and anxiety, but they are false beliefs. Think of a mental simulation of the future that has caused or is causing you anxiety and write it down.

Now use the following phrases from Karen Reivich and Andrew Shatte, co-authors of *The Resilience Factor*, to submit the thought to analysis. Write down these phrases with answers to vet your catastrophic thought.

"That's not true because…"

"A more helpful way to see this is…"

"A more likely outcome is _____ and I can deal with it."

Have these phrases handy on a Post-It note on your computer screen or maybe on your refrigerator, ready to swoop in with reality.

The Contagion of Secondhand Stress

The Delta pilot came bursting out of the locked door of the hallway that led to his commuter plane in Grand Rapids, Michigan, where his departure was stuck on hold. "What's going on here?" he yelled, throwing his arms in the air in exasperation. "I have never seen it take this long to get a flight off the ground!"

He was steaming, but one of the gate agents did not respond in kind. She said calmly, "It's a system problem, and we are working on it." She said it with a smile and didn't let the captain push her buttons.

After he turned around and went back to the plane in a huff, she told her colleague. "I don't know his job, and he doesn't know mine."

It was the perfect reaction to a scourge that spreads stress like a virus: the contagion of secondhand stress. She did two things that made her immune to his stress. She didn't take it personally and separated his emotions and the cause of them from hers.

I wish I'd had it on video as a teaching instrument for most of us who are little more than mood marionettes, picking up on the stress of everyone around us. The reality is we are born to be copycats.

Humans are designed to pick up on the emotions and physical expressions of others, thanks to brain cells called mirror neurons. These cells cause us to mimic the emotional states of others and behaviors from laughing to crying and yawning.

We've all experienced the stereo yawn. You don't even have to see the other person yawning to uncork an epic yawn yourself. Hearing it is enough to send your simulation equipment into the actions of sleepiness, even if you're not sleepy at all. The same goes for laughing and smiling. Have you ever caught yourself smiling in response to someone on TV who's laughing in an ad? *Wait, what am I grinning about? It's not even funny.*

It's all part of the equipment we have evolved as social animals to bond with others, size up threats, and increase our odds of being able to navigate the mysteries of the emotional world. Yet the simulation gear works too well when what we are mirroring is other people's stress, which we pick up in the form of secondhand stress.

Stress contagion comes from our ability to "catch" aspects of other people's emotions, which helps us understand how the other person is feeling, reported a study led by Stephanie Dimitroff. Understanding others is great, but do we have to pick up their stress in the process? As if we don't have enough angst of our own, we are also sitting ducks for the pass-along anxiety of coworkers, spouses, friends, bosses, family members, neighbors, and cable news commentators, passed along through mirror neurons.

One of the earliest studies to confirm the contagion of stress was the Trier Social Stress Test. The investigation showed that stress-related cortisol and alpha-amylase were released not just in the bodies of nervous people asked to speak spontaneously in front of a group of judges, but also in the observers watching the speakers. It's not just that we feel for them in their predicament. We feel just like they do, their chemistry mirrored in ours. It's amazing. It turns out that we are all highly talented emotional impressionists.

And it gets worse. Dimitroff and company wanted to see if viewing people in distress, watching people speaking in front of a group or watching videos of stressed-out individuals could cause a contagious cardiac response in the observer to reflect the jacked-up heartbeat triggered by the stress response. It did. The study showed a direct correlation, an increase in cardiac response that varied depending on the level of stress in the speakers or videos.

Subjects were able to clearly separate people who weren't in the stress zone from the subtle and not-so-subtle cues that pulse rates of speakers or people in the videos were racing. Being able to read others emotionally is a finely tuned art that aids social functioning, but it's hard to turn off, since it's an autopilot behavior.

8 Ways to Fight Secondhand Stress

To keep secondhand stress from piling on, you have to be able to find the "off" switch. You want to be understanding of the plight of others, but you also need some separation. You can't do your job if you are absorbing the anxiety and grief of others all day. This is a particular challenge for those who work in emotionally intense industries, from health care to social work and emergency services.

Here are some things you can do to resist the stress of others.

1. **Identify where the stress is coming from.**

Is it yours or is it coming from someone else? Ask: Whose stress am I picking up on today? The plight of someone going through difficulty is concerning, and you want to be understanding. As bad as it may be for them, though, their stress is not a life-or-death event for you. You are not under mortal threat, so the stress you are picking up from them is a false alarm.

2. **Talk to the person about the habit.**

If there is someone raising your blood pressure through impatience, anger, hostility, cynicism, unrealistic expectations, or negativity, call them on it. Let them know that a particular behavior of theirs is counter-productive and transfers strain to you and others around them. Tell them about mirror neurons and encourage them to leave their emotional hot potatoes in the microwave.

3. **Separate yourself from the event/person.**

Keeping distance between the emotions of others and your own is crucial. Like the Delta gate agent, you want to be able to see that the cause of the stressful behavior of others is not you but something in the head of the stressed person. For anyone working in emotionally challenging fields, such as social work or health care, you want to feel *for* your clients and patients, but you don't want to feel *like* them, because if you do, you run the risk of undermining your own health and ability to help them. Emotional distancing doesn't make you less caring, just less of a potential burnout case.

4. **Don't take it personally.**

Taking events personally is one of the biggest drivers of stress. It triggers the ego, which sets off a boil of emotions. In the case of secondhand stress, the art is to see that it's personal for the person doing the stressing, not you. The cause of what that person says or mirrors to you is within their head and subject to the irrationality of their caveman brain's fight-or-flight equipment.

5. **Exercise choice.**

Like guilt, secondhand stress is a manipulation by others. It may be unintentional, but it nonetheless takes your free will out of the process and leaves you a spectator in your own emotional life. That doesn't work for humans, since one of our core needs is autonomy, having agency over our lives. The next time someone mirrors stress, refuse to have them dictate your emotions. Tell yourself you determine the content of your life.

If I grab someone else's stress, then I will drop it, because it's not mine.

6. Stop mirroring the negative emotions of others.

When people transmit negative emotions, the default is to pick up on that cue and go negative too. Instead, don't respond in kind. React to complaining with positive body language and comments. Change the subject. Don't feed the beast.

7. Shift mood.

Moods are ephemeral. They can change in an instant. We don't have to go with the first rote emotion that comes up from our mirroring equipment. You can crowd out the negative emotions of secondhand stress by shifting attention to a positive event or exercise. Music is a great mood shifter, so have some handy that lifts you up and turn to it when secondhand stress bites.

8. Try a Secondhand Stress-Free Zone.

Take a cue from the social sanctions on smoking, and have your team or organization print up signs and bumper stickers to place around the office, declaring it a Secondhand Stress-Free Zone. Explain what that means, and that rampant stress transmission can be as harmful as nicotine.

When people around us understand that they are unwitting drivers of the poor health of people close to them, we can all start to get more control over our reactions, which will be healthier for the stress inflictors too.

Stay Out of the ER—Test Your Stress Level

Humans made it through the gauntlet of evolution because of our legendary adaptability. Cold, heat, bad food—we adjusted and kept on ticking. Yet adaptability is a habit that can threaten your survival when it comes to stress.

The adrenaline set off by the stress response masks the fact that your body is going down from the wear and tear of stress. It makes you feel like you're transcending it all, so you get used to the stress and adapt to it, leading to major health issues presenting in late stages.

It doesn't have to be this way. You can get an early jump on stress with regular stress testing. We do eye checkups, mammograms, and blood panels, but we are never taught to identify and manage stress. You need to measure stress levels on a regular basis, or you wind up at the mercy of a runaway medical train.

How do you know if you are in the danger zone? See the section below, where you can learn about the tests you can do to monitor your stress levels, from saliva to blood and treadmill tests.

If you are under a lot of strain, and even if you think you are managing the pressure, it may be only the mask of adrenaline. You owe it to yourself, family, and friends to take the miniscule amount of time needed for a stress test.

7 Stress Tests That Can Save Your Life

If you are feeling stress or having any of the classic symptoms—insomnia, digestion problems, high blood pressure, the total exhaustion of burnout—it's critical that you get checked out.

Basic stress tests measure the level of cortisol in your body to see if it's elevated. The stress response triggers your adrenal glands to produce hormones such as cortisol and adrenaline to help your body prepare to confront danger. Cortisol helps regulate blood pressure, the immune system, blood glucose, and affects a host of organs and systems in the body, including sleep, so you want to make sure it's not oversupplied.

High cortisol levels from stress cause a host of problems, from heart disease to diabetes and can increase the risk of depression. Interestingly, researchers have found that cortisol levels drop in people who have burnout, the last stage of chronic stress.

Burnout depletes all coping and energetic resources. Chronic Fatigue Syndrome and Addison's disease are also marked by low cortisol levels. Cortisol testing can determine if you have abnormally high levels of the hormone from stress or very low from burnout. You don't want either one.

You can also take a cognitive test to determine stress levels as well as heart exams, such as electro-cardiogram and exercise tests, and a blood pressure test.

Saliva Test

This may be the simplest stress test, one which checks cortisol levels at various times throughout the day. You leave a saliva sample in a test tube-like device and send it off to a lab for analysis. You can buy saliva test kits over the counter and online. Most experts, though, feel that the saliva test is less accurate than a blood serum test.

Cortisol Blood Test

A blood test is a good way to determine whether you have abnormal cortisol levels, high or low. Certain medications can interfere with test results, such as steroid drugs, estrogen, androgens, and anti-seizure drugs. This test is typically done twice in a day—morning and afternoon around 4 p.m. to track cortisol levels at high and low points. According to the National Institute of Health, the normal values for a test at 8 a.m. are 6 to 23 micrograms per deciliter (mcg/dL).

Cortisol Urine Test

A standard urine test can also check cortisol levels. The National Institute of Health reports that the normal range is 10 to 100 micrograms per 24 hours (mcg/24h).

Cognitive Stress Test

This non-invasive approach can be very helpful in identifying stress and the situations that cause it. The questionnaire can be used in conjunction with other tests, such as a blood test or blood pressure test to map out the larger picture.

Blood Pressure Test

Keeping an eye on blood pressure is an important tool to track the effect of stress on your cardiovascular system. Healthywork.com's Peter Schnall, one of the top researchers in occupational stress, says that it's crucial that you get your blood pressure measured, not just at the doctor's office, but also at work. The true state of elevated blood pressure may not appear in the calm of the doctor's room. He strongly recommends that you test BP at work to measure how your body is faring in the heat of the workday.

The CDC says normal blood pressure is 120/80 mmHg. According to the American Heart Assoc., Stage 1 Hypertension begins at a systolic number (the top number of your BP reading) of 140-159 or a diastolic number (the lower figure) of 90-99. Hypertension Stage 2 is a systolic of 160 or higher and a diastolic of 100 or higher, while a Hypertension Crisis is higher than 180 for systolic and 110 for diastolic.

Electrocardiogram Test (EKG). This test can find underlying issues of heart disease and hypertension. Electrodes measure electrical signals in the heart to find patterns of rhythms and heartbeats that may be a tipoff to problems. The devices have gotten very streamlined and much easier to use, and can spit out results on the spot, so you can get a very quick analysis of your heart health.

Exercise Stress Test. An EKG, though, may not always be enough. Brian Curin, co-founder of Little Kitchen Academy and former head of the Flip Flop Shops, can thank the exercise stress test for saving his life. An EKG didn't catch the massive jam in his arteries. Also known as a treadmill test, the exercise test measures the way your heart responds to physical effort, and the extra demands can ferret out issues other tests can't. This test pinpointed an array of problems so serious that Curin was advised to go directly from his test into surgery, where he had to have a quadruple bypass at the age of 39. Do yourself a favor and take the time for your health and get this test done.

Beyond monitoring and testing, if your office or department has a stress problem, don't ignore it. Fix it.

Reclaim Your Time

There's one more benefit of managing stress. Keeping stress at bay is one of the best time-management techniques. How much extra time for your work and life will you be able to free up when you can offload the dump truck of anxiety that has burned up so much of your time on the planet and almost all of it for nothing? A couple months? A few years' worth? Reclaim your time and mind with the stress-fighting strategies in this chapter and more critical tools coming up in the next one.

CHAPTER 5

The Hidden Blowback of Stress and Burnout

Fight Back with the Best Stress-Busting Strategies

G iven how important our bodies and minds are, you would think we would get a lot more instruction in how they work—and don't. But no. We all have to grope in the dark as if we were the first people on Earth who ever encountered stress, runaway emotions, and setbacks. How could there not be classes every year from middle school onward on managing emotions and stress and the impact of the mind on the body?

Instead, each of us has to stumble around the field of hard knocks before, if we're lucky, we learn that what we think can show up with a vengeance in our bodies.

Before we dive into strategies to control stress, I want to talk a little bit about a super-critical part of dealing with a crazy-busy world and its over-the-top pressures: the physiological blowback of unmanaged stress. This stuff really is a major danger to your health, not something you should just "take." Because when you take it, you get taken down by any number of medical issues.

Stress is a factor in six out of the seven leading causes of death in the U.S.—heart disease, cancer, stroke, lung disease, Alzheimer's, and diabetes—because it undermines so many crucial functions of the body. If we knew more about what it's doing to our insides, the world would take it a lot more seriously. Yet you're walking around. You look normal. What's the problem? It's just in your head, right?

Demands or pressures in your mind instantly turn into a full body reaction once the stress response is activated. The key to the potential health damage is how long the stress lasts. If the stressful event is brief, and there is no after-life for the anxiety it set off, it's not harmful.

The stress response was designed for short bursts, providing a sudden rush of power to our limbs to help us avoid danger. It was intended to last only a limited time, until we were out of harm's way. When the saber-tooth tiger left the neighborhood, so did the stress. Stress in small doses doesn't wreak large-scale havoc on your body. Stress that is chronic causes major harm to any number of systems and organs and can lead to trips to the ER and the loss of all coping resources, burnout.

Duration is the most dangerous thing about stress, because of the way the stress response alters your body for battle stations. With chronic stress, these and other realignments become the staging grounds for long-term damage. The effects of the constant rapid heart rate and higher blood pressure can lead to the nation's number one killer, cardiovascular disease, which includes conditions from heart disease to stroke to coronary artery disease. The heart, arteries, and blood vessels have to work much harder, but after a continuous period of excess emergency mode, things start breaking down.

The velocity of blood gushing through blood vessels like water through a fire hose starts wearing down the lining inside the vessels, causing little tears and pockets that attract a crowd—immune cells, foam cells of fatty nutrients, circulating platelets that promote clotting, fat, glucose, bad cholesterol, and plaque. It's standing room only inside your blood vessels along with a heightened risk for clogs that restrict the flow of blood through veins in the form of atherosclerosis.

And that's not the only way chronic stress alters the critical work of your circulatory system. The force of the blood flowing through veins is so great that it results in something really amazing. It causes more muscles to grow around the arteries to contain the load. Those muscles, in turn, can clamp down on the vessels, making them more rigid, restricting blood flow and increasing blood pressure further. You want to leave the muscle-building to the gym.

The collateral damage of chronic stress is extreme. It doesn't stop by denial or trying to will your way through it in a display of bravado. You have to actively challenge the stressor, show your brain the life-or-death threat is a fraud, or train the mind to catch the default. Here's a tool that can help by training your brain to not fall for the false alarms of stress.

Use an Implementation Intention to Beat Stress

One habit-busting technique can help you even before the fight-or-flight alarm goes off. It's called an implementation intention, and it was developed by Peter Gollwitzer of New York University to help with goal attainment. He studies what causes habits we don't want to go off automatically. He found that a mechanism behind habitual behavior can be trained to trigger a more productive response.

Habits are cause-and-effect-based. A cause takes place. Say you see some chocolate cake. Then an effect happens instantly. You scarf the cake. He developed a technique to prime the brain to have a different reaction the next time a cause of habitual behavior occurs. He created the If-Then statement to prime the brain to have a different effect: *If I see chocolate cake, **then** I won't eat it, or **then** I'll have some fruit.*

You say it out loud a few times, and it programs your brain to have a different reaction the next time the cause takes place. You remember you have to avoid the cake the next time you see it. He pairs the implementation intention with a goal-focusing exercise called mental contrasting. It reinforces the implementation intention with a benefit you will get by changing the habit you want to lose.

You can use an implementation intention to catch yourself whenever a reflex habit such as stress goes off. In this case, the if-then statement can be: *If I feel stress, **then** I won't take the bait.* This helps wake up the modern brain to the fraud of non-life-threatening stress, and it can help you catch yourself.

Prime your brain for a different effect for any habit by doing this exercise.

- What is your most important wish or goal about reducing stress?
- What is the most important positive outcome from realizing this wish?
- What is the most critical obstacle in yourself that prevents

you from realizing your wish?
- Use an implementation intention, an if-then statement, for your stress management goal.
- Create your implementation intention: "If I feel stress from (your stress trigger/scenario), then I will (your action) and not take the bait."

A Workaholic Will Die Before an Alcoholic

Of all the health problems triggered by stress, few are more vetted in the scientific literature than the connection between work stress and heart conditions. A host of studies has traced the link between job stress and cardiac issues alone.

Dozens of studies show the connection between job stress and heart attacks. Research by Mika Kivimaki of the Finnish Institute of Occupational Health has found that job stress may double the risk of heart attack and cardiovascular disease.

One massive meta-study conducted by Kivimaki and colleagues Jaana Pentti, Jane Ferrie, David Batty, Solja Nyberg, and Marcus Jokela examined seven studies, covering 102,633 people, on the association between work stress and mortality. It found that job strain in men with cardiometabolic disease (which includes everything from angina, to stroke, insulin resistance, and diabetes) had a higher rate of mortality than from high cholesterol, obesity, lack of physical activity, and high alcohol consumption.

It's a cruel irony, but chronic stress is the real life-or-death threat, not the social stressors that set off the fight-or-flight response. You have to turn off the false alarms that drive stress, or you put your health at a risk greater than gulping down platefuls of high cholesterol food or smoking a pack a day.

This is why a workaholic will die before an alcoholic. An alcoholic will have a long demise, while the workaholic has a sudden exit, thanks to a heart attack that could have been prevented with some basic stress management strategies.

Risky Repercussions

It's not just your heart that's at stake; your brain is too. An important meta-study on the connection between stress and stroke led by Yuli Huang found that high job strain increases the risk of strokes, or brain attacks, by 22%. The risk is higher in women, 33%, and for the most common type of stroke, ischemic stroke, which cuts off blood flow to the brain, job strain increases the stroke risk by 58%.

Stroke is the fourth leading cause of death in the U.S., affecting 800,000 people every year. It occurs when there is an interruption of blood flow to the brain, which prevents brain cells from getting the oxygen and nutrients they need, and they can die as a result. Stroke can lead to temporary or permanent disabilities and paralysis.

Meanwhile, over in the abdomen department, chronic stress is messing up your body's digestion equipment by putting the system on idle. It forces the stomach to cut down on acid secretion and bicarbonate and mucus production, which help protect the stomach. These and other changes can lead to gastritis, acid rebound, ulcers when combined with the Helicobacter pylori microbe, and irritable bowel disease.

Women with moderate to high stress levels were found in a 12-year study to have an almost two-and-a-half times increased risk of acquiring diabetes three years later. The other thing stress does to increase the risk of diabetes is make us choose unhealthy lifestyle habits, such as overeating, smoking, drinking, and lack of exercise that can contribute to Type 2 risk.

Stress constricts the brain to perceived worries and crises, which suppresses the urge to have fun, relax, or do activities that help you recover from stress. That's the last thing your ancient brain wants you to do, since it thinks you are on your last legs. It wants one thing, for you to keep ruminating about false beliefs, as if doing so is going to save your life when the potential is actually the opposite.

Track Your Warning Signs

The radical changes the stress response makes to your body's systems and organs to prepare you to survive a life-or-death emergency can lead to a swarm of symptoms. They are warnings you need to pay attention to, since the longer they are left unheeded, the more damage is done.

Keep a log of which stress symptoms show up for you. Where does stress occur in your body? What sets the symptoms off?

Here are symptoms to be on the lookout for. Check off which ones you experience.

Basic Stress Symptoms
Digestion, bowel issues
Insomnia
Rapid heart rate
Anticipatory anxiety
Overwhelm
Highly distracted
Memory problems
Fatigue
Withdrawal, isolation

Acute Stress Symptoms
Chest pain
Difficulty breathing
Very high blood pressure
Dizziness
Panic reactions
Loss of control
Angry outbursts
Mental confusion
Depression
Antisocial behavior

Stress Undermines Your Immune System

The need to maintain a strong immune system is a pretty simple concept to grasp. Without our built-in defenses keeping at bay a world buzzing with bacteria, microbes, parasites, and viruses, we are more apt to come down with any number of health problems. Long-term interruption of the immune system from stress causes a 40% to 70% reduction in the various metrics of the immune system function, reports Stanford's Robert Sapolsky.

Stress releases a flood of glucocorticoids such as cortisol into the bloodstream. They have been shown to interfere with the body's immune agents, such as lymphocyte cells, sidelining some and even killing lymphocytes.

As Sapolsky detailed in *Why Zebras Don't Get Ulcers*, "Give someone massive amounts of glucocorticoids, or a huge stressor that has gone on for many hours, and the hormones will be killing lymphocytes indiscriminately, just mowing them down. Have a subtle rise in glucocorticoid levels for a short time…and the hormones kill only a particular subset of lymphocytes—older ones, ones that don't work as well."

Clearly, then, the smart thing to do is to turn stress off and turn your immune system back on.

Why Sleep and Stress Aren't Good Bedfellows

One of the most common symptoms of stress and one I'm sure you are all familiar with is insomnia. Stress reduces the length of sleep—not just how many hours you sleep, but how often you wake up during sleep. A whopping 78% of participants in one study reported a link between stress and insomnia.

At the most basic level, stress is at odds with the concept of sleep, which is the act of closing up shop for the day and shutting down. The stress response is an activation agent. It drives arousal. It's a stimulant. It doesn't want to shut down for the night, because you are going to die, or at least that is the message being sent by an outmoded brain.

One of the hormones that the stress response floods your body with to help you survive a threat is cortisol. It's not a sleep aid. Sleep starts when cortisol is at its lowest point, and you are ready to wake up when it is at its highest level. Too much cortisol interferes with sleep regulators, activates the autonomic nervous system and increases alertness.

Acute and chronic stress have been found in studies of rats to decrease slow wave "delta" sleep, the deepest sleep, when the brain is less responsive to external stimuli, as well as REM, critical to our circadian sleep/wakefulness rhythm.

When stress suppresses the immune system, that also impacts sleep. The immune system is critical to the work of cytokines, which signal immune system molecules that regulate sleep. Without these elements, sleep is interrupted.

Stress-related insomnia causes many of the same problems that the stress that created it does—increased cortisol, fast heart rate, higher body temperature (which can also cause wakefulness) and oxygen consumption.

If you have insomnia, you are in a higher state of alertness, even though you are fatigued from lack of quality shuteye. Insomnia has been dubbed an "over-alertness obstacle" to sleep. That's exactly the modus operandi of non-life-threatening stress—overactivation and overreaction.

The Stress Audit

Stress is a tricky thing to manage because of the reflex nature of the behavior. Countering autopilot overreactions requires that you keep your awareness up. It's a daily practice.

You have to monitor reactions to demands and create backup systems that force you out of mechanical momentum to take the real pulse of how you are coping. Here's a tool that can help you do that.

Pull out your phone and set an alarm to go off at a time in the mid-afternoon. This is your daily Stress Audit. When the alarm goes off, ask:

- Where am I at with stress today on a 1 to 10 scale, 10 being the most stressed?
- If you are at 6 through 10, then ask: Where is the stress coming from? Identify the thought(s) driving the stress. What's behind the thought? What's behind that? What's so intolerable, difficult, or demanding that it is activating the survival gear?
- Then ask: Is the thought accurate? Is it useful? Is it life-and-death? When you see that the danger signal is false, not life-and-death, the stress response can shut off in three minutes.

How Stress Shreds Thinking, Shrinks Your Brain, and Makes You Stupid

If each of us had a blooper reel, our biggest blunders would come at times when we were late, rushing, on deadline, under pressure, times when we were under the influence of stress. That's when brains take leave of their faculties and default to impulsive actions that lead to regrets later.

Stress reroutes thoughts from the top floors of the brain to the lower ones—to the irrational emotions of the limbic system and to rote mode. You no longer have command of your chief productivity tool, attention. When rushing, you send emails with typos, put the wrong name on the message, forget attachments, or overlook important calculations and may have to do the task all over again. When late to a flight, you leave your smartphone charger cable behind and worry about whether the front door is locked at home. When stress sets off sudden anger or rage, you can lash out without thought.

A host of studies show that stress is a relentless saboteur of attention. It subverts intellect, and the mind can devolve to a state as reckless as that of someone who's had too much to drink. We do things under its command that we never would with full, unsidetracked presence of mind. That means stress has a major impact on all the things we need attention for—focus, discipline, analysis, and decision-making.

"Acute stress impairs the intention-based, attentional allocation and enhances the stimulus-driven selection, leading to a strong distractibility," noted researcher Jessica Sanger and colleagues in a study investigating the link between stress and attention.

The stress hormone of cortisol sends you on a chemical bender, a detour away from goals, focus, and the directed concentration of what's known as "top-down" attention (you choose what you pay attention to) to "bottom-up" attention, a survival mechanism that hijacks the higher brain in moments of perceived threat.

Studies show that chronic stress can lead not just to mental lapses, mistakes, and anger but also to impaired cognition, because of the impact of cortisol on the hippocampus and executive attention function. Stress undermines decision-making, judgment, attention, impulse control, mood, and social rapport, all of which affect your decisions and performance.

Stress and the cortisol it produces can kill brain cells and shrink the volume of the brain. One study that examined the brains of 2,231 women found that those with the highest cortisol did poorer on memory and cognitive tests, and their brains lost volume. Lower brain volumes and memory difficulties have been linked with higher risk for dementia later in life.

Stress also drives aggression. Through the crazy reflex of stress-induced displacement aggression, we take out stress on others. Studies show that stressed mice lash out and bite other mice. When they do, cortisol levels that indicate high stress drop. They and we feel better after transferring our anger or frustration to someone else. It's an invitation to conflict and back-biting, at least in the figurative sense—not a prescription for teamwork or trust. It's also a major driver of crime and police blotters the world over.

Stress also makes us not fully weigh the downside of a given decision. One of the reasons for this is that it reduces impulse control and discipline. The stress response overrides analysis for instant survival action. It's a kind of temporary insanity.

What About the Role of Work Systems in Stress?

While it's true that stress combusts within the mind of an individual, there is no doubt that the way workplaces are organized, and the structures of workflow and workload can drive people to overlap their coping banks and drive strain.

Employees, teams, and employers need to identify stress drivers that send nerves and performance south. Which tasks, deadlines, projects, operations, or workloads are driving unmanageable stress? Which adjustments can be made to systems, time management, information management, or support, so people don't have to work in an unsustainable, unhealthy way?

Speak Up for Your Health

When stress is impacting your health, you need to say something about it. The manager may be completely unaware of the problem, and chances are good you are not the only person struggling with the issue. Find a time to have a conversation and present a proposal to modify a chronic stress driver.

That means the fight-or-flight response is going every day, every night, jacking up blood pressure and heart rate and suppressing the immune system. Explain that the stress is affecting your health and that your symptoms are concerning, or, that you are on track for symptoms you don't want, from heart disease to stroke.

Assure the supervisor that you have no problem doing the work, yet the manner of the workflow, deadlines, or colleague conflict is counterproductive.

Propose a Stress Intervention

- Pinpoint the activity, task, person, or system driving the stress.
- Offer an idea(s) to change what's causing the stress.
- Start with an ideal solution you think will fix the problem.
- If that isn't agreed to, propose something that answers part of the problem.
- Ask for a counterproposal if there's no agreement.
- Suggest a trial of your idea. As we have learned, this is a great way to get something to change that otherwise wouldn't. If the adjustment improves health and productivity, it stays.

Stress Reduction Practices

Argue With Yourself

Mental health requires that you develop a healthy skepticism about thoughts in your head, especially ones that pop up when adversity strikes. Instead of accepting knee-jerk reactions, it's important to argue with the source of the problem, your brain.

This means submitting thoughts to the test of factual evidence. This can reveal how inaccurate the doomsday notions are. The process of rational investigation wakes up the modern brain, which can then step in and take command back from the survival equipment. It's called cognitive behavioral therapy (CBT), reframing unrealistic and exaggerated thoughts and beliefs that self-inflict worries, anxiety, and needless suffering.

Psychologist Albert Ellis was a leader in the development of CBT, which he saw as a more practical and rational way to solve emotional issues than traditional psychoanalysis. He believed that the problem at the root of most of our psychological difficulties is our thinking, namely, irrational beliefs that make us act out blindly without vetting the extreme thoughts we're reacting to. We will explore false beliefs further in Chapter 8, but for now, suffice it to say that we all have notions out of our consciousness that whip up emotional responses to negative events.

Researchers Katherine Richardson and Hannah Rothstein found in their meta-analysis of a host of studies on company stress management trainings that cognitive behavioral strategies "consistently produce the largest effects on psychological outcomes." It's the approach I use in my programs. The idea is to uncover the false belief behind a stressor or anxious thought by contrasting it with the most likely evidence of what is really happening. This allows you to turn off a stressor for good, instead of having it reappear continuously and have to address it with stress reduction processes over and over.

Ellis created the influential ABC Model to break down the illusions and mistaken beliefs that drive anxiety.

"A" stands for Adversity, the negative event, stressor or setback.

"B" is for Belief, the catastrophic thought that pops into the mind after a stressful event. But it's a false belief since it's being supplied by the ancient brain and the irrational emotions it triggers.

"C" stands for Consequences. These are the feelings, emotions, and behaviors in the moment of the stressful event that come from the belief, not the adversity.

"D" is how we deal with the stressor. We Dispute B, the false belief, by presenting all the evidence and facts of the case without emotion.

"E" is for Energization. We are energized when we resolve the stressor.

Let's try it now, by putting a stressful event or adversity of yours to the test with the ABC Model, followed by an innovative variation that attacks catastrophizing with positive emotions.

Deploy Your ABC's

The external event, the adversity, A, does not cause stress. You do, by ruminating about B, the false belief. That creates C, consequences—stress, anger, sadness. You have to challenge that thought.

Take a stressor that pushes your buttons. Now submit it to the ABC Model:

What's A, your **adversity** or the stressful event?

What is B, the false **belief** that comes from it? What is the worst-case thought—usually a threat to ego that is so intolerable it is turning on the life-or-death equipment? Is it accurate?

C stands for the **consequences** in your behavior—the emotions, feelings and thoughts that come from this belief. Describe your feelings and reactions in the moment of the stress reaction. You got mad, acted rashly, thought everything was ruined.

Now you unleash D. You **dispute** the false belief. Bring in the facts of the stressful event as a lawyer would. Focus on evidence, alternatives (there's more than one cause for the event, so why take the worst?), implications (how likely the belief is true), usefulness. Focus on causes that are changeable, specific, and non-personal. Write down how you will dispute the false belief.

Resolve the false belief, and you have E, **energization**. You are energized after solving the problem.

How to Dump Catastrophic Thinking

The University of Pennsylvania's Karen Reivich uses a strategy that combines the ABC Model with an innovative second step, going from identifying worst-case thoughts to best-case. Thinking of best-case scenarios brings in positive emotions, which help crowd out the negative emotions, slow down the frantic thoughts, enhance breathing, and allow you to come back to rationality to identify the most probable causes and a solution going forward.

You need to stop catastrophic thoughts immediately before they become entrenched in your brain. Use your modern brain to break down a catastrophic thought with the process below.

- **Get all your worst-case scenarios on a piece of paper or a screen.**
- **Now list all best-case scenarios.** Your brain is going to go—*Are you kidding me?? There's nothing good here!* Take a deep breath and think about possible positive outcomes. Let your imagination go, and in the process, the infusion of positive emotions acts as a fire retardant, lowering the emotional temperature, improving breathing, and returning rational command to your ship.
- **List the most probable case for what happened.** Just the facts, no emotional characterizations.
- **Based on what is the most probable case, create a plan of purposeful action going forward** to prevent this stressor from triggering you in the future.

Soothing the Savage Beast

The call of stress is not a low-key nudge to get out of harm's way. It's a raging, five-alarm fire that activates all the arousal agents in the body, especially emotions. White-hot emotions pour gasoline on the blaze, so turning them down is key to reviving the rational brain that can restore self-regulation and control.

Most stress reduction processes are designed to put out the emotional flames by either changing the mind through thinking strategies such as cognitive behavioral techniques—the ABC Model, Reality Response and thought labeling—or relaxation interventions that calm the savage beast through breathing and meditation practices.

Most of us today face a gauntlet of overstimulation with no space to think. We are so crammed with texts, email, and social media that there is fear of a quiet moment alone with thoughts. The irony is that if you ask people what they really want, more than money, most say a state absent of stress, peace. They want to shut down the blizzard of stimuli and pressures but have become codependent on all the busyness for the self-validation it is lousy at providing.

Relaxation practices, from progressive muscle relaxation to guided imagery and meditation, quiet the frenzy. This is because a relaxed physical state and a body activated by stress are incompatible. Relaxation processes cool the emotional temperature so that muscles can un-tense and the modern brain reassume command. A study at Stockholm University found that applied relaxation techniques are extremely helpful even in the most intense cases of panic.

Progressive Muscle Relaxation

Along with deliberate breathing and attitude breathing, progressive relaxation is what you want to do immediately after a stressful event triggers panic and thoughts of fear, doom, rage, or failure. It's a very simple but not widely used technique that's been around for a century.

Progressive relaxation was developed by a pioneering American doctor, Edmund Jacobson, a very early advocate for the role that relaxation strategies play in health. He discovered that stress can't take root when muscles are relaxed and not tensed, as they are when you're stressed. One of the advantages of progressive relaxation is that it's not a mental exercise. Sometimes when the mind is racing with irrational thoughts, turning off the mind with a physical practice can be the best strategy.

The idea is to relax the muscle groups of the body one by one, moving from the top of the body down to the legs and back up again. You tense the muscle group for five to 10 seconds firmly but not to the threshold of pain. Then you release it for 10 to 20 seconds, relax it, and then repeat. You do each muscle group twice on the way down and twice on the way back up again.

Start with a few deep breaths and then relax. Now clench your hands in a fist, which also tenses your forearms. Hold and feel the tension for five to 10 seconds. Then release your hands and arms and relax them for 10-20 seconds. Then do it again.

Next you tense the biceps (with a strongman pose) and upper arms. Then hold and relax. Then go to the forehead and scalp (scrunching them), eyes (closing them tight), jaw (opening your mouth wide), tongue (press the roof of the mouth), lips (form an "o"), neck (roll clockwise and then counterclockwise), shoulders (pulling them back and rolling them forward), chest (with a deep breath filling the chest, then relax), lower back (arch your back), then tighten the stomach, buttocks, thighs, and lower legs. Then head back up the body revisiting the muscle groups twice that you tensed on the way down.

It takes about 15 minutes for the whole process, after which the muscles and you are relaxed.

Meditation

At the top of the list for staying calm enough so you aren't triggered by stressful events in the first place are two secular meditation processes, the relaxation response and mindfulness. Researchers have found that these practices do two things critical for stress management and well-being. One, they increase your attention enormously. The more attention you have, the less stress, which is in the tenses you aren't in. They do this through the key to increasing attention, repeated focus on a target.

Secondly, both of these techniques reduce activity in the self-referential part of the brain that is always feeding your mind fearful survival chatter such as *How am I going to make it? What's going to happen? What's wrong?* These techniques greatly reduce the worry reflex and obsessive thinking as a result.

The relaxation response and mindfulness can be used during a stressful event, but they are best used daily to build calm and a habit of non-reaction that prevents you from being triggered by stressful events. See which works for you and then practice it regularly.

The Relaxation Response

Quieting the mind through the relaxation response is one of the most effective ways to reduce stress. I know, because I've been doing this exercise for years and years. On rare days when I miss my morning routine because of a super-early start, I feel the irritation and aggravation that precede stress come up easier. There are more mental sidetracks and detours to other tenses.

Dr. Herbert Benson, director emeritus of the Benson-Henry Institute (BHI) and professor of mind body medicine at Harvard Medical School, put the technique on the secular map in 1975 with his book, *The Relaxation Response*. His research distilled the essence of mantra meditation, such as Transcendental Meditation, into three basic actions—sitting comfortably in a relaxed position, closing your eyes, and thinking of a phrase—any phrase, syllables, or word you want—over and over in your mind for 10 to 20 minutes twice a day, once in the morning and once at night.

Benson's research has shown that the relaxation response lowers heart rate and blood pressure, which has made it a staple of hospital and clinic treatment for heart disease, high blood pressure, insomnia and other conditions associated with stress. One of Benson's studies found that doing the relaxation response regularly results in anti-oxidation and anti-inflammatory changes that help keep stress at bay.

It's extremely simple to do. Sit in a comfortable posture with your eyes and mouth closed and breathe through your nostrils. Then focus on the target—the key to increasing attention and, therefore, decreasing stress—repeating a couple syllables, a word, or phrase in your mind. You don't have to rush through it. If thoughts barge in, no problem. Just go back to the phrase again.

Through the challenges and passages of life, the relaxation response has been there for me, helping me stay focused and serving as a familiar safe harbor when things hit the fan. What you will notice if you do this practice or mindfulness is that it teaches your brain to get used to observing thoughts as they cross your brain without having to grab them or engage with them. You get in the habit of just noticing thoughts, then going back to your target—and the delight of not having to believe everything you think.

Mindfulness

Another offshoot of the meditation practices of the East, mindfulness has become a household name and is widely practiced and taught. Corporate America increasingly embraces it. Google has a renowned mindfulness program, while General Mills has been utilizing it since 2006. This scientific iteration of meditation and its study under the banner of Mindfulness-Based Stress Reduction (MBSR) was developed by Jon Kabat-Zinn, a former professor of medicine at the University of Massachusetts Medical School and author of best-selling books *Full Catastrophe Living* and *Wherever You Go, There You Are*. He founded the Center for Mindfulness for Medicine, Health Care and Society at the University of

Massachusetts.

As a scientist, Kabat-Zinn brought research and clinical practice to the art of meditation, detached it from its Buddhist contexts, and made MBSR a go-to stress reduction tool for everyone, even used by the U.S. military.

Mindfulness is much more than a relaxation technique; it's a way of living with full attention in the present moment. As Kabat-Zinn describes it, the practice trains the mind in "moment-to-moment, nonjudgmental awareness." You learn to avoid being diverted and triggered by the content of thoughts.

"The simple act of recognizing thoughts as thoughts can free you from the distorted reality they often create and allow for more clear-sightedness and a greater sense of manageability and even productivity in your life," Kabat-Zinn says in *Full Catastrophe Living*, which details his MBSR program.

This program is very effective at training brains to build and cultivate something that is in very short supply, awareness. It's a higher intelligence that is open and flexible enough to offer options other than meltdown when pressure, pain, and difficulties arise, as they do if you are a human on this planet. Building awareness of where you are, a much calmer and more insightful place to be than mentally traipsing through where you aren't, increases self-control, confidence, and resilience.

Mindfulness focuses on the target of the breath. The goal is to watch the breath as it fills your nostrils and then as it leaves on the exhale. If thoughts intrude, you notice them, let them go, and return to attention in the moment and watching the breath. Sit calmly and be aware of any physical discomfort or pains. These help you to stay present and not wander off into the mind's rabbit holes.

Here's an excellent description of the process and benefits of MBSR from Kabat-Zinn: "When we spend some time each day in non-doing, resting in awareness, observing the flow of the breath and the activity of our mind and body without getting caught up in that activity, we are cultivating calmness and mindfulness hand in hand. As the mind develops stability and is less caught up in the content of thinking, we strengthen the mind's ability to concentrate and to be calm. Each time we recognize a thought as a thought…we are strengthening the mindfulness muscle."

It's best to start with 5- to 15-minute sessions as you get your brain accustomed to quieting the usual cacophony. In time the goal of MBSR is to meditate 45 minutes per day, usually in two sessions. Even if you can only squeeze in 10 minutes, you get tremendous benefits. Stick with it, and you will become much more rooted in attention to the moment and less prone to reactive behaviors. There are many online MBSR courses available. It can make a big difference in all areas of your life.

Stress Reduction Apps

There are a host of apps that can help manage stress, worries, and moods, with many offering guided meditations from top teachers. Here are some of the options and monthly rates:

Breathe2Relax
A program designed to teach breathing techniques to reduce stress. Free
AnxietyCoach
This app, from the Mayo Clinic, uses cognitive behavioral therapy techniques to get to the root of fears and anxiety. $4.99
Simply Being
This affordable meditation app provides guided meditations and the sounds of the natural world to help you meditate. *$1.99*
Unplugged
Unplugged offers a host of guided meditations from top voices in the realm. Even if you don't have a lot of time, you'll find a meditation with your preferred length here. Monthly rate: $12.99. Annual rate: $69.99.
Insight Timer
This app offers a free version as well as a subscription plan for $9.99 per month. One of the most popular meditation apps, Insight Timer gives you access to a host of meditations.
Calm
One of the best-known relaxation apps, thanks to its national TV advertising, Calm has a large lineup of guided meditations. You get a basic course of meditation free. The subscription rate: One-week free trial, then $69.99 annually.
Headspace
This is one of the leaders in the meditation app world. You'll find meditations of all lengths and guides, as well as for kids, too. It also

has animations that help explain the dynamics of meditation. Rate: $12.99 per month.

Meditation for Fidgety Skeptics

This app provides a free, seven-lesson course in meditation. The program is rooted in science and stripped of spiritual components. Additional meditation and courses are $9.99 per month.

Yoga & Tai Chi

We can see through the dynamics of the stress response that there is a direct connection between mind and body, with anxious thoughts and stressful beliefs causing widespread collateral damage to the physiology. It works the other way too. A relaxed body can help quiet a restless mind. Yoga and tai chi are two of the best ways to align physical equilibrium with mental balance.

Each of these activities combines a blend of slow movements, deliberate breathing, and dwelling in the present moment. There are yoga and tai chi classes for rank beginners all the way up to the most advanced practitioners. These days you can find many of these courses online.

Beyond the calming nature of the activities, they also are great physical workouts, allowing you to stretch and keep muscles limber and in balance and overcome the weakening and atrophy that set in when lives get busy and sedentary. Tai chi is an especially effective tool to keep bodies responsive and healthy into your senior years.

Go online and you can find a wide selection of courses in yoga or tai chi. If you do an online class, it removes lots of excuses. No traffic, parking, other folks to worry about. Simply follow the instructor in the comfort of your home.

Exercise, Recreation and Hobbies

It would be nice if the research findings of leisure studies scholars at universities around the world could make their way into the public domain. Then we would know that one of the best tools to reduce stress is leisure activities, from aerobic exercise to hobbies and social outlets.

Aerobic exercise is known for its ability to calm the body and mind, thanks to the release of endorphins, which activate the brain's reward chemical, the neurotransmitter dopamine. After a run or long cycling session the body's natural tranquilizer kicks in, and that feels great.

What you might not know is that there is another agent produced by exercise that helps you get stress down. Researchers have found that aerobic exercise increases a peptide called galanin, which reduces stress too.

Studies show that engaged leisure pursuits increase positive mood, which crowds out the negative emotions of stress. When we immerse in activities that are fully absorbing, we get out of our heads and into the realm of experiences, which make us happier than material things. They also increase self-esteem and competence, which act as buffers against setbacks. Leisure activities cut stress and sadness and improved mood and interest in a study at the University of California at Merced by Matthew Zawadzki. Gardening, doing puzzles, and relaxing activities reduced blood pressure in an earlier study led by Zawadzki.

Leisure and recreational activities are medicine. I've spoken with doctors who prescribe vacations to help patients recover from stress and burnout. One therapist told me she encourages clients to start hobbies to get them out of the thought factory and the ruminations that perpetuate anxiety.

Zawadzki has suggested writing yourself a prescription to take 10 minutes three times a week for a leisure activity. We all have three 10-minute slots in the week. You can do this.

What can you prescribe yourself to get your mind engaged in something fun or engaging a few times a week that's not related to work? See if you can come up with three ideas.

Mastery activities that help you build skills have been shown to be the most effective way to turn off stress after work, report researchers in the science of work recovery. The possibilities range from painting to woodworking, ballroom dancing, flute, mandolin, archery, rock climbing, skating, bowling, running, badminton, softball, or learning a language. You will learn more about this area of stress-busting and life-immersion in Chapters 10 and 11.

Positive Emotions

We are learning more and more about how potent positive emotions are and that they hold a particular key to keeping the brain aligned and out of the negative rumination column. How powerful are they? The University of North Carolina's Barbara Fredrickson found they are capable of shutting down the physical symptoms of stress on the spot. Not bad. She calls it the "undo effect." The right positive thought can reverse the effects of the stress response on your physiology.

The power of positive emotions is stunning, and not based on platitudes but hard-core research by Fredrickson and her scientific colleagues. One of the most effective positive emotions, she discovered, is gratitude. Gratefulness brings a perspective that lets us know, that despite hardships, we still are blessed in many ways. It works wonders, as we will see ahead. Taking a concerted approach to increase the positive emotion count in your memory can counter the default to dwell on the negative.

Understanding, Avoiding and Recovering from Burnout

What used to be the domain of mostly the people industries—education, social work, and health care—burnout has become a problem for everyone. Burnout is enough of a concern that the World Health Organization upgraded its definition of it for the 2022 edition of its *International Classification of Diseases*, calling it "an occupational phenomenon" that comes from "chronic workplace stress that has not been successfully managed."

That stress most often comes from work overload and long hours, but it can also be caused, surprisingly enough, by a lack of challenge and work that's too easy. That triggers a sense of ineffectiveness and lack of achievement, one of the key domains of burnout.

The last stage of chronic stress, burnout is the final stop after a prolonged bout of stress that drains energetic resources until there is nothing left to handle demands. All that remains are the signal dimensions and symptoms of burnout: complete exhaustion—mentally, physically, and emotionally—depersonalization and cynicism, and an inefficacy that comes from reduced productivity and low morale.

Though burnout is caused by chronic stress, it is a different beast than mere stress. It's a multi-dimensional syndrome that hollows out vitality, drive, and esteem and undermines competence. It's a mysterious state to be in for most people who wind up with it, since they tend to be the hardest workers, the achievers, the most conscientious. They have always been able to bring more to the job than the average person—more endurance, stamina, intensity. But now it's gone. What happened?

A sustained period of high job demands outstripped coping resources. At a certain point, the backup energy supply runs out and exhaustion overwhelms all else. The resulting fatigue is so startling that the burned-out can hardly recognize the person whose name is on their driver's license.

It's hard to get rid of a medical condition you don't know you have, and that's often the case with burnout. Many people with burnout don't know they have hit this debilitating stage until their health, spouse, or colleague lets them know that there's something seriously wrong.

People with burnout who reach out to me say they have struggled to find what's behind their chronic exhaustion, lack of energy and drive, inability to perform their job with the command they once had, and the dread they feel about what they once loved doing. They have sought out doctors and searched online, trying to figure out where their old self went.

Unfortunately, the brain and body have limits that, if pushed long enough, drive you beyond capacity. For those who always defined themselves by their work ethic, burnout is not something they want to advertise to others, so they keep it inside. This causes more time to pass in a state of chronic stress, doing more damage to your body.

The Secret Scourge

Burnout has long lived in the shadows of the workplace, those with it suffering in silence and organizations remaining unaware of the toll it takes on productivity, the bottom-line, and top talent. The days of ignoring burnout are getting harder to pull off. A Gallup survey found that 23% of workers report being burned out very often or always, while another 44% feel burnout sometimes. That is two-thirds of employees.

Some 77% of employees questioned for a Deloitte survey reported they have had burnout, with 70% saying their companies are not doing enough to address it. Half of millennials said they left a job because of burnout.

This is bad news for any organization because the exhaustion and cynicism driven by burnout undermine employee engagement, research shows. The energy and commitment are gone. They distance themselves from coworkers and the company. Burnout is a relentless demotivating tool. Why would any company knowingly allow burnout conditions to exist?

They wouldn't if they understood its massive impact on the bottom-line. Health costs for burnout are much higher than that for other workplace maladies, driven by problems from long absences to hypertension to diabetes. It's clear from the data that ongoing stress management training and support is essential to keep chronic stress at bay and a steady stream of valuable employees from leaving the company.

Burnout decimates all energetic resources—stress hormones, physical and mental vitality, positive emotions, willpower, motivation, resilience. You wind up in a three-way shutdown: emotional exhaustion, physical fatigue, and cognitive weariness.

Emotional exhaustion is the chief element of the individual component of burnout. There's an interpersonal toll that comes by way of detachment and distancing from others at work and beyond the office. With energy and motivation low, there is reduced personal accomplishment, which contributes to low self-evaluation, confidence, and esteem. So burnout attacks from all sides, reducing competence and isolating you from others.

Even the thought of work can make you feel physically sick. It feels like failure. If you can't do your job anymore, can't work feeling this way, how are you going to survive? Existential fear circles the brain. The darkness has more than a little crossover with depression, and burnout can lead to depression.

Swiss, French, and American researchers concluded in one study that, as burnout symptoms increase, so do depression symptoms and that "the burnout process essentially reflects a process of depression." Burnout scholar Christina Maslach, whose "Maslach Burnout Inventory" to measure the condition is a standard in the field, has said that the burnout-depression study was faulty in its findings, skewing results to depression symptoms. She reported in one paper that "the two constructs are indeed distinct: burnout is job-related and situation-specific, as opposed to depression, which is more general and context-free." Still, she says the two conditions are clearly linked, pointing to several studies showing burnout leading to depressive symptoms.

The cost of depression to the U.S. economy is estimated to be more than $210 billion a year, with half of that attributed to loss of productivity in the workplace due to absenteeism and presenteeism (reduced productivity from those with depression) and some 45% to 47% due to medical costs. There are many causes of depression, but, clearly, burnout-derived depression is one that is completely preventable—if we can get past overwork myopia and the fallacies that make physiologies expendable and mental health a no-go zone.

The launchpad for burnout is a source of chronic stress that hasn't been managed. What is it? Here are some typical places to look:

- Long hours
- High workload
- Role conflict and job-person mismatch
- Poor organizational and social support
- No time for recovery
- Unfair treatment that destroys trust

A lot of the bullet points come down to excessive hours driving strain and stress, no recharging, and lack of support. It's important to know you aren't doing a 100-meter dash. You are on a marathon, and your body and mind need pacing and enough energetic nutrients to complete the distance.

If you feel you are on a burnout track, start taking time now to reduce excessive hours, identify and manage chronic stressors, and dramatically increase exercise and recharging time. When you can stop the drain of resources caused by stress, you can begin to increase energy and take on other issues that may be impacting the situation, such as not enough support.

The Difference Between Burnout and Being Tired

How do you know if you are just tired, or you're burned out? When you are tired, sleep, rest, and hobbies can help you recover from physical exhaustion. Your mind can shift mood and find a way around a problem.

With burnout, the fatigue doesn't go away even if you get all your sleep. The weariness is there every day, even on the weekend, as is the negative rumination and mental cul-de-sac.

Fatigue doesn't cause an absence of positive emotions or hijack the mind with false beliefs and bleak thoughts. It's a temporary physical issue. Burnout crowds out positive emotions with all-negative, all-the-time.

You might want to be by yourself for a moment if you're tired, but you are not going to close yourself off to the outside world for months on end. That's burnout. You retreat from a world that appears to care less about you. You don't care about it either.

When you're tired, taking part in fun activities energizes and restores mood and vitality. When you're burned out, things you used to do for fun no longer provide enjoyment. Pessimistic thinking clouds the brain with dire ruminations that can prevent even the thought of doing anything to feel good.

Health Conditions Caused by Burnout

Of course, there are many other ways to tell the difference between burnout and fatigue, namely, the host of health issues that come with burnout that are missing from mere tiredness.

As we have learned, stress radically reconfigures your body, shutting down digestion, suppressing the immune and tissue repair systems, and dramatically increasing heart rate and blood pressure. Since burnout is a condition of long-term stress, all those alterations have a long time to do a massive amount of damage.

Beyond the stress-related impacts, burnout also leads to behaviors that can create more health havoc. Burnout has been shown to be associated with eating more fast food, higher alcohol consumption, little exercise, and frequent use of painkillers. That was in a study of doctors and nurses, who should know better, but their medical knowledge and brains were compromised by burnout thinking.

Since the effects of burnout on health are largely unknown beyond exhaustion, let's take a look at all the impacts of this condition—physical, psychological, and professional—as detailed in a huge meta-study led by Denise Salvagioni that looked at 993 different studies associated with burnout. The most frequent health impact of burnout, she and her colleagues found, was coronary heart disease and hospitalization for cardiovascular diseases, as well as risk factors for heart disease—obesity, Type 2 diabetes, high LDL cholesterol—but there were many others.

Physical Consequences:

- Hypercholesterolemia—high cholesterol
- Type 2 diabetes
- Coronary heart disease
- Hospitalization due to cardiovascular disorder
- Musculoskeletal pain
- Changes in pain experiences
- Prolonged fatigue
- Headaches
- Gastrointestinal issues
- Respiratory problems
- Severe injuries and mortality below the age of 45

Psychological Effects:

- Insomnia
- Depressive symptoms
- Use of psychotropic and antidepressant medications
- Hospitalization for mental disorders and psychological ill-health

And there are plenty of impacts on the organization as well from talent that is demotivated and disengaged. Productivity plummets when burnout takes over a team or company. Its main characteristics—exhaustion, cynicism, and inefficacy—are the opposite of those of engagement—energy, commitment, and effectiveness—burnout expert Christina Maslach has reported. People who are burned out have low activation and involvement and no pleasure in the work they do, easy to see in their mood and performance, while engaged employees are energized and find pleasure in their work. It's no mystery which creates better performance.

Professional Effects:

- Job dissatisfaction
- Absenteeism
- New disability pension
- Presenteeism

Organizational Risk Factors for Burnout

Even though you can develop burnout from chronic stress and excess workload that comes from self-driven overperformance, burnout is also very much a condition driven by structural and organizational factors. Researchers have identified risk factors in organizations—burnout triggers—that play an instigating role in burnout.

The more we can become aware of these warning signs, which range from work overload to imbalances between the person and job, the more adjustments can be made to avoid the burnout treadmill.

Humans are the social animal, and that's certainly true at the office as everywhere else. We are designed to connect, relate, and support, and when that doesn't happen in overloaded organizations, people operating in isolation beyond coping resources can get trapped on the burnout circuit. Christina Maslach and Michael Leiter have documented that when we don't pay attention to the human side of work, there are consequences—bad health to bad performance.

"People who are burning out...invest less time and energy in their work, do only what is necessary, and are absent more often," she and Leiter report in *The Truth About Burnout*. "In addition to doing less, they do their work less well. High-quality work requires time and effort, commitment and creativity, but the burned-out individual is no longer willing to give these freely. The drop in quality and quantity of work produced is the occupational bottom line of burnout."

What they are describing is a decline in attitude and output that comes from disengagement in the work. As a result, no company would knowingly order up a prescription for burnout.

Group and interpersonal dysfunction in organizations can create burnout triggers. Here are six red flags identified by Maslach and Leiter, known as the Areas of Worklife Model, that can lead to burnout.

The 6 Burnout Triggers

1. Work Overload
Excessive workload is the most frequent factor for burnout. When demands constantly push physiologies beyond capacity, energy re-

sources are overloaded. Nobody wins when we do more than we can do well. If you are bringing work home and leaving late chronically, this doesn't end well. You might be able to handle the work of an ex-colleague who hasn't been replaced for a little while, but you and managers need to insist on getting support, or the department will soon be down another person. Excessive hours keep you from recharging and recovering from stress, allowing chronic stress to entrench and spiral.

2. **Lack of Control**

   Since stress is a function of how much perceived control you feel you have over demands, the goal is to find more autonomy and choice in how you do your job. More flexibility leads to more of a sense of control and more self-responsibility. More micromanaging from above leads to less latitude and more stress. Discuss ways you might be able to play a bigger role in decisions that affect your work, deadlines, schedules, how you manage email or other stressors that create a work environment that feels out of control.

3. **Insufficient Reward**

   When overload becomes the expectation, and there is no compensating reward for the extra effort or even a sense of appreciation, it is human nature to feel you're on the short end of the stick. This is the breeding ground for disengagement. Dubbed "high-cost, low-gain," the contrast between effort—long hours, tough deadlines, fast pace—and reward, in the form of wages, job security, esteem, promotion prospects or recognition drives aggravation, anger, and chronic stress.

   Doing difficult and demanding work without recognition or reward deepens loss of trust. A huge study of 90,164 individuals found that people whose efforts are met with inadequate rewards are 16% more likely to have coronary heart disease.

4. **Absence of Fairness**

   There is an implied contract for most of us that we will be treated in good faith. When that trust is broken, cynicism grows. In a world of downsizing and restructuring, many feel their efforts are not valued, promises are not being kept, and everyone is replaceable. This climate added to chronic overload can ramp up the withdrawal and cynicism of burnout.

5. **Lack of Community**

High turnover and constant changes within organizations can hollow out support systems and leave employees estranged as they try to do more than they are equipped for. Alienation is the route to cynicism and a sense that no one cares. The risk for burnout grows as trust fades. Be as proactive as you can and communicate with managers and lobby hard for support. Finding teammates and mentors who care can provide a critical buffer to the forces of overload.

6. Conflicting Values

People are more likely to embrace the vision of the company they work for when it reflects their values. Having a good fit with values can spur people to go the extra mile. But when those values are contradicted by policies or behaviors at odds with those values, the mismatch can lead to an acceleration of disengagement and withdrawal.

Burnout, then, can be deepened by social layers of organizational distrust and lack of support and reward. Employers need to guard against burnout in their ranks by making sure workloads are manageable, people have a sense of agency in how they do their work, and that there is a sense of community and strong support from others. Healthy workplaces are the lifeblood of success.

Interventions and the Road to Recovery

There are plenty of reasons for organizations to want to do something about burnout—low productivity, absenteeism, higher medical costs, and low morale and engagement. Yet there aren't a lot of interventions at the corporate level, such as proactive stress management training or attempts to address burnout triggers that are flashpoints.

Meta-studies on burnout among physicians have found that individualized stress management training, mindfulness, exercise, and improved communication skills were effective, while even better was limiting duty hours, rescheduling shifts, and reducing workload.

A stress management program for teachers reduced burnout by giving the participants the ability to increase perceived control over demands and reframe stressful parts of the job, using the Karasek Demand-Control Model. The teachers learned time management and prioritization to help with workload, how to avoid perfectionism, better communication skills with students, how to increase assertiveness to manage disruptive students, and reach out for support. It all added up to a significant reduction in emotional exhaustion and a big jump in control over their work environment.

Arnold Bakker, a prolific Dutch researcher who developed the Job Demands-Resources model, led an innovative study on burnout among teachers in the Netherlands. He identified various resource factors that could prevent burnout. In some cases, "work overload, emotional demands, physical demands, and work–home interference did not result in high levels of burnout if employees experienced autonomy, received feedback, had social support, or had a high-quality relationship with their supervisor," he and his coauthors found. When employees can decide how to take on demands, the autonomy mitigates emotional exhaustion. Feedback helps get permission to take a healthier approach or change a schedule. The study points the way to levers that can be used to reduce rampant burnout.

The usual approach with burnout recovery is individual coaching and counseling. Burnout is a very personal reaction to chronic stressors, so finding ways to change individual responses to stressors and the larger conditions of work aggravating them can change the equation from futility to action.

The path to recovery requires a change in thinking—the way you appraise and manage stressors—and specific adjustments to work style, such as cutting down on overworking. It also usually requires changes to schedules, workload, and support that necessitate conversations with leaders.

Finally, another critical piece of burnout recovery is building up crashed emotional resources, such as social support and positive emotions. You have to exit the depersonalization, cynicism, and futility that perpetuates the burnout state of mind. The best way to rejuvenate the brain and self-esteem is through activities that get you out of your head and into physical pursuits that bring challenge, exercise, and engagement, particularly with others.

Here are the key areas to focus on to turn burnout around. For each of them I have provided stories from the trenches illustrating how coaching clients of mine were able to put burnout behind them and shift to healthy work.

Burnout Keys and Success Stories

1. **Manage or Eliminate the Chronic Stressors Driving Burnout**
   Burnout is a condition of excess—too many hours, too many demands, too little support, too much conflict with a coworker. To get it under control, you need to first identify the stressors draining your coping resources. What are they? To fix them, there may need to be boundaries for coworkers, bosses, and clients; conversations about priorities; more perceived control over your tasks and deadlines; and changes to the stressors that keep the danger signal going.

   If you are overextended, set up a meeting with a supervisor to let them know your plate is buried by other plates on top of it and that, while you want to do the best possible work, the situation is making that not possible and that it's impacting your health with burnout, which massively affects productivity and engagement. Suggest ideas on how workflow or an unviable schedule could be altered.

   Burnout Success Story

   For one of my coaching clients, Jill, there were two problems driving burnout, an impossible workload and a stressful coworker, the latter setting off the triggers of a toxic community and unfairness. Her job had a mission she loved, helping the environment, but the environment in the office was making it unviable for her to serve that cause.

   She agreed to speak to her manager about the problems and was ready to leave the company if there were no changes to the status quo. It was affecting her health. The manager loved her work and talents and didn't want to lose her, so he proposed another position in the company in which the workload would be moderated, and she would not have to deal with the difficult individual draining her motivation. She agreed to the new arrangement, and it solved her burnout problem. If you bring talent and hard work to the table, your company doesn't want to lose you. Be confident in your abilities. It's hard to find good employees.

2. **Get More Support and Resources**
   In the era of lean staffing, not having enough resources to do your job is a big burnout trigger, causing too many to work too long without a chance to recover. More responsibilities are added without a change in job description, and suddenly, you're doing the job of two

or three people.

That is not going to end well for all the reasons we've discussed in these pages—the limits of your physiology, stress, heart disease, etc. Make your case for the need to increase staffing. Studies show it can make all the difference for you and the organization.

Burnout Success Story

Intrepid Lotte Bailyn, MIT Sloan work and organization studies professor emerita and a co-founder of the Collaborative Interactive Action Research group, which has performed many fascinating interventions inside organizations, has demonstrated what happens when staff is overburdened because of a lack of personnel—namely, productivity plummets.

Bailyn and colleagues investigated an insurance company whose underwriting had gone south as staff worked late into the night and on the weekend. After interviewing and observing, she concluded that the company was understaffed because of recent cuts. The firm wasn't excited about bringing more positions back, so Bailyn proposed a trial. Bring on some temporary staff, train them, and see if business improves. They brought in the extra help, and lo and behold, new underwriting and productivity increased, reversing the firm's downward spiral. The chronic all-nighters disappeared. The company wound up keeping the temporary staff. Consider offering a trial like this if you don't have enough able bodies to go around.

Burnout Success Story

The support issue can be severe at startups and rapidly growing companies. I had a client who was working at a typically understaffed tech startup. Alex had expected to put in long hours for a new company, but the responsibilities kept growing. Meanwhile, the owner hadn't kept his word on equity share, didn't listen to my client's concerns about the markets the company was going into, didn't support him in front of malcontent employees who reported to him, and went to great lengths to avoid having a conversation about the problems.

My client finally put his issues on the table, but nothing changed, so he decided he had to leave the company. And, yes, that's a success story. When you have serious burnout and the health risks that come with it, you need to be prepared to go elsewhere if the future holds nothing but more of the same hazardous conditions ahead.

3. Recover Crashed Resources

On the physiological level, since burnout drains all energetic resources in the body, recovery means you need to replace crashed emotional, mental, and physical resources.

Studies show one of the best ways to spur the recovery process is stepping back from work and participating in active leisure pursuits. Vacations, for instance, can cure burnout, by helping to regather crashed emotional resources such as a sense of social support and mastery, which recharge the self-worth engine. It takes two weeks, though, for the recuperative process to occur, so you'll have to be able to stand having a holiday that long. I think you can handle it.

Hobbies and active leisure have been shown to increase the positive emotion count, which helps push out the exclusively negative state that comes with burnout and realigns the emotional balance.

Because burnout keeps you in a cynical, negative place, you need to play a trick on your mind to force yourself to do recovery activities when your attitude is dark and can't be bothered. The goal: just show up physically at the activity site. And keep showing up.

Burnout Success Story

After months of long hours out of town on a major project for a food manufacturer, my client Charles was tapped out. He was overwhelmed, not sleeping well, feeling guilty if he only worked an eight-hour day, and highly stressed to the point that his manager asked him if he needed some help. That's how Charles found me.

He realized he needed to speak up and set boundaries, which tend to be few and far between when you run factory assembly lines that go around the clock and are prone to snafus. He identified the life he wanted to have and the obstacles at work that were in the way. We focused on moderating his work shifts, sensible boundaries, and getting more support. He had conversations with his manager about more staff, and he set new perimeters for his prickly staff.

Charles also needed "a life to come home to," as he told me, so getting leisure and recreational activities on his agenda was part of the strategy to help recover crashed resources. He got together with friends he hadn't seen for ages, went to concerts, and started living his life. "Having, achieving, and sustaining work-life balance has been simply amazing," he told me.

And it got better for Charles: After the adjustments he received a promotion and was nominated for an award.

Take the Burnout Test

If you think you might be experiencing burnout, take the short test below. The Shirom-Melamed Burnout Questionnaire, from burnout experts Arie Shirom and Shmuel Melamed, measures stress on the three levels that comprise the burnout condition: emotional exhaustion (EE), physical fatigue (PF), and cognitive weariness (Cog).

Answer each of the statements below by indicating how often you have the feeling during working hours. Almost always = 7 points; very frequently = 6 points; quite frequently = 5; sometimes = 4; quite infrequently = 3; very infrequently = 2; almost never = 1. Add up your scores for each of the three categories. See below test for score range.

1. I feel tired. (PF) _____
2. I feel physically fatigued. (PF) _____
3. I feel physically exhausted. (PF) _____
4. When I get up in the morning to go to work, I have no energy. (PF) _____
5. I feel fed up. (EE) _____
6. I feel like my emotional batteries are dead. (EE) _____
7. I feel burned out. (EE) _____
8. I feel emotionally fatigued. (EE) _____
9. I feel I am not thinking clearly. (Cog) _____
10. I have difficulty concentrating. (Cog) _____
11. My thinking process is slow. (Cog) _____
12. I have difficulty thinking about complex things. (Cog) _____

Men whose scores average 3.0 to 3.75 and women who average 3.6 to 4.0 are at the high end of the burnout range.

Put It Into Practice

I hope you know a bit more now about how stress impacts your health, work, and life and how to combat it. Now it's time to put a plan together to put the new behaviors to work. Check off which of the following stress management strategies we have discussed that you will use to keep stress at bay and when you will use them—for which scenarios.

Stress Relief Strategies Checklist

1. **The Stress Audit**. Put a daily alarm on your phone. When it goes off, rate your stress level on a 1-10 scale, 10 being the worst stress. What's causing the stress? What's the thought driving it? What's under that? What's under that? Is the thought accurate? Is it life-or-death? If not, turn the danger signal off. The threat is bogus.
   When will you do the stress audit?

2. **Thought Labeling**. Instead of saying, *I can't handle this*, label it as just a thought or feeling. *I'm having the thought/feeling that I can't handle this*. Look *at* the thought, not *from* it.
   When will you use this technique?

3. **Attitude Breathing**. Take deep breaths for two to five minutes from your belly through the nose. With each breath, think "stay neutral" or "I don't react," which wakes up modern faculties after a stressful event and untenses muscles.
   When will you do this exercise?

4. **The Reality Response**. Break the stressor down into three parts to reframe the false story of stress. What's the false story (the worst-case scenario)? The most likely story (just the facts of what happened)? What's the new story going forward, utilizing the facts of the most likely story to forge a solution for this stressor the next time it pops up?
   When will you do this exercise?

5. **Challenging Catastrophic Thoughts.** Contest the catastrophic thoughts of your errant survival equipment by using a process based on Albert Ellis's ABC Model of identifying false beliefs and the work of Karen Reivich at the University of Pennsylvania. Step 1: Write down your worst-case stories. Step 2: Your best-case scenarios. Step 3: The most likely story of what happened. Step 4: Your purposeful action going forward.
   When will you use this process?

6. **Deliberate Breathing.** This exercise helps untense muscles, increase the flow of oxygen, and is a great tool to use right after a stressful event. Breathe in through your nose from your belly

to a count of five. Breathe out to a count of five. Do this for 2 minutes.

When will you do this exercise?

7. **The Relaxation Response.** Increase your attention and reduce fear and anxiety by doing this exercise for 10-20 minutes in the morning and evening. Sit comfortably, close your eyes, and think of a couple of syllables or a word or phrase repeated over and over in your mind. You can make up a phrase or phonetic sounds. When thoughts stray, just come back to the target, the phrase, word, or syllables.

    When will you do this exercise?

8. **Mindfulness.** Repeated focus on a target is how we increase attention and reduce stress. The target here is your breath. Sit quietly and breathe normally, watching the air flow in through your nose and then out again as it leaves your body. A daily practice of 45 minutes split into two sessions, is recommended. You learn how to let intrusive thoughts go and not be triggered by them.

    When will you do this exercise?

CHAPTER 6

Be Quick, But Don't Hurry

Opt Out of Time Urgency and Reflex Rushing

No doubt you have gotten that refreshing greeting from a harried colleague. "Hey, did you get that email I just sent?" they ask, five minutes after they sent the message.

They can't help themselves. They are afflicted with a scourge at the root of the unsustainable workplace: time urgency, the need to race through the day as if you were a wildebeest in training. Pretty soon you're going to get another call from a colleague. "Hey, did you get that email I haven't even sent yet?" That's where it's going.

Time urgency is another of the unconscious habits that drives the reflex work style. I call it the "crazy" in crazy-busy because it turns on the crazy part of your ancient brain, which misinterprets hurry-worry as if every minute was a life-and-death emergency, which is the cue for the stress response to activate.

We assume that being a blur is a good thing, but the research shows it's not, and there are a lot more repercussions to it than time-stressed calls. The term "time urgency" comes from the medical world, where it is a risk for coronary heart disease and heart attacks, not to mention a trigger for other stress-related medical conditions. Besides health problems, time panic drives behaviors that sabotage performance and relationships—crisis mentality, irritability, anger, and needless mistakes that happen when the rational brain is hijacked by fight-or-flight emotions.

The need to race nonstop is a hidden foundation of much of the stress in workplaces today. Time pressure is one of the most potent stressors. Real or perceived time pressure increases strain and stress, which leads to exhaustion, as stress burns up energetic resources in the body.

People with high time pressure report problems with work-life balance, which shows up in taking more sick days and higher health care costs.

Subjected to time constraints, brains default to stress and panic in the form of impulsive behavior. Drivers who are time urgent, for instance, drive faster and make more risky maneuvers. As a study led by Kathleen Kowalski-Trakofler put it, "Competence in judgment is always compromised under stress."

How badly can time pressure damage thinking and presence of mind? Consider what happens at airport security checkpoints, where the time urgency of your flight deadline collides with the time frenzy of those behind you in the security line. The result: some 90,000 to 100,000 bags, purses, phones, and other items left behind every month at TSA security stations. This includes $926,030 in currency and coin each year lost in the frantic scrum to make flights while rushing.

The rush hour has turned into an all-day, every-day affair, not because of rampant emergencies but, instead, because a tide of hurry-worry, stoked by instant technology, has made every minute of the day seem like an emergency and every email seem urgent. It's a self-perpetuating loop.

Nonstop motion makes everything appear urgent when you haven't taken the time to think about what is urgent and what isn't.

Time urgency equates commotion with motion, busyness with productivity, and any incoming messages and notifications with urgency. What the frenzy keeps us from considering is whether there is a real business reason behind the speed, or if it's just the only pace we know. In fact, it keeps us from considering anything at all other than the momentum of action. The result is a false belief that makes you believe you have to be going at breakneck speed every minute of the day.

Obviously, there are deadlines that have to be met and fast-breaking issues that land on our screens that need quick turnarounds. That's part of the territory. We have to move swiftly, but not before we think about what it is we're doing and why we're doing it. When time urgency extends beyond due dates and crunches to all the time, even at home, it's a major saboteur of work-life balance.

Moderating speed goes against every instinct in the crazy-busy age, but it's the first step to recalibrating the race that pushes you to go faster than your physiology is built for. The job is not a sprint to the death.

The Speed Trap

It used to be that time urgency was the province mostly of Type-A personalities, the super-competitive, hard-driving types who are not good at waiting and get annoyed with those moving in slow motion around them. These days, though, most people are caught up in the stampede. We have become hooked on instant gratification, mostly supplied by devices, which makes everyone want a response to every message yesterday.

Time urgency is a fixation with the passage of time, a compulsion to jam as much as possible into each minute and stay busy every second. It's an attempt to control the clock, which, of course, isn't possible, so it leads to irritation every time the world makes you deviate from your speed goal.

As someone on the A team myself, I know this beast well and its constant nagging to get stuff done. It makes sense that Type-A personalities would be fair game for time urgency. It's part of the competitive drive to take out achievement needs without mercy on clocks and unsuspecting to-dos. There is positive reinforcement of the behavior from others and the culture, so we keep racing.

The research, though, tells us something different: Time urgency is a speed trap, a time management saboteur, an indiscriminate rush that leads to frenzy and cognitive errors. Productivity is not a function of how busy you are or of constant commotion. Rote busyness is simply mechanical momentum, movement without awareness of whether the commotion is moving things forward or where we are going or why.

It's mobility that we want, not a badge of busyness. Saying constantly how swamped we are only intensifies time anxiety. Mobility comes from the opposite of rushing—space for reflection and focused attention on the task, not the time. This places us in the moment, instead of having to keep a part of the brain on the finish line. You get the work done faster without the ticking time bomb.

The solution is to pace yourself, instead of blindly barreling ahead. You have the power to do that, to say, *No, I'm not going hyperventilate over this task. I can do it without stress and more attentively when I don't race.* Yes, you want to move quickly, but you don't want to do it in a way that is counterproductive. The great University of California at Los Angeles basketball coaching legend John Wooden had a brilliant description of how we should approach a swift result. He told his players:

"Be quick, but don't hurry."

On the basketball court, hurrying triggers forced shots, turnovers, and charging fouls, because it sets off impulsiveness, out-of-control moves, and stress-addled emotions. Being quick, though, means you move swiftly but under control. You are not under control when sprinting on time urgency because every minute in that state needlessly simulates the pressure of the last seconds of a tied basketball game.

Your Mind on Hurry-Worry

The rushing state of mind is very similar to being drunk. You do things in your rushing state you never would in your sane mind. Like go ballistic at a market at the 10-item or less checkout counter, when someone is over the limit. You are ready to go off on the granny who has 25 items. I talked to a clerk at my local market, and she said nobody wants to work that line in her store because everyone in it is insane. Fights break out. Over what? Usually, a self-appointed deadline to get somewhere else, like the dry cleaners.

Time urgency kicks your thoughts down to the lower brain of rash and rote behavior. It's a ticket to re-do's, skimming minds, chronic stress, and an unsustainable pace. Daniel Kahneman dubbed the type of mental activity that takes over your brain under time pressure and the stress that it unleashes System 1 thinking. Author of *Thinking, Fast and Slow*, Kahneman says we have a two-speed brain, one for emergencies, System 1, and one for analyzing, planning and evaluation, System 2, or slow thinking.

When you are rushing, you are using the autopilot of System 1. It's a shallow, quick, impulsive mode that looks for easy answers and doesn't have time to mull alternatives. Your mind seizes on what's familiar, recent, defaults to cognitive biases, and doesn't look for deeper solutions. Kahneman says that when we are engaged in a mental sprint, we are effectively blind from the myopia of System 1.

You use the deliberate brain, System 2, for planning and rational analysis. This is why managerial activities that require complex decision-making and long-term future planning are hindered by time urgen-cy, because that all needs System 2.

Studies have shown that time urgency damages the ability to make well-thought-out decisions, since stress comes with it. As time urgency increases, it drives retaliatory decision-making and mistakes without an analytical process. Since it makes you think everything is an emergen-cy, time frenzy feeds crisis mentality, which makes people feel they have the right to interrupt anyone at any time, which only turns up more hurry-worry for the interruptee as forward progress is stymied by the interruption.

Researchers investigating the nature of attention have uncovered a complex network that depends on a reflective capacity. Alertness and "orienting," picking your spot of focus, help you take in and respond to matters you notice, and executive attention, a higher-brain processing function, allows you to make an informed decision based on what you have paid attention to. Time urgency and its default to System 1 turns this process into a knee-jerk response, with an instant reaction you may regret later.

A key part of executive attention, called "effortful control," which regulates your impulse control, gets short shrift when you're hurrying or getting disrupted. The result is a hit to your ability to "shift focus delib-erately, engage in planning, and regulate one's impulses," notes Maggie Jackson, author of *Distracted*.

The stress of time pressure activates the emotional center of the brain, and, when it does, rational cognition gets waylaid. Decision-mak-ing during stressful emergencies can have an assortment of impacts, from decreased vigilance, to reduced capability for working memory, and a quick end to evaluating alternative options.

Just the perception of time urgency is enough to undercut perfor-mance. In a study on time pressure in negotiations by Carsten de Dreu, some subjects were told they had plenty of time for the assignment, while others were told they had limited time. Performance decreased for those who thought they had time constraints.

We can see from this how the mere belief that you are under time pressure, created, say, by yourself, can create the same effects as real time limits. It's a false belief of ceaseless frenzy and frazzle that must be jetti-soned.

Identify Crazy-Urgency Traits

The first step to tackling the speed habit is to identify the behaviors that keep you in frenzy and frazzle mode. Check off the traits below, as reported in the research, that apply to you. If you are a Type-A, you check them all. Sorry about that.

- Type-A behavior
- High level of impatience
- Need to race through every task
- Irritability when others don't move fast enough
- Frequent clock-checking
- Talking fast
- Eating fast

Rush-Hour Symptoms

Another clue to runaway time stress is how the anxiety manifests in your body. Use the signals to activate awareness, stop rushing, and take a breath or five. These are going to be the same symptoms as stress.

What are the physical symptoms of rushing and time anxiety for you? Tightness in the neck? Racing stomach? Rapid heartbeat? Write down your warning signs and be aware when they go off that you could be caught in a speed trap.

When you catch yourself racing and there's no reason for it, stop, breathe deeply, and tell yourself, "It's not apocalypse now."

Why Irritability Is Hazardous to Your Health

Like all habits, time urgency is an autopilot behavior that happens out of your awareness. This allows the stress response it sets off, also on reflex, to alter key systems in your body undercover, causing any number of health issues.

The dangerous pattern you want to avoid is this: Impatience leads to irritability, which leads to anger, which leads to clogged arteries.

It's time urgency's irritability/anger threshold that is the danger point for health issues. Irritability is defined as a proneness to anger. It is both an enabler of anger and a low-grade form of it. It is the famed short fuse that some have temperamentally, and others have conditionally. The more irritable you get, the better the odds that anger will erupt.

Irritability and anger are a tag-team. They operate as cause and effect in a cycle generated by an obsession with the passage of time and the need to fill it as quickly as possible in the most productive way. Of course, bending time to your will is difficult, since there's no willing partner on the other side.

When you are ticked off, simmering inside, any little spark can set off anger, which has been shown to be a major risk factor for cardiovascular issues. It's no surprise, then, that time urgency has been shown to increase the risk of heart attack. On top of that, people high in time-urgent speech patterns—in other words, you talk fast—are also most likely to report burnout due to emotional exhaustion and depersonalization.

Anger can triple the risk of developing heart disease, even for those with no history of it. A huge meta-study on anger as a heart attack trigger found that an anger outburst two hours beforehand can more than quadruple the risk of myocardial infarction, or heart attack.

That's because anger and particularly hostility do their damage through activation of the stress response, which jacks up heart rate and blood pressure. Hostility has been linked to increased levels of C-reactive protein, which can form plaque and restrict blood flow. It's such a red flag that one study by the Boston University School of Public Health suggested hostility is a better predictor of coronary heart disease than high cholesterol or smoking.

The real threat of anger is its staying power. It keeps you in a prolonged state of emergency and high blood pressure, which can suppress the immune system for hours.

The irritability set off by time urgency has been connected to the frustration that comes from a blocked goal. That makes sense. Traffic, coworkers, and progress not moving swiftly enough all fill the blocked goal thesis. In fact, time urgency makes every event in the day a potential source of aggravation, because little in real life happens as quickly as you want it to. It sets an impossible standard on turnaround time, while locking you into self-inflicted irritation.

No Letup

The insidiousness of time-urgent behavior is that it doesn't end with the workday. It follows you home, making you want to fill every minute of your off-hours with something productive, which makes it very hard to relax. The hurry-worry whip insists you keep getting things done. Do you really want to get your life "done"? How about experiencing the life that whizzes by without you when you are in a time-urgent state?

The irony of time urgency is that in the frenzy for speed, we actually slow ourselves down.

1. Compulsive time-checking creates chronic self-interruption.
2. Each check of the time self-inflicts needless stress that sends the mind on a journey to irrational emotions and other tenses.

With friends like yourself around, who needs enemies? *OK, let me check the time and see how stressed I can make myself.* Clearly, we all have deadlines to meet, but a little impulse control can go a long way.

Manage Ego Upset

Irritability is one of the ways that humans excel at tripping themselves up. It pushes others away, entrenches negative emotions, sets off anger and stress, keeps you in a bunker of me-against-the-world, makes you unhealthy, and hands over the keys to your life to your ego.

One way to keep this behavior away is to treat yourself as the enemy, or at least your ego.

- **Make it a competition between you and your ego.** When irritability starts up, making you the most important person in the world, tell yourself: *Chill. The world doesn't revolve around me.*

- **Slow down your body.** If you're rushing for nothing, deliberately walk slower or get in the longer line at the market. *Take that, time urgency.* Act the opposite of the time nag, using the extra time to do some deliberate breathing (inhale to a count of five; exhale to a count of five) to restore your higher faculties and step off the runaway train. You are in charge, not hurry-worry.

The Mental Block of Busyness

Of all the things the time-urgent are too busy for, saying you're too busy isn't one of them. We always have time for that. Busyness, the state of being constantly preoccupied, often becomes more the purpose of our work than the act of doing the task.

Busyness feels productive, even if there's no real intention behind the commotion. Racing every minute becomes a part of your identity. A state of constant busyness validates us as performers to such a degree that it winds up being a mental block.

If you tell yourself there's no time, there isn't any. If you think, *I'm too busy,* you are. Maybe you're too busy to have that extra conversation you need with a colleague to move a schedule around to help with overwhelm, too busy to sit down for 15 minutes to plan priorities. Or maybe you are too busy to see people outside work. Who do you need to put on your calendar for a call or a visit? Are there parents you haven't seen for a few seasons? Friends?

Maybe, though, you have time for it all, if you tell yourself a different story—that you are not in an Olympic race and you do have time when you don't take the bait of self-defeating "hurry sickness," as it's called in the scientific literature.

We learned in the last chapter how self-talk drives false beliefs that cause stress. The same thing is true when the belief of busyness becomes your self-definition. Every time you tell someone you are too busy it reinforces the belief that constant activity is the marker of self-worth and who you are, and it fuels more busyness. Resist telling others, "I'm busy," as if that was your first name, and you stop perpetuating the belief behind time urgency.

Underlying all time urgency is the belief that you must go faster than you are going at any given moment. The anxiety to be where you're not makes wherever you are inadequate, which leads to an ungratified life.

What's the Emergency?

When everything is an emergency, it's vivid evidence of a habit of false urgency, and crisis mentality along with it. To catch yourself, you need to bring up awareness. Whenever you are racing and rushing, pause and ask yourself this question.

Is it an emergency or is it a speed trap?

Almost all the time the answer will be: Speed trap!

You can also prevent yourself from hopping on the speedway in the first place by using an implementation intention to plant this question deeper in your brain. As we learned in Chapter 5, the implementation intention uses an if-then statement to seed the brain with a behavior you want, instead of the habit. Say this out loud six times:

If I'm rushing, *then* I'll ask: Is it an emergency or a speed trap?

Qualify the Rush

One of the key elements of sustainable performance is understanding that not everything coming at you has the same value. Qualifying the incoming is critical. Just because email and phones chime instantly for your attention doesn't mean it's urgent.

To keep rushing under control, question the speed requirements of a given task and identify if it is truly something that has to be jumped on now or whether you can get to it in the afternoon or two days from now. Does it have to be done in the next hour or two or by the end of the day? That's urgent. If not, do it later and move on to something that is.

I like the approach that Gil Gordon, author of *Turn It Off*, takes to an essential piece of time management: prioritization. He says there are two questions you have to put to every item rattling your brain.

1. What's the value of doing it now?
2. What are the consequences of waiting?

Client projects would take priority over an email to a colleague. Items from leaders and managers are at the top of the list, so you want to be sure you have a clear idea of what they want. Customer support would have priority over research on a new project.

Time urgency explodes with overwhelm, so having a way to manage the volume of to-dos is critical. The brain is not built for storage. It's a processing center. Having multiple to-dos and unfinished items clogging up your mental bandwidth is an automatic trigger for aggravation and stress.

A couple of decades ago productivity guru David Allen, author of *Getting Things Done*, had an insight about this problem. He noticed that when you have unfinished business, the undone nags constantly and gets in the way of whatever you're trying to get done. He discovered that you can solve this issue by getting to-dos out of the brain and onto a piece of paper or screen with a next physical action attached. This tells the mind that you are on the way to handling the task, so it stops badgering.

He calls it closing "mental loops," making sure the unfinished items have a trajectory to completion. It's a trick you can play on the brain and a big assist, since it tells the part of the brain that confuses to-dos with survival needs that the item is under control. Years later, researchers at Florida State University were able to prove Allen's idea. They found that when you have unfinished business, the anxiety of the undone intrudes into whatever you are working on and hinders task performance.

Allen's prescription is to do it now, if the task is under two minutes, do it later if the task isn't urgent—and designate a time when you will get to it—or delegate the item. The central organizing principle is the next action. For all the things on your list, you jot down what the next physical action is for that item. Do you pick up a pen? Send an email? Whatever the next thing is write it down and you start to map a trail out of the task wilderness. Let's try it.

Put two of your to-dos to the prioritization and next-action test.

Task 1

Urgency of doing it now
Consequences of waiting
Next physical action

Task 2

Urgency of doing it now
Consequences of waiting
Next physical action

Avoiding Time Underestimation

When you are dogged by hurry-worry, one of the afflictions that comes along for the ride is a knack for underestimation. Since time is of the essence, the drive to do everything speedier jacks up estimates with forecasts that reflect when you would like to finish in an ideal world. The result is unrealistic deadlines that can't be met but can be stressed over.

Realistic time estimation is critical to putting the brakes on schedules careening out of control. The faster you estimate turnaround times, the more work that's going to be given to you that you won't be able to deliver on time. Build in more time to complete tasks to allow for interruptions, mistakes, Murphy's Law, and the inevitable "scope creep."

We all know that almost every project takes longer, costs more, and gets bigger. Building in additional time and resources beyond your first take provides a buffer to allow for enough time and a lot less time urgency.

When estimating how long a project will take, add an additional 20% for scope creep. It's better to under-promise and over-deliver than the other way around.

Productivity apps can help you organize your time better. For instance, RescueTime shows on your computer or phone how much time you spend on various categories of your job, from communication to scheduling to social media, as well as the time you spend on various websites. It also analyzes what time of the day you are most productive, which could be a very handy insight.

There's another kind of deadline that causes racing pulse rates, the arbitrary self-deadline. Every day we concoct times that we have to do various errands or chores by, and then stress over these voluntary time-tables, if we don't get them handled as planned. Avoid setting yourself up by seeing non-urgent items as the non-emergencies they are and by turning self-deadlines into more approximate targets.

Here are some keys to help make your days less hectic.

Tips to Rush Less

- **The desk does not have to be cleared at the end of each day.** Don't give yourself impossible agendas.
- **Don't do tasks just to get done with them.** When the goal behind a task is to get done with it, so you can get to other things that need to be done, you keep one eye on the future and that drives time urgency. Make the goal intrinsic. Do the task for the sake of it. Do it to do it, and you keep full attention in the present.
- **Limit time-checking.** Each time you check time, you lose time and gain stress. Never check a clock when you're late. It's not going to get you there any earlier and only makes time panic worse.
- **Always leave 15 minutes earlier** for appointments than you think.
- **Don't hold yourself to the false crises of self-deadlines.** Give yourself a break from self-inflicted, random time targets. When you're racing to get to the market for no reason, smile at the comedy of it and avoid the speed trap.
- **Never worry about anyone else's hurry-worry.** It's in their head, not yours.

Get to the Base Camp

There's nothing like a major project to egg on time urgency. You feel the nag badgering away at you to get going, but it's so big, how do you get started with no time? Take a page from one of the top mountain climbers, Ed Viesturs, the first American to summit all 14 of the 8000-meter peaks in the world (above 26,246 feet).

Getting to the top of one of those giants is a project to the 10th power. Viesturs told me it's too intimidating to look at the top of the mountain. Instead, he keeps his focus on getting to the base camp each day where the team will sleep for the night.

You can use this strategy with your big to-dos. Break them down into base camps. Tell yourself you're going to spend 30 minutes on it every day, first thing in the morning before you even glance at an email. By the end of a week, you will have made considerable progress to the point that the project will start to feel that it's on the way to being handled. Keep making it to your base camp for a few weeks, and you can put that assignment in the under-control category.

The base camp approach also works for your biggest priorities for the day. Choose your chief to-dos for the day and make their completion your base camp. No matter how much comes across your desk and the mountain of to-dos begins to resemble a Himalayan peak, keep your focus on getting to the base camp by workday's end.

Time Management to the Rescue

Getting organized is the answer for time-crunch woes. This can be scary for time-urgent souls, since it's an input exercise, which always takes a backseat to speed and output. Yet you have to take time to make time work for you.

We are all capable of prioritizing. What happens when you have a four-day holiday weekend coming up or a vacation? You tend to get everything caught up, make decisions you have been putting off, and get rid of clutter. You just need to use that skill the rest of the year.

A good time management system can reduce time anxiety throughout the day. There are several good comprehensive programs, including David Allen's *Getting Things Done* (GTD) and David Tracy's *Eat That Frog*, which is a good introduction to time management. Allen's program is one of the best. I got a lot out of his GTD workshop. He gets down into the granular, and nothing is left to procrastination.

Task apps are also worth checking out. Todoist gets your projects on the calendar, assigns priority to them, and can assign tasks to others too. The popular note-taking app, Evernote, lets you mark your tasks via audio, writing, photos, even sketches.

You can get control of a lot of loose ends and even email with the project management software Base Camp. It's easy to use and helps you know quickly where you are at on every to-do. It lets you add clients and unlimited videos. One of my clients, JamesandMatthew.com, an advertising and marketing firm in Boston, was able to dramatically reduce email by moving messaging out of in-boxes to Base Camp and encouraging only the most needed messages to be sent.

The key to getting organized—and to work-life balance—is planning. Keep a log of how you spend your time over a workweek, and certain patterns will emerge—where time is wasted, where you are over-committed.

The perception of time changes from tormentor to something manageable when you set the terms of engagement with tasks, and you are in control, instead of the deadline, stack of to-dos, or device.

Managing time is a daily practice. Make conscious choices every day to resist false urgency, your own and that of others. Here are some venerable organizing principles to bring order to chaos.

Organizing the Frenzy

- **Identify your top time thieves.** What are the time sinks in your day that need boundaries and limitations—such as social media, email, meetings, and personal calls? How can you cut them by 10%, 25% or more?
- **Do time estimates of all your key tasks.** It's easy to be overly optimistic on turnaround times. Analyze how long it takes to do each of your regular tasks. When you take an assignment, you will know how much time to budget for it.
- **Prioritize first thing every day.** Take 10-15 minutes each morning and determine your priority goals for the day. Separate out the most urgent from the important. As you plan, the anxiety lowers, and you feel more control over the day.
- **Determine the contours of your to-dos.** How will you know when you're done with them? What metrics can prevent you

from going at the task too long? Map out what the finish line looks like. This is important for perfectionists.

- **Qualify tasks by effort required.** Once you have determined a priority list, rank the items by which require the most effort. Do those at a time you have the best concentration to get them done more swiftly.
- **Identify tasks from the pile that are not within the scope of your job duties.** Can you say no to any of these? Where should they go?
- **Delegate or reschedule.** If you have more than you can do well, talk to supervisors or colleagues about how the work or the schedule could be changed.

Cultivate Patience

"Patience" is a word you normally hate to hear, because it usually comes up when you have lost yours. Being reminded that you need to take a minute when you are in a state of time frenzy doesn't go over too well, since you are on the edge of fight-or-flight.

In a time of permanent rush-hour, patience seems like a relic of another time, something from a do-gooder's list of manners that develops character and all that. Yet this increasingly rare act of discipline is the antidote for the speedway mind.

Instead of seeing patience as a waste of time, see it as a strategy to save time by avoiding mistakes, conflicts, and time burned up by stress. Patience doesn't mean moving at the speed of a tree sloth. It is acting deliberately, with informed performance, thought before action. It's crucial to sustainable performance, and only you can make it happen.

The gift of patience is that it is something within your control. All you need to do is take a breath, recalibrate the false urgency of frenzy, and exercise this act of discipline to turn down the blood pressure, bad mood, and irritability. Patience is a choice to resist the stampede and work and live with conscious intention.

If you want a long life, make patience your go-to strategy. It can prevent a host of serious medical conditions, particularly heart problems that come from aggravation and anger. Patience can also ensure that you don't shorten your perceived time on the planet when you race nonstop. You miss a lot of life blazing in constant busyness. As you get older, you realize just how short your time here is. Why make it go by even faster in a frenzy of hurry-worry?

When you have the awareness and patience to be fully present for every moment, you enlarge the experience of your day and the passage of time. Your memory isn't a blank by the end of the day because you have been paying attention to the experience of your time here.

Here are some ways to expand time by building the skill of patience.

Let Go of the Future
The anxiety of time urgency comes from trying to control future time, a talent none of us have.

Accept Delayed Gratification
Impatience demands that your needs be satisfied now, even if there's nothing you can do about making that happen. Patience is the exercise of not having to have a payoff instantaneously. Find gratification in the intrinsic experience of what you're doing, and you don't need to rush to the next hit of external validation.

Flip the Script on Impatience
When something or someone is taking longer than you want, if it's not an emergency, switch the story from how long it's taking to being grateful for something in your life. *I'm lucky to be alive today. I'm getting three meals a day. I'm healthy unlike so many others.* The stress is shut down by the appearance of positive emotions, which kick out the negative and the irritation with it.

Activate Tolerance
The raceway mindset is easily stoked by people and processes that aren't up to our standards. The judging impulse jacks up the irritability quotient. Cut some slack, criticize less, and relate more. Tolerance breeds a calm, relaxed focus that can't be shaken by what others are or are not doing.

Avoid Knee-Jerk Reactions
Don't engage with instant emotional responses. Withhold judgment and allow time for the neocortex to kick in with rational appraisal. Make nonreaction your new default.

Check the Ego
Impatience and irritability are both incited by an unchecked ego.

Time urgency makes you take time letdowns personally. See the bigger picture. You are one of 7.8 billion and counting.

Relax

I'm a track and field fan, and it has always intrigued me how the fastest humans in the world, 100-meter sprinters, invariably say after winning a race that they relaxed well during the sprint. What they mean is that, even though they were blazing, they were focused on their form in the moment, not the clock, so they weren't tensed up or constricted.

The answer to time urgency is, as it is for the world's fastest humans, relaxing into full attention and engagement in whatever you do.

CHAPTER 7

Set the Terms of Engagement

Control Devices, Distractions, and Interruptions

I had an encounter in New York with a classic example of where the reflex work style has taken us. I was leading a work-life balance training for a large consulting firm. Prior to the event, I was at the sink in their office building's empty rest room when I heard a loud ring. It wasn't my phone. I didn't see anyone else around, but then I heard some rustling behind one of the stalls. Sure enough, somebody's in here. Now what do you think happened next? Did the guy pick up the phone on the can?

Oh yeah. "Hey, how's it going? I'm doing great!"

I'm thinking, No! No! No! Don't go into detail about how great you're doing right now. Too much information. Dude, you're on a commode! Don't you have any idea where you are?

Let's face it, half the time these days we don't know where we are, because we've lost one of the basic management tools, boundaries. The devices are running us, instead of us running the devices. And just reacting to it all without managing it drives us down the autopilot road to stress and burnout.

We have to set boundaries and manage the incoming, or we wind up at the mercy of a lot of unconscious behaviors that make our days much harder than they have to be.

How many times have you felt you had to check email even though *you just checked it* five minutes ago? Answer: countless. In fact, the more you check email, the more you have to check it. Interruptions erode impulse control, so you lose the ability to regulate your impulsivity. With willpower gone, you can't help yourself. Americans check their phones 96 times a day, reports a survey from Asurion, a tech support company.

That's a migraine right there, if not whiplash.

It's not just email-checking that you can't control when impulse control leaves the building. You lose the willpower to control impulses for any habit, from Jim Beam to Haagen Dazs.

The addiction element of devices is no joke, say researchers at Rutgers University. "Addiction to technology can be equally damaging to the mental health of the worker" as chemical and substance abuse, says Gayle Porter, professor of management at Rutgers and co-author of a study on email addiction.

Technology is helpful when humans are in charge of it. Most of the time these days, we're not. We're at the mercy of unbounded inboxes, information overload, distractions, intrusions, and interruptions.

One executive at a supply chain conference told me he feels a semblance of control if he can get his email box down to 200. A couple people in the training I led at this event were getting more than 300 messages a day. That means doing email at home to catch up, which drives exhaustion, crowds out recovery options and shreds work-life balance. Executives from Pepsi to Starbucks to Microsoft told me they were drowning in messaging and digital interruptions to the point they can't keep up with it all and feel like they're constantly falling behind. They regularly ignore dozens of emails every day because they can't physically deal with them all.

What we don't understand about digital devices is that they are supposed to work for us, to help us, not barrage our working memory and survival equipment all day. The humans are supposed to be in charge.

When devices and interruptions are in control, we feel out of control, and as a result, wracked with stress. At just about every organization I see, large and small, it's triage mode—just reacting to the bombardment.

Yet we are not helpless—and can't be, because the digital assault is snuffing out the key to productivity and sanity: attention. When we are not in charge of our attention, we are also not in charge of self-control, motivation, and mind-wandering.

Chronic interruptions shrink attention spans, drive stress by overwhelming mental and emotional resources, and trigger mistakes. An interruption averaging 2.8 seconds—say, one of those blinking notifications on your computer screen—can double the risk of error, a study by researchers at Michigan State University and the U.S. Naval Research Laboratory found. Increase the length of the interruption to 4.4 seconds, and you triple the chance of a mistake, which doesn't do wonders for performance. An Intel study found that lost productivity from information overload alone amounts to $1 billion per year for a company with 50,000 employees.

The surge of email, texts, chat apps, and social media notifications in recent years has led to a tipping point of terminal distraction and always-on availability. One entrepreneur, who co-founded a cloud-based service management software company, told me he was getting a thousand messages a day at one point. For a while, he barely slept, taking calls from customers from his bed. His health started to suffer. He gained weight and became anxious from the never-ending assault.

It's time for an intervention. The research shows we don't have to be digital punching bags. We can create rules, norms, and systems to wring order and attention out of chaos.

Reflex vs. Science

Look closely at the information overload problem, and you will see a familiar culprit at the root of it: unconscious, autopilot behavior. No thought, just reaction.

Let's compare the reflex work style to what the science has to say about how productive our instinctive digital behaviors are. We assume that unbounded, constant messaging is the way to get more done. We don't do anything to stop it, so it all just avalanches on us. The research, though, says something quite a bit different. A study at Kings College in London found that interruptions undermined IQ by ten points. Interruptions make us stupid by making it hard for working memory to function while being blown up by distractions.

One of the gospels of the digital age is that multitasking speeds up work. You try to do a couple of things at once as much as you can, thinking you are more productive that way. Wrong. Multiple studies from the University of Michigan to Vanderbilt University have found that multitasking doesn't speed you up. It slows you down. Multitasking is not so swift.

David Meyer at the University of Michigan says multitasking can cut productivity by 40% and more. The reason is that we can't multitask cognitive tasks as we can manual ones. I'll have more on this in a few pages.

Another assumption made when in the trance of mechanical momentum and hurry-worry is that answering an email won't take long, so you will just hop over and take care of it. Nope. Gloria Mark, a professor of informatics at the University of California Irvine, found in her research that every email results in a loss of 25 minutes. We do the email, maybe another one or two, get distracted by social media or stop for a conversation with someone.

How much time do you lose every day from email? For someone getting 126 emails a day, the average for most American workers, according to the Radicati Group, it adds up to more than a third of your workday doing nothing but email. And it doesn't end when the workday does. Some 82% of people check their work email at home after hours, reports Statista.

This, obviously, has a major impact on work-life balance, since it cuts into time you can be spending on other responsibilities and recharging activities. We all share responsibility for self-inflicting email and device overload, and we all can play a role in fixing it.

What Was I Doing?
Minding Your Working Memory

The siege of interruptions and fractured attention spans is taking a special toll on one very crucial part of your ability to stay on task and get anything done: working memory, or as it is better known, short-term memory. Unlike the deeper reaches of long-term memory that span your life, working memory has a remarkably limited capacity. The expanse of the brain is reduced down to only the most relevant core concurrent thoughts to a given task.

You can only hold in your mind three or four thought chunks for only a few seconds. This makes working memory very vulnerable to intrusions and distractions, which blow up the tenuous link between thought associations. *Where was I again?* By the way, if you have maxed out to four thought chunks in the moment, you are more likely to divert to a distraction. Too much effort makes the brain want to bail to something easier.

Continuously paying attention burns up a lot of attention resources and energy, so you are restricted to the amount of stuff you can hold in mind while working on them. This is why working memory activates brain neurons only temporarily. Long-term memories go through processes that change neurons and their connections, allowing them to imprint in our brains.

Working memory is the unsung hero of attention, and you need to wall it off as much as possible from distractions. It uses controlled attention to join tenuous thoughts into an idea that leads to an action.

Though it is very limited, working memory can call on any memory or idea in your brain to help complete the cognitive or physical action. Information overload, interruptions, and aging all affect working memory negatively. Senior moments come from slippage in thought retention.

Studies show that the better you are at controlling your attention, by both laser focus and keeping out irrelevant content, the better your working memory functions. The goal in a tide of distractions, then, must be protecting fragile working memory from the unbounded hammering— and doing what you can to increase your short-term memory skills. One thing shown to increase executive attention skills like working memory is an eight-week mindfulness training course, as documented in a study conducted by Amism Jha, Jason Krompinger, and Michael Baime.

Interruption Management

Managing email and devices is really about managing interruptions. The toll of the e-barrage comes from the constant assault on concentration as you are forced to shift from primary task to secondary items or more, most of the time unrelated to what you're doing. Interruption management is a concept crucial to performance that gets even less attention in most companies than information management.

Interruptions trigger detours that tax working memory and increase the time it takes to accomplish tasks, all of which drive stress and mistakes. You can't pay full attention to what you are doing when you are being interrupted.

When an intrusion occurs, "It sets off a chain of random events, with people switching activities," Gloria Mark, an author of many studies on the impact of email, told me. On average, she said, "You work on two intervening tasks before you get back to the original task." For example, you might be at work on a marketing project one minute, then shift to an email from a customer, then head off on a trip to LinkedIn.

Mark followed 35 managers, engineers and project leaders for three days. She found that the average time people spent on a single task before being interrupted or switching to something else was a whopping three minutes. The amount of time they worked on a device before switching was two minutes, 11 seconds. Flash forward 10 years, and Mark said the average time on an activity had shrunk even further, to one minute, 15 seconds.

Not surprisingly, researchers Brian Bailey and Joseph Konstan discovered that interruptions slow us down, causing up to 27% more time to complete a task.

How annoying is it when you're focused on a task, almost done with it, and you get sidetracked by an interruption? This echoes the blocked goal thesis behind impatience. We get irritated and shortly afterwards, angry, when our progress is stopped by an intrusion. Bailey and Konstan found that interruptions increase anxiety and annoyance 106%. And herein lies a very important lesson for every team and organization about interruptions. They make anything you're trying to do seem harder than it is. Interruptions come with a big side of stress.

The point at which performance plummets is when the interruption turns into a disruption, when progress on the primary task is compromised by the leap to a notification or text and it winds up taking longer to complete. That was precisely the story at a software company that makes color printers. The firm was having serious problems getting a new product designed and on the market. Engineers tasked with creating a new model had to work at night and on weekends for months on end to meet their deadlines.

Then-University of Michigan researcher Leslie Perlow, now professor of leadership and senior dean for research at Harvard, stepped in to investigate. After a few months she determined that it was a case of chronic disruption. She discovered that the engineers were being interrupted so often they didn't have time to think and couldn't get enough done during regular hours as a result. With everyone falling behind schedule, a crisis mentality developed, in which people felt entitled to interrupt anyone at any time. Because the engineers had to do their work at night or on the weekend, when it was quieter, the issue was driving work-life balance and morale issues.

Perlow proposed a new work style, one designed to manage interruptions, instead of letting them run wild. She called it Quiet Time. The idea was to set aside zones to give engineers the space to do their work without the usual flood of email and intrusions. Days were divided into periods in which the team agreed not to interrupt each other and periods of normal contact. There was a no-interruption zone to start the day, from 8 a.m. to 11 a.m., followed by regular contact from 11 a.m. to 3 p.m., and then another no-interruption zone from 3 p.m. to 5 p.m. The results of her research speak for themselves:

- 8 a.m. to 11 a.m. No-Interruption Zone: Productivity increased 59%
- 11 a.m. to 3 p.m. Normal Contact: Productivity increased 42%
- 3 p.m. to 5 p.m. No-Interruption Zone: Productivity increased 65%

These are huge gains in performance. Even in the normal contact zone, productivity soared, since minds had been focused from the no-interruption zone earlier. And what is usually the worst time of the day for performance, the low-energy afternoon swoon from 3 p.m. to 5 p.m., when bodies and minds operate as if stuck in a vat of molasses, turned in the best output, an astonishing 65% jump in productivity.

Perlow's work shows the impact of interruption management on productivity, thinking, concentration, stress, and results. Every organization needs to be investigating ways to build no-interruption zones into their systems. Exploding working memory every couple of minutes with unbounded messaging and noisemakers is not a prescription for productivity.

Quiet Time brought massive increases in performance to Perlow's group. The engineers wound up finishing the new software on time and with dramatically less overtime—and won an award for their product to boot.

Fear Fuels the Siege

The messaging siege is held in place, not by any law of productivity, but by run-of-the-mill fear—thoughts and theories about what might happen that we have no ability to know, since we are not seers. The prevailing fear is that if we don't let technology run unfettered, if we aren't available 24/7, that teams, clients, or managers won't be able to have the contact they need. We'll miss important communications, and relationships will wither.

These are false beliefs that crumble in the face of facts, experience, and science. Perlow's Quiet Time productivity gains tell us this. Companies such as Deloitte and U.S. Cellular that have instituted email-free Fridays so people can think and get work done free of the messaging blitz have found that productivity and rapport increases with less email availability. People are actually talking to each other instead of just sitting back and clicking.

When we let fear call the tune, we wind up overdoing it at the sacrifice of health, life, and the work itself. Boundaries, again, are a mandatory organizing instrument in an always-on world. We need not fear them.

Imagine if there was no email, no texting, no mobile apps, and you had to get work done. Impossible, right? That's the way it was before digital devices showed up. Big companies and small firms alike survived and thrived with only telephone lines. We can survive too with a lot less e-overload.

Almost everyone I meet understands there is too much messaging—employees, customers, and especially managers. All levels of the company want something done about it. When you let someone know that you are starting a new information management program and clarify your availability and preferred contact time, they are almost always okay with it, because they have the same problem.

Overcoming the fear of managing messaging is about preparing everyone with the right expectations. Yes, we will continue to have contact, but it will be within an understanding of what an emergency is and an agreement on availability and response time. There's no fear involved when the ground rules are laid out. Instead, people feel more confident that they can rely on spelled-out perimeters they wish they had.

Hold That Interruption

You can significantly minimize the disruption factor of interruptions with a couple of simple strategies.

1. University of Minnesota researchers Bailey and Konstan

say to defer action on the alert barging into your work until you are done with either the thought or task you are on. Even holding off a few seconds before responding can prevent a disruption, where you lose track of what you are doing, and then it takes longer to get the task done.

2. You can also keep an interruption from becoming a disruption by deferring an interruption until you have written down where your thoughts are and where they are headed before you take the interruption.

You Are the Boss of Your Attention

Time management, information management, interruption management, stress management—all are about finding ways to protect and harness working memory, so that we can complete a thought, a task, a conversation without being sidetracked by counterproductive impulses, emotions, and habits.

Beyond its importance to getting the job done, attention is the architect of all you see and touch. What and who you decide to pay attention to in your life turns out to be your life, what you have chosen to select out from the myriad options. In this way, you are the author of your journey on this planet simply by what you spend your time focused on.

The digital heist of attention has reduced minds to scattered, superficial retention that can't hold interest or encode data in memories. It is stealing attention from our work, kids, family, friends, and interests.

The siege is intense, but you can fight back. If you have enough attention left to decide you want more of it, the damage can be undone by limiting cognitive intrusions and opting for an attention style that builds more focus.

Out of all the things your brain could focus on right now, your attention at this moment is on this sentence. This is because you are using what's known as *top-down* attention, or controlled attention, in which your goals lead you to choose what to concentrate on. You set the terms of engagement, leaving the executive attention function of your brain that controls what you attend to fully in control.

On the other hand, you also have another kind of attention, one you don't choose, called *bottom-up* attention, which is dictated by someone or something else. Bottom-up attention is part of the survival equipment. When you hear a loud noise, a siren or a car backfire, your attention instantly shifts to the potential threatening sound. It triggers a startle response that stops everything else you're paying attention to so you can focus on potential danger.

This same process happens with all the digital interrupters in your life. The cavalcade of rings, chirps, buzzes, and pulses from email, texts, apps, phones, and notifications are all bottom-up intruders. They arouse defenses, hijack concentration, and suck you in.

"There's a thrill to it," Winifred Gallagher, author of *Rapt: Attention and the Focused Life*, told me in an interview. "Your texts and e-mails are like video games. There's a stimulus and rewards."

"Yet you are the boss of what's in your head," she added. "Attention is a tool, and you can take charge of it. It's a matter of knowing when you want to use your top-down attention, and then you have to suppress the bottom-up stimuli. Otherwise, you become a victim of stimuli."

Impulse Control vs. Instant Gratification

You may remember the famed marshmallow test, the Stanford study that measured the ability of children to delay gratification by not immediately eating a marshmallow (or a cookie or pretzel in later tests) sitting right in front of them. Children four to six years old were told that, if they could hold off for 15 minutes and not gobble up the goodie, they would get two marshmallows.

Most of them couldn't get through a minute without downing the treat. In later studies, the researchers found that those able to delay the reward had better SAT scores, educational accomplishments, and body mass index. If you did the same test on adults today, swapping the marshmallow treat out for a screen with a new message, they couldn't go thirty seconds without grabbing it.

Being able to manage temptations and delay gratification is essential to productive working and living. Interruptions and messaging undermine a mechanism essential to both self-discipline and attention: impulse control, making it harder to summon the discipline to focus on anything.

The executive attention that directs your concentration is located in the frontal lobe, home to the decision-making and analytical gear. A part of your executive attention is home to the discipline you need to sustain attention. It's called effortful control, and it regulates impulse control. You need it to stay on task and prevent detours, but interruptions erode this crucial mechanism.

Too many interruptions, and you become a victim of stimuli, chasing them mindlessly. You can't regulate your impulsivity. You are at the mercy of whims and instant gratification. You check email you just checked minutes ago and make a beeline for the brownie or margarita.

Temple University researchers Henry Wilmer and Jason Chein found that excessive use of mobile devices is associated with weakened ability to delay gratification and increased impulsive behavior. The study discovered that mobile tech habits, "such as frequent checking are driven most strongly by uncontrolled impulses and not by the desire to pursue rewards." Compulsive device use, then, isn't triggered as much by the positive reinforcement of an email response at a certain point, but simply by an irresistible urge—due to impulse control malfunction.

You can see it in action every day with the text-walkers of the world, heads down in their phones, blithely stepping off curbs and into oncoming traffic and winding up in ERs or mortuaries. Text-walkers have plunged off piers, fallen down open manholes (that one is on YouTube), tumbled downstairs, and walked straight into swimming pools and fountains (also on YouTube). I saw a text-walker, buried in his phone, crossing on a red light on a major street in my town, with two lanes of cars backed up to five in number. Horns honked, but he had headphones on and didn't even look up. He's lucky to be alive. We may need some new citations, such as walking under the influence or maybe reckless ambulating.

Inability to regulate impulses is something you would expect from a baboon or a drug addict, but now tens of millions of people have entered the no self-regulation zone. I was at a concert, lost in a spellbinding performance by one of my favorite artists, keyboardist Gerald Clayton. The moment was rapturous. The lights were dim. And then they weren't. Three phones flashed around me, as their owners defaulted to scrolling Instagram and email. They missed a great show.

Constant stimulation begets more stimulation, which crowds out focus, assessing, and evaluating. Without impulse control, instant gratification is the guiding instinct.

Unplug For Your Brain, Kids, and Dog

Constant interruptions from email- and social media-checking shrink the size of the attention and goal centers of your brain and increase the size of the habit-formation centers. If you don't manage this reflex, it can go from compulsion to addiction.

Mental health centers around the country now offer therapy for technology addiction, many for teenagers, who spend a boggling 11 hours on screens per day on average. But increasingly, adults need to break the screen habit as well.

I see way too many people walking on a gorgeous day, head down in the phone, oblivious to where they are, not present for the experience of their life. I see friends theoretically out together but not talking to each other, all buried in phones as if they were random strangers.

Put down the devices, lift your head up, and behold the offerings of planet Earth. Look at your surroundings, the sky, the dazzling flowers in that yard. What about that architecture? How did they do that? Don't let the phone delete you from every scene you are in or relegate you to a bystander in your own life.

We take devices from our kids who overdo it and put them on an electronic timeout. Why not prescribe the same medicine for us? Detaching from screens is critical for the brain to reset, repair impulse control, focus, and think.

Do it for your partner, your kids, friends, and dogs, all of whom don't have your attention when you are glued to the phone. Walking the dog has turned into a text-walking experience, with the poor pooch wanting to do his business, but the owner, head down in the device, is plowing ahead, yanking the dog along. It's like man's best friend is not even there. That's even true for the kids of some text-walking moms pushing strollers, which is alarming.

It's not only dogs who are lonely. Researchers were puzzled by a huge increase in depression among teenagers, which had doubled by 2019 from seven years earlier. They discovered a compounding factor. The number of teens reporting high levels of loneliness had been stable at 18%, but since 2012 the number doubled, rising by about the same amount all over the world. A study led by Jonathan Haidt and Jean M. Twenge found the culprit: smartphones. Adolescents were cut off from the world by their digital sidekick.

In a *New York Times* article about their findings, Haidt and Twenge wrote poignantly about why it's so important we, our coworkers, and our kids extract ourselves from the self-isolation of excessive phone use. "The smartphone brought about a planetary rewiring of human interaction. As smartphones became common, they transformed peer relationships, family relationships, and the texture of daily life for everyone—even those who don't own a phone or don't have an Instagram account. It's harder to strike up a casual conversation in the cafeteria or after class when everyone is staring down at a phone. It's harder to have a deep conversation when each party is interrupted randomly by buzzing, vibrating notifications."

Unmanaged phones and devices remove us from those with us. That is sad, frustrating, and maddening. How do you feel when you're trying to have a conversation with someone, and you're talking to the crown of somebody's head as they gaze down at the phone? In my experience, people feel unheard. Unimportant. Unessential. In some cases, unloved. In other cases, insulted. We all hate this. Let's change it.

Starting now, let's make a vow to improve communication and respect for everyone we interact with by putting the phone down when you are talking with someone, or they are speaking with you. Pay courtesy forward, and let's see if we can make a change.

There's also another side effect of phone and email overdosage that underscores the need to disconnect. If you look at a screen every time you have a spare moment, you won't have any thoughts to process when you are sleeping that night. If your brain is always fixated on a screen or doing tasks for that matter, the parts of it charged with processing and reflection—key to memory—known as the default mode network, are sidelined. The network only activates when your brain has downtime. Your brain needs rest to do important cognitive work.

Sleep is essential to forming memories, finding patterns in the events of the day, and solving problems, but your brain can't do its job if there is nothing upstairs after a full day of zombie phone staring, because you haven't had a moment for any thoughts to process.

It's critical to build in unplugged zones to turn down the noise, allow the mind to reset, restore concentration, spur imagination, relax and have a few thoughts to process during shuteye.

Take a page from the screen guidelines for kids and try these habit-busting behaviors:

1. No devices at the dinner table
2. Bedtime curfew on devices
3. Play outside more with no screens

Which times at night and on the weekends could you set aside to disconnect and unwind? Could you do a whole weekend day unplugged? How about an hour or two every day without a screen?

Attention Deficit Trait

As self-regulation capacity is reduced by interruptions, so is your attention span. This creates a constant need to shift to the next quick escape/stimulation/instant payoff and away from anything that requires effort and discipline.

The result is high distractibility, impatience, and flitting from one thing to the next. It's a condition that Massachusetts psychiatrist Edward Hallowell sees a lot these days. His patients think they have Attention-Deficit Hyperactivity Disorder (ADHD), but they don't. They have a variation on that theme he calls Attention Deficit Trait. You are born with ADHD. ADT is a byproduct of information overload and interruptions "filling our heads with a cacophony of mental noise" until the brain "loses its ability to attend fully and thoroughly to anything," Hallowell notes in *Driven to Distraction.*

As with ADHD, those with ADT have trouble organizing, planning, or seeing things through to completion, since they are drowning in a sea of distractions and to-dos. Once high producers, people with this condition bounce from one task to the next and find themselves falling behind, which in turn increases time urgency and anxiety as they try to catch up.

The constant disruptions feed a feeling of being overwhelmed and not able to cope, a signal to the ancient brain to set off the stress response. It's a default to System 1 thinking, marked by rash, impulsive behavior and impatience.

With ADT, you can't resist the temptation for something easier, so you jump from one task to another to a browser to social media. This leads to poor concentration, rushed output, mistakes, and longer turnaround times.

The Myth of Multitasking

It's not enough that we have everyone else interrupting us, but we add to it with self-inflicted interruptions such as multitasking. We have grown up thinking multitasking is a good thing, but when it comes to cognitive tasks, it's not. It's a descent into simultaneous inattention. If you are a dedicated multitasker, before you scream, I invite you to do the exercise below this section, and you will see what I mean.

Even the most adept multitasker will "crash and burn" trying to resolve simultaneous conflicting language demands, says David Meyer, the cognitive scientist at the University of Michigan we met earlier.

Diverted attention is hazardous to work and life. You wind up sending the wrong person your email. You can make a colossal mistake on a price quote or seriously misunderstand a conversation. Or you can find yourself in a truly hazardous situation, such as driving while using a cell phone or texting.

There's a belief that some people, say, young people or women, are more adept at multitasking. No data supports that. When it comes to simultaneous cognitive multitasking, none of us can do it.

Yes, you can do a couple of manual tasks at one time like a juggler in the circus, but when it comes to two cognitive tasks, there is only one neural channel for language to flow through. If you are on the phone with someone and doing an email at the same time, you are not doing them at the same time. You are switching back and forth. In that switching there is a cost: stress.

It stresses your brain neurons out to have to keep jumping back and forth from the primary to the secondary task. Each time they switch they have to stop and try to remember where they were the last time they were there and where they were going. That slows you down. That causes strain from cognitive overload.

By the way, you are also using the language channel when you are driving, because you have to look at road signs. Again, you can do only one task involving words at a time, which adds up to serious risk when you are on the phone in the car. Either your conversation is going to suffer, or worse, your driving will. No wonder the National Safety Council reports 1.6 million car crashes a year due to cell phone use while driving. Texting while driving is many times more dangerous and is responsible for one out of four car accidents in the U.S.

"When you perform multiple tasks that each require some of the same channels of processing, conflicts will arise between the tasks, and you're going to have to pick and choose which task you're going to focus on and devote a channel of processing to it," Meyer told me in an interview.

Meyer has been at the forefront of research for several decades on how the brain processes information and copes with multitasking. He investigated the brain's speed, accuracy and memory in information processing while working with psychologist David Kieras for the Office of Naval Research. A study Meyer co-wrote on the limitations of multitasking went viral in 2001, setting off the first awareness of the counterproductivity of this habit.

"If you have a complicated task, it requires all your attention, and if you're trying to spread your attention over multiple tasks, it's not going to work," he said.

That's heresy in a time-urgent world. Meyer admits that multitasking is not only getting more prevalent, but it's also "very often highly inefficient and can be dangerous to your health."

Creativity and innovation don't come from people who are multitasking, he pointed out. That sends thoughts from the higher brain to the rote and emotional parts, the so-called "low road," where mistakes and impulsive behavior live. "You ought to be setting aside large chunks of time where you just think. Einstein was not multitasking when he was dreaming up the special and general theories of relativity."

Since multitasking cognitive tasks can't be done, we need another solution to get this brain strainer under control. Instead of trying to do multiple things at once, do what your brain was made for:

Do one thing at a time.

Shift to alternate tasking for all cognitive work. You are on one email or conversation at a time. When that is over, you take on another task with 100% attention. Not only do you prevent self-interruption and fractured working memory, but you also reduce stress in a big way. You're not racing with one eye on the next couple of to-dos. You have full attention on what you are doing, which means you get the job done faster. That's smarter work.

Unless you prefer the mistakes, meltdowns, and overwhelm of trying to do what your brain can't.

So, You Think You Can Multitask?

One of the best illustrations of the difficulty of doing simultaneous cognitive tasking is an exercise that was given to me by David Meyer. Try it right now. It only takes a few seconds. Then have your whole team try it.

1. Count out loud from 1 to 10 as fast as you can.
2. Now recite the letters A through J as fast as you can.
3. Good single tasking. Now put them together and say each number and letter together: 1-A, 2-B, 3-C, 4-D, as fast as you can until you get to 10-J. Don't slow down.

How did that go? Still think you can multitask? It doesn't get any easier than letters and numbers. Think what's happening when you are trying to multitask complicated thoughts and ideas. We can't do it.

Connectivity Pressure and Message Overload

The confessions began to tumble out. One woman at a work-life balance workshop I was leading in New York raised her hand and said sheepishly, "I take my smartphone to bed."

"So do I," chimed in another consultant quickly. "I've been sleeping with my phone for years," offered a third woman.

This is what I call unrequited love. You give your device undivided love and attention, and what do you get for it? The attention span of a gnat. Constant interruptions. And the dings of messages from other time zones in the middle of the night.

Don't get me wrong. Email is a very handy tool. It's just that there are no widespread, agreed-upon norms to manage it and prevent its overuse and abuse. The approach to email overload so far has been to just react to the incoming, get up earlier, stay later. But that's not viable in a 24/7 digital world.

Email is by far the choice for the most annoying bottleneck at any company I visit. Everyone hates the constant barrage, the reply-all lists they have no idea how they got on, the fear of missing a critical message amid the pile, the lack of a respite from the server firehoses spraying their in-box.

In her research Gloria Mark at U.C. Irvine found that the more time people spend on email, the higher their stress levels. In addition, Mark's study participants—across all job duties and titles— told her the more time they spend on email, the less productive they feel at the end of the day.

There is no shortage of reasons why unbounded messaging is at the top of the list for driving stress and burnout. Tonnage, velocity, and inescapableness come to mind. All add up to the automatic trigger for the survival gear to go off: more than you perceive you can handle. And, of course, there are many more impacts. One study identified these critical culprits, which go to the core of the role information overload plays in compromising mental health and work-life balance:

- **connectivity pressure**, the perceived need to stay connected outside office hours
- **increased workload** from the inexhaustible flow of messaging
- **inner obligation for availability** even if not expressed explicitly

The study, led by Katharina Ninaus and Sandra Diehl, examined the use of information and communication technologies in companies in Austria and Hong Kong and featured comments from participants that detail the crying-out-loud need for boundaries. Here are comments from two different people in the study:

I feel as I if have to be available at all times. For instance, when I'm in the car, I check my emails at every red traffic light.

I permanently check my emails, sometimes even in the middle of the night. I wake up and automatically reach to my phone. I feel pressured to do so.

It could be that we are all in the *Twilight Zone* and that the takeover of Earth by machines is complete. However, if humans are still in charge, then it behooves us to go after the three overload drivers laid out in this study. What can we do about these agents of overwhelm and burnout?

Talk About It. Connectivity pressure and inner obligation for availability both have to do with the lack of communication and expressed intentions about work outside office hours. Discuss with managers and teams reasonable boundaries on checking email and working after hours. What are the expectations? Constant checking? I think not. Get agreement on stop times. If there are times when there needs to be contact after-hours, define the kinds of scenarios. If it turns out the expectation is for constant contact at night and on the weekends, that is a prescription for burnout and major turnover problems and not tenable in the long run.

Measure Increased Workload. The velocity of information technology means there is much more coming at us—more projects, more emails to answer, more texts, more people who expect turnaround times faster than can be done in business hours. Do time diaries for two weeks and see how much time it's taking to do your various tasks, how much time email is sucking up per day (include an estimate of the amount of time you spend on work email at home), and then determine how much you can legitimately do over the course of the day versus the workload you have just because more can be squeezed through a medium of perceived urgency. Analyze the results and together with your team adjust workload, response times, deadlines, message volume, and expectations to reflect the metrics of reality.

It's time to stop assuming and start getting a clear understanding on all the issues driving information overload—availability, open-ended tasks that run chronically late into the night, and deadlines that are based more on time urgency than on project accuracy. It's a win-win for all when we do the job without having to pull all-nighters and endurance heroics. We have to set the right, not the most instantaneous, expectations.

Spay and Neuter Your Email

The single biggest problem with email is the volume. It's just not sustainable. We have to cut the tonnage. Email is multiplying like oversexed cottontails. Every email has offspring, and they have offspring. A single message creates six messages on average—three going, three coming back, say researchers, as we try to tease out an answer and go back and forth until someone gives up.

Even at the standard average of three minutes per email, that's 18 minutes down the tubes for every email you send. Add it up. It's time to spay and neuter email. The sooner we can see email for the digital rabbit it is, the sooner we can get the population down.

Email has overwhelmed our lives because it's convenient. We don't have to physically interrupt someone with a call or pop-in. In the pre-email days, the message had to rise to the importance of a phone call before it caused someone to reach out and dial. This helped to limit messages to the most important ones. There are zero inhibitions to clicking an email. It's imperative we create some.

Solving the email overload dilemma requires a proactive offensive to tackle the lack of rules and structure that feed unbounded messaging. There are three main paths to do this.

1. **Cut the Volume.** Reduce incoming and outgoing totals to manageable levels.
2. **Cut the Amount of Email- and Device-Checking.** Slash the constant interruption of notifications and reflexive email-checking with a designated schedule done at your choosing.
3. **Create Rules for E-Tools.** Work with your team and organization to establish standards and norms for email, texting, chat apps, and interruptions, so that everyone is on the same page with best practices.

How to Cut Message Volume

I was working with a group of managers at an aviation company. They were commiserating about their tangles with email, when one man raised his hand. "I don't have an email problem," he said.

Jaws dropped around the room and a hush came over the crowd. He had an identical job description to the rest of them. How could he not be buried in email? Then came his reveal: "I just tell my people that I would rather be contacted by phone and that an email has to be important before sending it."

That's it? Yep.

Sometimes solutions are easier than we think. Clear communication about how to be contacted can change click-first behavior. These conversations are almost never had, though. In the vacuum of non-communication clicking goes wild. With no boundaries, there are no restraints on shaky impulse control to not overdo it. Once again, boundaries are the key to sustainable performance and work-life balance. The email overload-solving manager shall lead the way for us.

1. **Ask others to please only send an email if it's important or needs an action and try the phone preference gambit.**

Talk with your colleagues, where most email comes from, and tell them you have embarked on a new information management program that is helping you be more productive and improve your work-life balance. The vast majority will understand and ask how they can get in on the program.

As for the phone contact, almost everyone hates talking on the phone these days, so you won't get many takers, and that's the point, to help others hold fire.

2. **Write in the headline or body of the email, "No reply necessary."**

Letting folks know they don't need to come back to you with another email can go a long way to reducing message volume. You will get across clearly that you are trying to keep the volume down and let others off the hook. You'll make a lot of new friends this way.

3. **Get off reply-all lists you don't need to be on.**

The number one beef everyone has against email is reply-all. Most of us are on too many lists, and we need to get off as many as we can to make a dent in the volume. One of my training participants shared a story about being copied in on the news that one of their medical clinics had ants. Did this nurse manager really have to know about that? Answer: No. Sit down with your team and organization and find ways to reduce reply-all. Leaders may think they are being inclusive with frequent email contact and reply-all notifications, but it's counterproductive. Constant messaging drives stress and eats up time for people to get their jobs done.

Do an inventory of the reply-all lists you are on. Request to be taken off lists that aren't essential, and then go have some champagne.

4. Send less mail.

You can control how much email you personally generate. Before sending a message ask if it's really necessary. Does it need to be sent? Is it urgent? Can it wait? Think of the person on the other end of the email who has to open it and deal with it, then respond—and then go through several more back-and-forths from both of you.

5. Use an email to set up a phone conversation that can let you handle all the points of an issue in a brief conversation.

We assume speaking with someone takes longer than an email, but often it's quicker, because we don't have to go through the repeated reply emails over days to settle something. Using email to set up a phone call or personal meeting saves multiple back-and-forths.

6. Try the 100-Foot Rule.

If most of your messages are coming from colleagues who are sitting within 100-feet of your desk, get up and deliver the message in person when possible and appropriate. This saves six messages and also increases rapport. If you want to get a little more exercise, make it 500 feet. You are not on a plane with turbulence. You are allowed to get up and move about the cabin.

7. Limit texting to emergency only.

Remember when texting was only used for personal business? Now it's another go-to interrupter that adds to the pile of message overload. Create boundaries to keep it at bay. Try to get agreement on some restrictions on texting, when it's okay to send one, such as emergencies, and when it's not, most of your workday.

8. Keep personal messaging to a minimum when you're at work.

Tell family and friends to limit contact during the workday. You can connect at lunchtime or on breaks. You have too much to do and not enough time to do it. If you can't get it all done because of all the interruptions and sidetracking, it comes home with you and impacts family and friends that way. You want to move socializing to your hours outside the office. Obviously, you can be available at work for family and personal emergencies.

9. Check out Messaging Apps.

As I'm sure you know, there are a bunch of apps designed to put messages in one place that you and teams can access when you want. They range from Slack to Microsoft Teams, Chanty, Facebook Workplace, Mattermost, Google Chat, to Flock. This can be a useful place to stick FYI and informational email. The jury is out, though, on whether these tools cut volume. Slack channels, for instance, have a habit of proliferating and can increase the volume of mail. Make it easier to create email, and volume rises.

Project and task organizing apps such as Trello and Asana can be helpful in placing everything on easy-to-see boards. A host of other email organizing and de-cluttering apps claim to help you get your inbox down in size. They range from apps that move less important messages and cold calls into folders that cut down on triaging (SaneBox), to a system that arranges your calendar meetings a few days before your event, so they don't overflow your box for weeks (Boomerang, Streak), to a tool that organizes folders in two columns, instead of one scary single column (Sortd).

Slash Email- and Message-Checking

Just as important as cutting the volume of email is reducing the number of times each day that you check email on whatever device. This means finding ways to put organizing and willpower in charge.

There's no reason to have your computer and phone chiming like deranged glockenspiels all day or blinking annoying notifications. Turn off message software and turn it back on when you want to deal with it, and you can shut down the sound and light circus.

Some 68% of us keep email on autocheck all day. If you are not required to maintain nonstop vigilance, turn your email software off. Put your phone on silent. One study found that, if your email software is set to check every five minutes and send you a notification each time, that is a potential of 96 interruptions over the course of an eight-hour day. How can you get anything done? Add heaps of texts and Slack messages on top of it, and you are in brownout mode by lunch.

However, if you turn off your email software and phone and check messages at a designated time, say every 45 minutes, you stop the interruption festival, slashing the number of times your startle response is triggered from 96 to 11. This leads to the key rule of breaking the email-checking habit:

Turn off email and visual notifications and turn them on again according to a set checking schedule.

This way you are in control by organizing the incoming, and that keeps the stress down. People who choose their own checking schedules also report higher productivity at the end of the day. No doubt reduced stress plays a role in that.

Checking every 45 minutes is a big improvement over nonstop but still too much. Researchers at Oklahoma State University say two to four times a day are the most productive email checking schedules. That gives you up to four times to get back to someone. Gloria Mark recommends three batching sessions per day, where you plow through for a half-hour or so.

Manual checking at a set schedule offers the least interruptions and maximum productivity. I have had financial advisers who formerly checked every five minutes who have adopted a four-time schedule, and their lives and stress levels have been transformed. If you can do it within your job responsibilities, try limiting your message-checking to once an hour, and wean yourself down from there.

Lose Email Weight Fast

A designated time when you check messages cuts interruptions and increases perception of control over the email beast. As you take charge, the aggravation level drops dramatically. Most messaging behavior is done reflexively. Let's pause for a moment

and assess your current messaging style and how it could be better.
- How many times do you check messages each day? How much could you cut that amount by?
  - Identify a goal for an email-checking schedule. Can you set a manual schedule of hourly checking? Can you do four times a day?

Stop Checking Messages After Work, on the Weekend, and on Vacation

Email-checking soars when there are no agreed-upon norms on availability and what constitutes an emergency. The fear of the latter drives massive amounts of message-checking in hours off-the-clock, and it doesn't have to.

A lot of the scrolling in off-hours comes from a fear that we might miss something important, like an emergency. No one wants to not be there if something big breaks. This counterproductive and counter-work-life balance habit can be stopped right now by doing two things:

1. **Have your team define specifically what an emergency is and what it isn't.**
2. **Have an understanding that emergencies should only be handled by phone. No email.**

These clarifications get everyone off sentinel duty. You know in the future you will be contacted by phone or text if something that constitutes an emergency takes place. This allows you to get back to family, recharging, and life without the threat of a potential critical email that could come at any moment. Despite the best vigilance of email-watching, messages get lost, buried, misinterpreted, and sent to spam folders. When you need to get hold of someone NOW, call them.

Everyone needs to have a clear understanding of what constitutes an emergency or something extremely urgent that demands an instant response. Spell out which scenarios are in the emergency category and which are not.

Yes, it's handy being able to get messages wherever you are. Technology has enabled you to be productive in Ubers, airports, pet stores, and 7-11's—but also at your kid's play, during dinner, at a Sunday picnic, and even on vacation. As we have learned, work expands to fill the available time—and that's all the time unless we make some of that time unavailable.

Because somebody emails you on the weekend doesn't mean you have to respond or even check mail until Monday—if you have an understanding of what's inbounds and what's out of bounds. The president of a New York book publishing firm told me that it's convenient for her to email staff on the weekend, but she doesn't expect them to answer. But how many of her employees feel obligated to reply in the middle of their weekends? A lot of them when there's no stated permission to not respond.

Have the conversation on availability. Do you need to be checking work mail on your holiday, for instance?

That should be a No. Checking email on vacation sends you mentally back to work in the middle of your mai tai. The separation from work is the point of the vacation and the recuperative benefits it provides. If you are still in contact on holiday, you are not getting the work recovery scientists say is crucial to reviving mental health and performance.

Developing a clear sense for what contact is out of bounds after work hours is critical to be able to recover, recharge and take care of personal responsibilities, and it leads to our next email precept:

Negotiate a personal perimeter zone to limit off-hours e-contact.

One manager at IBM told me he was able to carve out 6 p.m. to 8 p.m. as a no-contact zone for time with his family. Others let it be known that they don't check email on the weekend. What about a conversation with your manager, client, or customer that creates a carve-out that work email only arrives during work hours? Grant that there are emergencies and busy periods but get agreement on the concept. Most can agree to this, since they face the same dilemma, though workaholics may not. Make it your mission to identify and propose a perimeter that would be workable in your company.

Create Rules For E-Tools

Unlike the introduction of the telephone, which was adopted over a long enough period that the culture was able to develop rules for how to use it, e-tools arrived so suddenly and overwhelmingly that they were running the show before anyone knew how to use them effectively. We have language on the phone that clues in the other person that the conversation is ending. "I'll let you go now," was a favorite of my mother's.

The good news, though, is that, since there are no rules, they are up for grabs. That means we can set some. Norms and rules for the non-abusive use of e-tools manage chaos, reduce the time spent on messaging, and help you get your life back.

We need self-management strategies to manage compulsive checking and prioritizing, but organizations also need a norms guide to establish a code of digital contact. It's not hard to come up with ideas for rules. We all know the stuff that drives us crazy. Asked what rules they would like to see placed on email, employees at companies I've worked with have volunteered:

- Deactivate the reply-all function
- Disable visual email notifications
- Never expect an immediate response from an email
- Pick up the phone and call, instead
- No email between 8 p.m. and 6 a.m.
- Don't send one-line "thank you" and "got it" messages
- Think before you send a message. Does it have to be sent?
- No expectation to check email on days off and vacations.

Obviously, this is a wish list. What is feasible for you in your workday is going to vary with the type of work and management you have. Most people can refrain from the two- and three-word response emails and turn off visual notifications. There is a much longer list of things you and your company can do to manage email overload and interruptions.

Now it's your turn. Get together with your team and create a list of rules and norms that can get everyone on the same page to control messaging run amok.

How To Increase Your Attention

I have always been fascinated by prodigies, who by the age of 10 can play complex classical or jazz music as well as the pros. What switch is turned on in their minds that isn't in the rest of our brains? We are starting to get some answers from researchers working with these gifted children.

It had been assumed that off-the-chart IQs helped prodigies reach their heights, but studies show that a high IQ isn't the main factor. Eight music, math, and art whizzes were found to have IQs ranging from 108 to 147 in an investigation by Joanne Ruthsatz and Jourdan Urbach. Yet there *was* something the subjects had that very few others do, a finding that seems to go to the heart of the mystery. Every child in the study scored higher than the 99th percentile of their peers in one area: working memory—short-term memory. Six of the eight kids measured in the 99.9th percentile.

These kids all have an incredible ability to "store and sort information," to pay exceptional attention to detail within the moment, a time when thoughts are normally very tenuous. Musical prodigies seem to be able to hold notes in memory while processing incoming data. They have the ability to maintain complete attention, and with that laser concentration, burn the information into their brain neurons. They may also have exceptional long-term memory as well. One of the prodigies had memorized more than 100 pages of classical music before the age of four.

Increasing your attention may not wind up in a gig at Carnegie Hall, but it is something that can dramatically improve your work, mood, satisfaction, impulse control, and resistance to distractions.

The good news is that you don't have to memorize Mozart to improve your attention quotient. In fact, it's the opposite. It's the lack of complexity and, instead, **focus on a simple target** with repetition that builds your executive attention. The act of sustained concentration on a target trains the mind to focus and resist distraction.

The focusing activity can be as basic as counting—backwards, that is. That's not something you do every day, so you have to pay more attention. And therein lies the key to the mental discipline needed. Let's give it a try right now.

Countdown to Concentration

Count from 100 to 0 backwards in your mind. You don't have to rush through it. Go down the numbers methodically. If your mind strays to a movie you watched or a trip to the store, bring your thoughts back to the next number down the line until you get to 0.

How did that feel? How would you describe this experience in a word? Hard? Easy? "Relaxing" is what most people say. If you are able to slow your racetrack mind enough in this exercise, you will feel calmer.

The lesson: It's relaxing to pay attention. When you are absorbed in the moment, you don't have anxieties and stressors intruding from other tenses. It makes the exercise a great stress reduction tool. It's a minute-and-a-half that stills the mind and restores concentration. Do it several times a day for focus but also stress relief. The more attention you have, the less stress. People I work with tell me that this exercise has become a go-to tool in their day for stress relief.

If you want to increase your attention further, try counting backwards every third number from 100. If that seems difficult, good. That is what helps the concentration—effort. You have to focus when it's hard. When things are easy, the brain goes into rote mode and actually stops noticing in great detail. It's been there, done that.

Focus on a Target

The counting exercise gives you a taste of the dynamic behind the most effective attention-building process: meditation. Meditating is just a longer version of counting. The style I use, the relaxation response, uses a mental phonetic process, usually a meaningless sound, a couple of syllables, as the target, instead of numbers. Choose two syllables of sound and sit quietly while repeating them over and over in your mind for 10 to 20 minutes two times a day. Practice this process for a week, and you will see changes. You will feel more focused, less prone to rumination, less aggravated and annoyed.

Studies have shown that Buddhist monks, who spend hours in meditation every day, have more attention than the rest of us. The physical size of the attention center in their brain is actually larger. A study that examined the attention prowess of American meditators at a three-month mindfulness retreat in the mountains of Colorado showed that they were more accurate on a series of tests measuring concentration than people not in the program. Their attention also improved as the retreat went on.

Increasing attention has not been high on the agenda in recent decades. Instead, all the energy has been focused on ever-increasing velocity, stimulation, and disruption. The prevailing vibe is that it's desirable to have your attention assaulted, a sign of busyness, popularity, status.

The reality is that most of us would like to reclaim mental faculties and attention spans from the cacophony. There are many ways we can stop the brain drain, from exercise to meditation and better sleep. Use as many attention strategies as you can to keep your brain sharp and the stress down.

That is the goal of meditation, building attention to have full awareness in the moment, not being waylaid by the time machine in our minds. It should also be the goal of anything we do in work or life, engaging fully with what is, instead of unreal mental wanderings.

7 Focusing Strategies

1. **Use more top-down attention.** When you choose what you pay attention to, you focus the lens and concentration comes with it. On the other hand, you want to avoid the bottom-up attention brigade of devices and interruptions that diverts you from the high brain.
2. **Cue your brain.** Studies show that you can increase focus by telling your brain before a task that you are going to pay attention to it like a laser. If you have a task that demands extra concentration, signal your mind beforehand and perk up the neurons. Say it out loud. *I'm really going to focus on this.*
3. **Use headphones.** The mission of attention is to shut out the noise and distractions as much as possible and focus. One of the best

tools to accomplish that goal is a good pair of headphones. If you have open-office talking and high din level, go with noise-silencing headphones. I use headphones and listen to instrumental music. This does three things that help focus: 1) It drowns out the background noise, 2) It provides constant positive emotions that help increase my energy and outlook, and 3) Music orders thought, providing a focused runway for my concentration within the contours of the musicscapes and keeping everything else out. The music can't have lyrics, though, because language distracts.

4. **Take breaks.** Stepping back from cognitive strain is one of the best ways to refresh the mental screen. Intense focusing load creates a need to reset. "When you increase the metabolism of the brain, it comes with byproducts that need to be cleared out and cleaned," Borna Bonakdarpour, an assistant professor of neurology at Northwestern University who studies aphasia and dementia, told the *Washington Post*. He recommends a break of 20 or 30 minutes after two hours of focus.

   Giving the brain a break every couple of hours by doing something physical, such as stretching or walking, allows the thinking gear to recover.

5. **Block out focus zones on your calendar every day.** The white space in your calendar is gold when it comes to opportunities to hone your attention equipment. A focus zone lets you set scheduled time for concentration without interruptions. All the things we have talked about in this chapter are part of the tool kit for building focus zones. The more you can set the terms of engagement with devices and interruptions for unadulterated concentration, the more you will be able to dial in full attention.

6. **Do skill-building hobbies.** Activities that force you to pay attention to the rules of the event and that build both mental and physical skills keep you fully absorbed in the moment of what you are doing. Dancing, orienteering, chess, playing a musical instrument, and learning a language all increase mental focus.

7. **Get more sleep.** A well-rested mind brings a lot more self-discipline to the table to stay on task. Sleep deficit undermines vigilant attention, working memory, long-term memory, and decision-making.

Harnessing Peak Alertness

Just because you are out of bed and walking around doesn't mean you have stellar attention. There are other factors that are crucial to the quality of attention even if you have all the interrupters at bay. Physical vitality and energy give you more impetus and drive to stay on task. They can help rev up the chief tool of concentration: alertness, an item we all should be much more acquainted with.

The difference between hearing someone speak and remembering what they said is alertness—not to mention learning. This may be why people who have a high level of alertness are apt to also be higher achievers.

As we saw with musical prodigies, one of their gifts is intensely targeted working memory. Break that down, and we're talking about sustained alertness in the moment. The challenge is that alertness is variable, depending on the time of day, mood, nature of the task—novel vs. repetitive—stress level, how late you were up the night before, and amount of caffeine guzzled. Yet there is a reliable way to take advantage of the one time every day when you are at your most mentally alert—harness your innate rhythm of wakefulness.

Some of us, and that includes me, are morning people, or larks, people whose wake-sleep cycle runs early. They get up at the crack of dawn and are fully charged even without caffeine by 7 a.m. Others are night owls, whose peak energy tends to be late afternoon or 11 p.m. at night.

Your alertness is at its lowest ebb obviously when you are sleeping, but there is also another plunge at midday, because we are biphasic creatures. We are wired to sleep two times a day, though we pretend that is not the case. The conventional wisdom says you get tired after lunch because of what you ate, but it's actually your biphasic urgings that are the culprit. If you look at car accident reports, the most accidents occur as drowsiness sets in from 12 midnight to 6 a.m. and from 12 p.m. to 4 p.m. in the afternoon.

The maligned siesta is in line with your biphasic nature, and as a result, your health. A study by the Harvard School of Public Health and Athens Medical School that tracked 23,681 men and women in Greece found that regular nappers had a 37% less risk of dying from coronary artery disease. Occasional nappers had a 12% less risk. Those are big numbers that make a huge difference for your health and worth adding a power nap of 20 minutes to your day.

Which circadian rhythm do you have? If you are a morning person, your peak alertness can range from 7 a.m. to 10 a.m. (or even earlier, 5 a.m. to 8 a.m.). Night owls have more alertness from 3 p.m. to 5 p.m. In general, alertness increases in the morning until the afternoon swoon hits at noon. There's another increase around 6 p.m., as attention rises after the mid-afternoon dip. You may not have exactly the same time available every day, but try to find some space within your alertness zone for full focus.

You can use this quirk of your biology to turn your peak alertness zone into a focus zone to work more effectively. Choose an amount of time that you can set aside within your peak concentration period to do your work without interruptions. Then create an autoresponder message for your email telling others that you are on a project and will be back at the time your focus zone ends.

Put your most important tasks, the ones that require the most thinking and assessing into your zone, things like planning, writing, creating. Harnessing peak alertness with a no-interruption zone is going to allow you to get your work done faster and take on the tough tasks that tend to get procrastinated.

Identify Your Focus Zone

We can all find ways to block out time on our calendars for deep work, think time, and undiverted attention with a no-interruption zone. Can you set aside 30 minutes to do uninterrupted work? How about an hour? Make sure the focus zone coordinates with your wakefulness peak.

- What is your peak alertness time?
- How much time can you set aside within that zone to work without interruptions?
- Which tasks and activities will you do in your focus zone?

Put the Humans Back In Charge

There are growing signs that information overload and the distraction cavalcade is causing some companies to try to draw the line. Intel has experimented with Quiet Time at some facilities to contain interruptions, while, as we learned, accounting firm Deloitte and U.S. Cellular are among firms that have instituted email-free Fridays.

As an indication of how embedded messaging habits are, the companies got pushback from employees when they learned they couldn't send email on Fridays—the kind of reaction you would expect from folks with a tech dependency. Yet, after a few weeks the panic subsided. Once the emotions calmed, they could see the interpersonal and focusing benefits of reducing the email and interruption load.

Add rapport and community benefits to the list of putting the humans back in charge. It builds trust, social resources, and the teamwork we all say we want more of. Why not have your team try an email-free Friday or no-interruption zone? Strike an all-in-one blow for time management, information management, interruption management, and human relations.

CHAPTER 8

The Power of Possibility

Build the Engine of Resilience: Optimism

Oscar Wilde once said the difference between an optimist and a pessimist is that the optimist sees the donut, the pessimist the hole. That might give the pessimist an edge in dieting, but that approach is an albatross in most areas of life. You don't want to deny the negative, since it's part of life, but clinging to it can lead to bad outcomes in your work, relationships, and especially your health.

A wide body of research shows that optimism is a major asset in life. Optimism boosts performance on the job, increases success, and people with positive affect, the outward sign of an optimistic personality, make more money than pessimists. That's a nice incentive to de-grumpify. It's also a clear social advantage and a sought-after quality in relationships.

Who would you rather work with or hang out with, someone who brightens the day and supports you, or someone who habitually sees negative events and anxieties on the horizon?

People with an optimistic outlook believe that good things will happen in the future or that the road ahead will be favorable, because they can control key outcomes. It's easy to see how that could benefit your health—less stress, and as a result, less high blood pressure, fewer heart attacks, and less depression—but the impact is truly amazing. Optimistic people live an average of 11% to 15% longer than pessimists. People who are optimistic have a lower risk of heart disease or any disease. They take care of their health better.

Optimists manage stress and negative emotions more effectively, preventing chronic inflammation and a flood of stress-related health problems. The payoff: Optimists in a meta-analysis covering 209,436 people had 35% less heart disease and cardiovascular conditions. In a Dutch study of a thousand seniors optimists had 23% of the cardiovascular disease death rate of pessimists—and only 55% of the death rate from all causes.

This same pattern holds in large population studies. The Women's Health Initiative measured 94,000 women and found that those highest in optimism had 30% fewer coronary deaths than the most pessimistic. Women were given statements to agree or disagree with, such as "in unclear times I always expect the best" and "if something can go wrong for me, it will."

Those statements capture in a nutshell the self-talk of the optimist vs. the pessimist—and the world of difference between them. What you tell yourself about why things happen to you and what you expect will happen in the future plays an astonishingly important role in your life.

Optimism is a hidden elixir for much of what ails us, a free medication we all have access to. A positive approach energizes, broadens opportunities, uncovers solutions, vastly improves work-life balance, and, best of all, makes you happier.

Meanwhile, pessimism makes you hold on to negative emotions and stressful events and ruminate about them, activating stress hormones such as cortisol and system changes that undermine your cardiovascular, digestive, and immune systems. Pessimism causes inflammation that can lead to a host of health conditions.

Optimism has another awesome power too. It helps you bounce back from setbacks and adversity. When you respond to negative events with an optimistic form of self-talk known as explanatory style, it helps you pick yourself up, recalibrate, put the event in the rear-view mirror, and move on. As a result, optimism is key to resilience and a savvy stress management strategy. In this chapter you will see how optimism can help you persevere through challenges and difficulties and find a path to a brighter day.

Are You Born An Optimist?

Optimism is such a successful personality trait, you would think evolution would have selected it out for as many of us as possible. As you may have noticed, that didn't happen. It can seem sometimes that we are surrounded by grumps, cynics, critics, and complainers. And worst of all, that cast can include us. Looking on the brighter side doesn't get a lot of airtime on the nightly news, but we all have the machinery to do exactly that more often, even if you are a pessimist by nature.

Yes, nature does play a role in outlook, though not as much as it does with introversion and extroversion—39% to 50% and more in some studies. Heredity is thought to be responsible for about 25% of your positive or negative set point, according to Lewina Lee of Boston University's School of Medicine. A big chunk of your outlook is formed in childhood and adolescence through your own experiences, upbringing, and environment in the form of explanatory style, the self-talk you evolve to explain why bad things happen to you.

Dwelling on negative events is a specialty of humans, part of our hyper-tuned survival equipment. "The brains of humans contain a mechanism that is designed to give priority to bad news," Nobel laureate Daniel Kahneman has written.

If everyone had a sunny outlook back in caveman/cavewoman days, you wouldn't be reading this, because the species would not have overcome the daily threats to life and limb. Caution, skepticism, and not poking the bear are valuable tools in the arsenal. You don't want to have an optimistic lawyer, accountant, journalist, or engineer. You want people who will ask the hard questions and be as skeptical as possible in certain walks of life. Pessimism has its place in the world. Setbacks happen. We all have bad days, sometimes bad months. You just want to make sure you submit negative events to the analysis of your neocortex and that you can move swiftly out of the pessimistic feedback loop.

This is the role that optimistic thinking plays in extricating minds from the mental morass of adversity, helping to put you on the road of resilience. It's very similar to the strategies for managing stress that we have discussed. It's all in the appraisal of the negative event. A reappraisal of bad events as temporary, for instance, helps you find a much quicker way forward.

Like stressful events, the emotions that create them are especially temporary, though it doesn't feel that way in the moment. Loss, defeat, anger, or sadness can be overwhelming. Yet they are passing events that blow in and out like clouds drifting in the wind. One minute you're outraged, the next you are laughing. One day you feel defeated, another day you're jubilant. It's hard to believe all these emotions can live inside the same head.

It's a question of being able to see the dark cloud's fleeting nature when you're under it and the brighter day beyond it. It turns out that it's much easier for optimists to flip a negative into a positive, something documented in a study led by Jason Moser of Michigan State University. He looked at brain scans of people who were shown negative scenes in photos and then tasked with finding a positive way to interpret them. The brains of those prone to worrying and pessimism had to fire up much of their gray matter to do this, it was such an effort for them. Meanwhile, optimists were able to complete the task by barely breaking a neuronal sweat, with a fraction of their brains lighting up compared to the pessimists. Optimistic framing was a habit for these folks, so the assignment was second nature.

The fact that optimists are able to get control over events is key to the kind of optimism we are talking about here. It's a psychological strategy firmly rooted in possibility, not a denial-of-reality Polyannaism. The science of optimism shows that its central skill is not pretending the negative doesn't exist, but, instead, countering it with positive action so it glances off and doesn't stick around. Optimism is problem-solving.

This is the essence of resilience, using flexibility to broaden thoughts and actions, reframe events, and persevere through tough demands, knowing they are not going to last forever. The key levers that help you get through difficult times—self-control, reappraisal, a long-range view, and persistence—are all enabled by optimistic framing. They are available to all of us when we trade reflex emotional reactions and their false beliefs for the skills of a much savvier self-talk.

You can get started on the reframing skill of optimism right now. I want you to think of something negative that happened in your life recently. How could you turn it into a positive? Write down how you can see this event so that it opens another door, another vantage point for you to move forward.

Explanatory Style: The Hidden Director of Your Life

You don't know it at the time, but in your childhood and adolescent years your brain is forming a story, one that will be crucial to navigating the tough events ahead. It comes in the form of self-talk that becomes your go-to explanation for why bad things occur in your life. Depending on the style of the explanation, either optimistic or pessimistic, you will react to an event in dramatically different ways—either treating it as a one-off and moving on, or as something lasting and defeating.

The discovery of explanatory style was a scientific breakthrough that revealed one of the most important tools in the arsenal for healthy minds. Early in his career the University of Pennsylvania's Martin Seligman, one of the pioneers of positive psychology, set out to investigate the source of depression. What he discovered was the power of pessimism to freeze minds in harm's way, a paralysis of futility he called "learned helplessness." "Some people stop trying to avoid pain and accept it as inevitable. They give up," he wrote in *Learned Optimism*. The question was why.

British researcher John Teasdale had part of the answer. He thought it was about the kind of explanations people use for why things happen to them. If you could change their explanations, these people could climb out of the darkness. Meanwhile, two young graduate assistants, Lyn Abramson and Judy Garber, were convinced that it wasn't a single explanation but a habitual pile of them, a style of self-talk. All three joined Seligman in a historic research paper that introduced explanatory style to the world in 1978.

What they established is that the way we frame negative events is one of the most critical factors in human flourishing or flailing. The recipe for depression, Seligman says, is "preexisting pessimism encountering failure," and then ruminating endlessly about it.

The story you tell yourself when bad things happen either aggravates the situation by locking you into pessimistic thoughts, or it gives you the opportunity to learn from the event and be resilient and bounce back. And let's face it, given the number of times we are knocked down on the journey, getting back up again is the real story of success. Optimism and pessimism are belief systems that either inspire reflex persistence or futility in difficult moments.

When a setback occurs, the mind leaps to two instant questions: Why did it happen? And, what's next? You immediately want an explanation for the situation and try to project the cost of the event into the future. The answers are very different depending on whether you are an optimist or a pessimist. The ready-made explanations come in three flavors or domains. If you have a pessimistic explanatory style, you take a negative event as **permanent, universal, and personal/internal**. If you are an optimist, you respond with the exact opposite route—**temporary,**

specific, and non-personal or **external.**

Pessimists think they will never escape the adversity, that it's going to affect every aspect of their life forever, and they take it personally, getting their ego and its runaway emotions into it. *I'm not smart enough. I'll never make it.* A relationship doesn't work out, and, instead of chalking it up to experience, the reaction is: *I'm not good enough for anyone.* Obviously, these are exaggerated false beliefs, but in the emotion of the moment they feel very real.

This pattern can seal you into a worse-case-scenario bunker that becomes self-reinforcing the longer it goes unchallenged. A pessimistic explanatory style can lead you to reel for months from even small setbacks, obsessing over pessimistic and catastrophic thoughts about the permanence of the negative event.

Beliefs of disaster and futility drive stress and a host of health conditions. People with a pessimistic explanatory style are more likely to have coronary artery disease or die from a heart attack. If you are a serious pessimist, you can get more easily depressed, your achievements can be undermined, and your immune system can take a beating, leading to many more health issues as you age than for the optimist.

Optimists take a more flexible approach to the why and what's-next questions. We are back to the power of the agile mind. They see the problem as **temporary, not permanent.** The predicament is not going to last forever. It's not the end of the world. Your life is not over. It's merely an obstacle, and you will overcome this one like all the rest. The mind stays open and looks for solutions.

The optimistic view doesn't fall for the exaggeration that the setback spells doom pervasively for every aspect of life. Instead, you see the impact is **specific** to the circumstances of the event, report, conversation. **One time, one place.** Keep repeating that like a mantra.

And optimists have one of the best habits you can have—they don't take setbacks personally. When you let an aggrieved ego set off a flood of irrational emotions, that just makes getting the event behind you all the more difficult. Anger, fear, and embarrassment blind you to the instrument that can extricate you from the fantasyland of false beliefs, the rational deductive logic of your prefrontal cortex. You are in the world and bad things happen in the world. You don't have to let your ego compound the difficulty by convincing you that the world has a target on your back.

What Are Your Reflex Explanations?

Reflex emotional explanations get in the way of smart responses to adversity. Understanding your go-to self-talk style after a negative event can help you respond in the most productive way. Which of the domains below of negative explanatory style are challenges for you? How can you avoid them next time they pop up?

- Taking negative events permanently
- Taking negative events personally
- Taking negative events globally, affecting your whole life
- What are the why and what's-next explanations that immediately came to mind after a recent adversity or setback?
- Why did the event happen? Was it because you did something wrong? Was it someone else's fault?
- What were your thoughts about the future as a result of the event? Everything ruined? The event was a one-off? You'll never get past it? Next!

Dire Straits: Pessimistic Explanatory Style

You probably have a pretty good sense of whether you lean optimist or pessimist. Worriers tend to be in the pessimist camp, since anxiety about the future comes with that explanatory style. The half-empty glass would make you less of a risk-taker or a cautious one. Optimists are more inclined to try something new, though they can get out over their skis without enough real-world intel on what they're getting into. The glass half-full, though, leads to more self-belief and a feeling that things will work out.

Certain words can lead down the pessimistic track. You are what you say. "I'll *never* get my chance," or "This *always* happens to me." "You *always* think of yourself and not me." Terms like *always* and *never* exaggerate the event, ratcheting up emotions. They are prime facilitators of the first two domains of pessimistic explanatory style—**permanent and universal**.

In the initial aftermath of a failure or setback, it's normal to have feelings of permanence and pervasiveness cloud the brain with thoughts of doom. Yet a pessimist believes the cause of the adversity is internal— their fault—and that the situation is global and unchangeable, while the optimist can rally to get back up, because he or she knows the event isn't forever. It's **changeable, specific and external**.

Viewing bad events permanently creates the learned helplessness in the face of hardship that Seligman found in his research could lead down the road to depression. Why bother? It's only going to get worse. That thinking style keeps you in a quicksand of pessimistic thinking.

One of Seligman's examples shows just how massive the gulf is between the two styles of self-talk and why it's so important to know which style you use and how you can adopt an optimistic explanatory approach. Someone who takes a setback as permanent would think, "I'm all washed up." Meanwhile, in the temporary framing of optimistic style, the personalization and endless ego doom are swapped out for "I'm really exhausted."

We are not statues. We are living, breathing, fallible creatures who make mistakes on a planet where accidents and failures occur. Disappointments and duress are part of the human package, but we don't have to be knocked off course for months or years from them. We can challenge the fictions of permanence and pervasiveness.

The domain of permanence controls time, how long someone is going to give up. What is your pattern? Do you tend to get over troubles quickly, or do they linger and spell long-term calamity? Permanent pessimistic style explanations come straight from the ancient brain's reflex of catastrophic thoughts and its jump-off-the-cliff, fight-or-flight, all-or-nothing bag of self-defeating tricks.

As you now know, you can't trust the worst-case stories of the ancient brain and its dire take on what is going to happen in the future. Not only can we not predict what's going to happen, but we also don't have a clue as to how we are going to feel in the future, known as "affective forecasting," the emotional affect we expect to have.

For one, the emotions of the present overwhelm all else, so you can't see out to another time accurately. Imagining the future in a highly negative state is not going to come up roses and banana splits, since how you feel now is going to dictate the color of the future.

"People profoundly misestimate their emotional responses to future scenarios," reports a study led by Harvard psychologist Daniel Gilbert. "In particular, people overestimate how long their negative responses to various outcomes will last." The simulations we dream up cause emotional reactions that then influence the feelings that would exist in the prediction. You stack the deck against yourself.

Oz Sanchez was a 25-year-old Navy man riding his motorcycle in San Diego when a car ran a stop sign, crashed into him and sent him flying off a 12-foot embankment. He landed on his back on a pile of rocks. He suffered a spinal cord injury just a few days before his wedding. In an instant all hopes for the future were obliterated.

He would be in a wheelchair the rest of his life. "It really took a toll on me," Sanchez told me. "I went into a very dark area, depression." He didn't want to live.

Perfectly understandable. What could be more permanent than a spinal cord injury? The blow seemed too hard to bear. Months and months he lay in a body cast. Feeling helpless was a new experience for Sanchez, who was a proactive personality by nature. His friends and family tried to encourage him, but it was bleak.

One day at the hospital, though, he saw a wheelchair with a handcycle used for racing. It touched off a curiosity, one of the most important ingredients in finding a new path forward. What if? Could he do that, pedal with his hands and compete in a sport?

The idle thought turned into a goal to try, and the cracks in permanence began. He began to build his upper-body strength and endurance, empowering acts in themselves. After a year of training, he entered a 10K race and finished it. It was exhilarating not to feel helpless. He was back in touch with his core needs of autonomy and competence, which we all need to feel gratified. Sanchez learned that he was not permanently exiled from movement, life, and achievement. He could change and adapt.

He threw himself into his new passion and built his strength and conditioning to compete in handcycling marathon races. He would go on to become a multiple world champion in the sport of handcycling. He won a gold and a silver medal at the Beijing Paralympic Games, the gold for winning the wheelchair marathon. Today, he is a renowned athlete and motivational speaker.

Sanchez's inspiring tale shows how optimists can see adversities as challenges, instead of threats. They focus on what they can control and put all their energies into that, while pessimists focus on parts of the issue they can't control. Optimists attack the things they can influence, while pessimists avoid.

Sanchez is not alone in his comeback. Studies show that the majority of people who suffer spinal cord injuries go back to the well-being set-point they had before their accident. We are remarkably resilient creatures—when we see setbacks as changeable and adjustable, keys to optimistic explanatory style.

It would be hard to think of a setback more permanent than being a paraplegic, but even that isn't enough to stop the resilient human spirit. Sanchez found the silver lining, the glimmer of another way of viewing things, when he let his curiosity about the handcycling wheelchair lead him forward to a life he couldn't have imagined otherwise.

The second domain of pessimistic explanatory style, known by various terms—**pervasive, global, universal**—controls how widespread you think the impact of the adversity will be on your life. It's another crazy exaggeration, multiplying permanence and helplessness into every corner of life. You are no good at anything, because one thing tripped you up. This is nonsense. Global explanations make a person give up on everything, which is very dangerous. They shut down all paths of escape.

Personalization is the third domain of the pessimistic explanatory style trinity. It controls how you feel about what has happened to you. It ratchets up the emotions by turning the trouble into assaults on the ego. The blame floods in: *You're a loser for life, there's something wrong with you.* These punches fuel even more catastrophe, striking at the core of self-esteem and identity.

How we respond to challenges can be a nail in the coffin of permanent worthlessness or an opportunity. The personal lane of pessimistic self-talk is a massive opportunity to outflank one of the biggest sources of pain and suffering in life—the ego. It's a fragile construct that is easily offended and affronted, and unless we manage it, we get in our own way. It doesn't have to be personal. It can be a business decision. It can be an angry person. It can be an opinion. It can be someone who's not a nice person or vengeful. It can be someone who is wrong, made a bad choice, or is delusional.

What seem like personal ego attacks can have many other interpretations, if we don't instantly personalize the event. Most of the time, we can rise above the flotsam and jetsam of an addled brain acting out. We can separate ourselves from reflex thoughts of personal pain in the same way we get distance from stressful thoughts with thought labeling. "I'm *having the thought* that this is personal." Managing thoughts is the key to resilience and happiness.

Even if it is personal, resist the reflex reaction that will only make things worse. Yes, for egregious personal attacks—libel, slander, misplaced blame, injury, assault, firing without cause, criminal behavior—we have to stand ground and fight back, but usually the personal explanation rears over much more minor affairs. You don't have to get triggered every time. You also don't have time in this blip of a life to waste on a triggered ego.

Focus on What You Can Control

Oz Sanchez was able to reappraise his situation as a paraplegic by focusing on what he could control, not what he couldn't. You can do the same thing with difficulties in your life.

- Identify a current stressor or challenge. Write down all the things that you control in the situation and what you don't.
- Now take one or two of those elements that you control and think of actions you can take to change the situation for the better.

Bounce Back With Optimistic Explanatory Style

Unlike the fictional apocalypses of pessimistic explanatory style, optimistic self-talk is rooted in adaptability, openness, and resilience. It's about not giving in to futility and finding ways to resolve the situation. You don't have to be an optimist by nature to exercise optimistic reframing of events. Anyone can do it. You simply reverse the false explanations of pessimistic style, **from permanent to temporary, from universal to**

specific, and from personal to non-personal.

First, you counter the self-talk of permanence by reframing the forever trap. The goal is to see negative events as one-time, one place, the result of multiple causes, not just the most dire, and of circumstances that are changeable, not locked in forever.

You can flip pessimistic self-talk by adopting the language of optimistic explanatory style, which sees time as the transient realm it is. Words such as *sometimes, recently, lately,* and *maybe* keep setbacks in their rightful place, as painful, tough, but restricted to a time and place and thus survivable.

There's a parable from a couple of millennia ago in what would become China that shows the power you have to defang the false belief of permanence and signal that you are not out of options. In the story a farmer's horse runs away. A couple thousand years ago, that was a big deal. As a result, neighbors and friends come by to console him. That's terrible, they tell him. What bad luck. The farmer says, "maybe."

The next day, the horse returns with six wild horses. Now the friends are back telling him how great this stroke of luck is and celebrating his good fortune. The farmer's response: "maybe." The next day his son tries to ride one of the wild horses and is thrown and breaks his leg. The neighbors return, bemoaning the injury. It's horrible, really bad luck. The farmer says, "maybe." The next day soldiers come by to conscript his son into the army, but he is spared because of his broken leg. Now the friends and neighbors are back to tell the farmer how fortunate he is. His response: "maybe."

The lesson of the story is that we can't get too high or too low in a world with as many sudden twists as the one under our feet. "Maybe" acknowledges reality as it suggests the potential for better circumstances. It recognizes the indisputable fact that situations and people don't stay the same; it's all impermanent. It is our failure to accept the true nature of things, change, that is a key source of suffering.

My mother, who was a super-optimist, was a big advocate of "maybe." When things didn't work out, she was always there with a "maybe next time..." to signal that things change and could be different tomorrow.

Optimists don't box themselves in with "permanent" language. They move forward with a belief in other possibilities than worst-case. They don't have to know exactly how they will bounce back, or the exact route of future events needed to extricate themselves from a challenge.

Instead, they have a belief that somehow they will solve the issue, overcome the obstacle, get where they need to go. "Somehow" has always been my preferred word of persistence when the way forward is fraught and hazy. *I don't know how but somehow* is a phrase I've told myself over the years when faced with difficulty and an unknown path ahead. You don't have to know the future, which is good, since we are lousy at predicting it. You can act anyway, moving in the direction of where you want to go. Each step brings more knowledge that can lead eventually to the vicinity of where you want to be.

The optimist also has something else that makes it easier to overcome and persevere—more positive emotions, which are the lifeblood of optimism—than the pessimist. Positive emotions help crowd out negative emotions, which keeps dwelling on the bad stuff at bay.

A more positive outlook creates space in the mind to attack the problem, instead of stewing in negative emotions. Optimists rebound by seeing adversity as a challenge. Their minds try to find options and ways around the adversity. Optimists also reach out to others, which gets them out of their heads and the false beliefs circling there to take in other viewpoints and support. In addition, optimists exercise more and eat healthier food, which keeps energy and vitality high.

The Self-Talk Gulf

Positive behaviors make optimists more resilient when troubles strike, and you can use their strategies to be more resilient too. Let's start by looking at the vastly different stories/beliefs created by pessimists and optimists for the same event. Here are three examples of the permanent pessimistic style (on the left) and an optimistic version of self-talk on the right.

Pessimistic Permanent	Optimistic Temporary
I'll never amount to anything.	I'm frustrated today.
I can't get past what she said.	She had a bad day.
I'm going to be fired.	The boss is in a bad mood.

Look at the gulf between these explanations. It's a Grand Canyon of difference in how you respond and act in a stressful situation. Each of the temporary explanations limits the story to a momentary cause that will blow over and be gone, while the permanent talk revs up catastrophic thoughts into the future. Find a cause of the situation that is changeable and specific—one time, one place—and you are on the way to bouncing back. Now it's your turn:

- Identify a current adversity and a permanent pessimistic story for it.
- Reframe it with a temporary explanation.

Pervasive and global explanations blow everything out of proportion. Catch yourself when a setback or mood extends the trouble of a particular problem to everything else in your life. Find a cause that's specific to the circumstances of this event and doesn't balloon into imagined unlimited damage everywhere.

Pessimistic Global	**Optimistic Specific**
I can't do anything right.	I didn't study for the test.
There are no opportunities.	That company didn't have openings.
I'll never be able to live it down.	I misspoke. It happens.

Your turn:

- Identify a global explanation for an adversity you have had.
- Reframe it with a specific explanation.

One of the trickier domains to flip to the optimistic side is personalization. To most of us, everything negative coming our way feels personal. The ego is always working overtime to make sure we come out on top, that we are right, better than others, and that slights are not tolerated. Yet it pays to take a more detached view. In fact, strong self-worth doesn't need constant stroking. It can handle slings and arrows. And so can you when you detach from the personalizing element of negative events. There are many other reasons things don't work out, so you have to catch the reflex to assume personal failing and reframe it. The key is to shift from an internal explanation, a cause being a personal flaw or imperfection, to an external and specific reason. Here are some examples.

Pessimistic Personal	Optimistic Non-Personal
This always happens to me.	The mechanic is lousy.
I said something wrong.	They took it the wrong way.
I'm not good enough.	I'll give that assignment another try.

Show how you don't have to take it personally:

- Identify a pessimistic explanation for a negative event that you took personally.
- Reframe it with an optimistic non-personal explanation.

When you look at the pessimistic stories, you'll notice that all of them are declarations of impotence. *I can't do anything about it. It's pointless. Nothing I can do.* Pessimistic self-talk shuts off the only way back from the adversity—action. It's characterized by passivity that internalizes the issue and doesn't do anything about it.

Responding to events with learned helplessness is counter to everything the science knows about what makes for thriving humans—our ability to adapt, to turn difficulty into challenge, and the need to write our own script. We are not here to observe but to participate in the journey. Pessimistic explanatory style would have you deny your deepest aspirations, which is why something we never think about—increasing optimism—needs to move from the realm of research studies into practice in our daily lives.

Good Events Are Permanent

Get ready for a little whiplash. Now that I have urged you over and over to not take negative events permanently, pervasively, or personally, that is precisely how you need to see good events. What? You have to flip the script when it comes to good things.

When positive events occur, you want to see them as something lasting, affecting your life globally, and you want to take them personally. You're not lucky. The good stuff appeared through talent or your own effort. You did something to make it happen. You deserve to have positive events happen to you. You are worthy.

Optimists explain good events as the result of permanent traits, abilities and universal causes. People who believe they generate good things have better esteem. Celebrate your role when good things happen—but avoid over-broadcasting it.

How To Increase Your Daily Optimism

It may not seem like it, but there are more neutral to positive events than negative that happen to you in a given day. You just don't notice them, since the mind is fixated on problems and threats, a remnant of the ancient survival mandate. This habit is more than an annoying nag and an accelerator of pessimism and cynicism. It clogs your mental space with incessant orbiting worries, which squeeze out the antidote to this rut: the positive emotions of optimism.

Optimism is not the default state for most of us. Do nothing to encourage or develop it, and it won't be around much. Without this weapon of resilience, you are going to hang on to stress longer, ruminate more, and be subject to wild false beliefs. Luckily, you can do something about it with strategies that force you to notice the positive moments in your life, cultivate positive emotions, and engage in active leisure pursuits and hobbies that increase positive mood.

The most effective technique for building daily optimism is the *Three Things That Went Well* exercise. I've been doing this proven process for years. It works very fast, but you have to stick with it for a lasting impact on your thinking and daily mood.

It's a simple habit designed to get you to notice the positive things that happen every day that you miss when your mind is fixated on problems. It's an exercise in gratitude, a powerful optimism engine.

Three Things That Went Well

Step 1
Each night before you go to bed take a few minutes and identify three things that went well that day. Write them down in a

journal or on a screen. Or at the minimum, think of them when your head hits the pillow.

Maybe someone let you in front of them on the road and didn't run you off the road. That's a plus! Put it on your list. Or you looked out your window and saw a beautiful sunset. You were present to your day for five seconds. Write that down. Or maybe something went well at work. You had a good conversation with a colleague. You got something done, solved a problem, tackled a challenge.

Step 2

Now ask why each of those events happened. Why did that good conversation at work happen? Did you initiate it? Did you say something that made it fun? What made you stop to look at the sunset? Was it an accident? How can you do it more often? Why did the motorist let you in front of him? Are there good people in the world? You weren't driving aggressively? You were in a relaxed mood? Think about what put you in the vicinity of the positive event. Can you find that vicinity on a regular basis?

After a few days you will start to notice positive things that happen in your day—the parking spot right in front, the clerk who changes your mood with a friendly banter—and will say to yourself, as I do, "That's going on my list tonight." Instead of going to bed thinking about problems, you go out on a high note. I'm usually asleep by the third item.

Studies show people doing this exercise feel less depressed after just one week. One of the reasons is that it populates your mind with positive emotions, and they counter the negative brigade that likes to be in charge of your thoughts. Get the positive count up, and the doom crew has to shut up for a while.

Building Resilience

During a long glacial period between 123,000 to 195,000 years ago, the ancestors of our species were reduced from about 10,000 to a few hundred souls living in caves on the southern coast of Africa. There were no North Face jackets, no George Foreman grills, no Tempur-Pedic beds, no central heating, no markets, no farms, no doctors, no medicine. Somehow, generations of these hardy souls managed to get through 70,000-plus years of deep freeze to go on to populate every corner of the planet.

Humans are very resilient. We've survived the eons by adapting to changing climates, societies, conflicts, and beliefs. We have found ways to shift preconceived notions so that we could manage pressures and problems. An agile mind made all of it possible, and mental adaptation remains the key to resilience today, especially when it comes to jettisoning inaccurate beliefs that set off the survival gear and make it hard to recover from challenges.

False beliefs are a major cause of rigid minds. They feed brain neurons inflexible, ready-made explanations for negative events that keep you stuck in reaction rehash. Unfortunately, we are unaware of the reflex beliefs that run our reactive machinery, since it happens out of our consciousness. It's time to flush out these pains in the brain, so we can manage them.

There are surface beliefs, knee-jerk beliefs about why a negative event happened. There are **thinking traps** that spawn instant reactions without thought. And there are **icebergs**, beliefs buried deep inside that can explode like TNT out of nowhere when triggered.

Unconscious beliefs cause errors in logic that psychologists call "cognitive distortions." They pretend to be the real story and con you into taking their inflamed emotional bait. That keeps a lid on productive emotions and prevents problem-solving.

Contesting and changing false beliefs is crucial to building resilience, since their stories write, produce, and direct our problems. As we learned with the ABC Model of Albert Ellis, beliefs lead to consequences—the anger, fear, panic, or crazed fantasies you think are real when a belief abducts rational thinking. Beliefs operate in predictable patterns, triggering certain emotions depending on which belief the adversity produces.

The belief of a future threat, for instance, triggers anxiety and fear.

Future threats can include thoughts set off by uncertainty, job insecurity, or an upcoming meeting or exam.

The belief of a violation of rights causes anger.

Triggers for this belief range from territorial incursions to who-moved-my-cheese events to insufficient respect and road rage.

A belief of loss or loss of self-worth results in sadness and depression. Loss comes in all sizes—financial reversals, loss of friendship, family loss, job loss, and betrayal.

Use the patterns above to tie the emotion to the belief that set it off. When there is fear and anxiety, you can look to uncertainty as a culprit. Opt out of mental simulations of the future, and you can keep this trigger at bay. Remember, we are terrible predictors. We can't do it.

If you find yourself erupting in anger because you feel someone didn't respect you, and you have been stewing about it for days and can't let it go, catch yourself. Sit down and trace the anger back to a violation of some kind. Then get separation from your thought. You are not the thought. Look at the thought, not from it.

Surface beliefs, also known as tickertape beliefs, are the why and what's-next thoughts you have while in the middle of a negative event or adversity. They are responsible for how you feel and behave as a result of the event, so if you can manage them, you can prevent a lot of stress and crazed delusions. They lead to the permanent, universal, and personal beliefs you learned about with pessimistic explanatory style.

The "why" category stories are personal or non-personal. *It's my fault. I'm no good. It's their fault. They are out to get me. They always make it hard for me.* The "what's next" thoughts slap a knee-jerk cause on the event and project the future exaggerated fallout. The bias is for permanent Armageddon, because the forecasting is done with the full activation of stress and the irrational thoughts it sets off.

As with optimistic explanatory style, the key is to counter beliefs of permanence and universality with their opposite domains—temporary, specific, and non-personal—and look for causes other than worst-case. When setbacks send you down Forever Road, which of the phrases below can you deploy?

"It's temporary."

"It's not life-and-death."

"One time, one place."

"There are other causes than worst-case."

"I have no idea of what's going to happen in the future, because I'm not a psychic."

Okay, that last one is a bit long, but it can shut down the projecting. These phrases bring back the 21st-century brain. Don't just think them, speak them out loud. The experience of spoken words can trump bogus thoughts by shutting off the silent spiral of pessimistic and panicked thinking. The earlier in the stressful event you can fight back the better, since extreme, pessimistic thoughts take root the longer they go unchallenged.

Icebergs are deep beliefs, buried out of awareness, that can make life difficult for you and the people around you and spark conflict. These thoughts represent core assumptions about the way you think you, others, or the world should or shouldn't or must or mustn't behave.

They are felt with total certainty to be true and result in behavior you think is admirable, but they are false and harmful. Take an iceberg that is common among fire and rescue professionals: *I shouldn't need any help.* Under this belief, you'll find another iceberg: *It's weak to reach out for support.* People in this profession see horrific trauma and anguish. Bearing it on your own isn't viable. The mental blowback of this iceberg can lead to substance abuse, alcohol dependency, and divorce.

Since icebergs are beliefs about what we or others must do or situations that must be a certain way, they are considered inviolate. Any transgression of the belief triggers a big emotional response. If you want to uncover an iceberg, look for sudden emotional explosions out of proportion to the situation. For instance, overreactions to criticism, security checks at airports, territorial issues.

I used to think I could avoid traffic on Los Angeles's notoriously packed freeways by driving at times with less traffic, but I'd run into slowdowns and parking lot non-action just the same. That would trigger my iceberg, which, I discovered, was *there shouldn't be traffic,* a ludicrous belief in a city with more than 13 million people in the metro L.A. area.

Icebergs on the career side can range from *I should be respected by everyone at all times,* to *my motives shouldn't be questioned,* to *I must never fail at anything,* to *no one should touch my desk.* These beliefs set you up for anger, stress and repeating the pattern over and over. Absolutist thinking is the opposite of agility and about as rigid as it gets. It consigns you to self-sabotage when the iceberg is triggered.

The first step to melting icebergs is to identify them. Find areas of your life that push major emotional reaction buttons or that drive you beyond your capacity, such as long hours. What thought is driving the counterproductive behavior? *Everything I do should be perfect. I must work longer than anyone else to succeed. I shouldn't take a vacation, because that's for slackers.* Reframe the thought from the extreme, tyrannical iceberg to an attitude that reflects reality.

Challenge the iceberg. For instance, can you prove your work ethic without having to pull all-nighters and risk health and shoddy work? Are there others around you whose work ethic is respected who aren't over-performing? Can you have more confidence in yourself?

Listing reasons for the opposite of your iceberg to be true helps shut down the bogus belief, as you recognize the convincing evidence is on the other side. For my iceberg, there were plenty of reasons why there *should* be traffic on the freeways of L.A. There should be traffic because there's weak public transit, commuters live far from their jobs, and there are millions of drivers.

If the iceberg is *I shouldn't fail,* you can make a list of the opposite to be true here as well. *Life is all trial and error; it's just a question of how many errors. I didn't put in enough time on that project. The timing was wrong. There are no guarantees about any outcome.* If you're honest and confront the iceberg, you learn from the experience. If the iceberg stays buried, you eat yourself up with denial or self-loathing, and it can happen all over again if the lesson isn't learned.

Fire and rescue crew professionals should need help because they see trauma and terrible things. They should need help because thinking about the pain and sadness of what they encounter leads to negative and depressive rumination. They should need help because post-traumatic stress syndrome is common in the field. They should need help because of the impact not dealing with emotional trauma has on their families. Weigh the iceberg against reality, and it loses its hold.

Knee-Jerk Thinking Traps

We depend on the mind to help us think our way out of adversity, but it makes matters worse when it defaults to "thinking traps," which respond to negative events with a rigid thinking style. Thanks a lot for the "help," brain. Thinking traps offer wrong explanations in the heat of the moment that mentally constrict options to worst-case. It would have been nice to know about these troublemakers much earlier in life, so we could have saved a lot of anguish over the years. Let's review some of the most common thinking traps.

Jumping to Conclusions

When an adversity sets off the stress response, your mind reverts instantly to raw emotion and the telltale impulsiveness of System 1, or fast, thinking. There's no vetting of the worst-case thoughts that flash before you, no analysis. It's just immediate, rash, exaggerated calamity that would be tossed out of your gray matter, if your modern brain was in charge. But it's not. The ancient brain is running the show now.

As a result, the false belief of **jumping to conclusions** has free rein to scare up whatever doomsday visions it can. *I missed the deadline, so I'm going to be fired. Jim has been very quiet lately. He's probably plotting against me with the new boss. She should have been home by now, and she's not picking up her phone. She must have gotten in an accident.*

Instant takes without valid data and supporting information lead to a lot of angst for nothing, not to mention actions that can be dangerous. When a negative event sets off dire conclusions before the facts are in, step back and take a timeout. Ask yourself which facts lead to this conclusion and which facts don't. Identify other explanations and best-case stories as well. It helps to get the reflex thought out of the mind, where it remains in charge, and onto a piece of paper or screen, or detail it out loud to a partner or friend. Wrong conclusions don't look so believable when you see them in print or someone else can vet them.

Mind-Reading

The next thinking trap is **mind-reading**. We've all done plenty of it, thinking we know what someone else is thinking—usually, convinced someone isn't thinking highly of us. It's an assumption that can lead to anger, conflict, withdrawal, and just plain off-base attitudes about others. *They think they're better than me. He gave me this assignment at 5 p.m. when I'm ready to go home, because he has it in for me. She should have known what I wanted her to do.*

When you have wrong assumptions, you have wrong beliefs that lead to wrong behaviors. The place to start reversing the trap of mind-reading is to stop assuming and start communicating. Get more information. Ask clearly what the person wants or if they understand what you want. Get more clarity on assignments, instructions, and goals. Work on better communication with your supervisor or colleagues, with your partner, and kids. Vagueness is not your friend. Go with who, what, when, where, why, and how, as they say in the journalism business.

The "Me" Trap

The biggest mental trap is that we are often unable to see outside our own heads. One of the side effects is the "me" trap, believing that everything that goes wrong is somehow your fault. Everything becomes a verdict on what you didn't do right. The me-trap can lead to guilt, sadness, and pessimism.

There's a difference between a healthy sense of responsibility for things that don't work out and the instant belief that if someone is mad, had a bad outcome or day, the project or the home front is not working, that you are the sole cause of it. You let others down. Maybe you are not up to the task if everyone isn't happy. The me-trap generates thoughts that attack the core need of competence and can make you go into flight mode. Have patience. Don't push the emergency slide button.

Catch yourself when this trap goes off and find other reasons that could play a role in the situation. The delays of others. Unrealistic deadlines. Unnecessary rudeness. Overwhelming workload. Someone's unchecked temper or negativity. Information overload. Remember that all the causes are temporary, one time, one place. Many challenges will have more causes than you.

The "Them" Trap

This is the opposite of the me-trap. You blame everyone and everything else for your problems and setbacks. It's a nonstop battle with a world conspiring to keep things from going the way you want. *I didn't get that promotion because Jeff blind-sided me with that deadline. This weather is killing my motivation. That figures they would seat me here in the back. I never get any respect.*

Those caught in this trap can't take responsibility for anything that goes wrong or any criticism. The ego is too fragile to handle mistakes or slights. The belief-consequence pattern for loss or loss of ego is anger, marinaded in resentment, tunnel vision, and aggression.

If you have a lot of anger, this trap might be a culprit. Yes, you can be treated badly, and for anything egregious, you need to speak up, but if you are experiencing a lot of anger in your life, you need to find a way out of this self-sabotage. As we have learned, anger is one of most dangerous stress agents and a driver of cardiovascular disease and heart attacks.

Think about what role you are playing in the anger event and what you could change about the scenario the next time, so your response to a demand isn't a default thinking trap. There's actually a benefit to admitting your own miscues—learning from mistakes so they don't happen again. How can you not react to anger scenarios in the future? Be more patient? Not take the event personally?

Catastrophizing

Anything that overloads your perceived ability to handle it, whether consciously or unconsciously, is a catastrophe to a brain designed to panic your physiology into fighting or running from mortal danger. As we have learned, catastrophizing is something humans do well and often. It was a great spur to avoiding imminent demise 150,000 years ago, but it's not so useful for non-life-threatening issues that push your buttons today.

As you learned earlier, catastrophizing can lead to counterproductive emotional reactions that spiral into more and more exaggerated scenarios. *I lost a big sale, so I may not be in the company plans anymore. If I get laid off, then I won't have the money to pay my mortgage, support my family. I'll be on the street,* etc.

But you don't have to be a hostage to your brain's knee-jerk flights of fantasy. You can go into action to defeat catastrophic thoughts with that four-part technique to stop catastrophic thoughts in mid-apocalypse we talked about earlier: Get all worst-case stories out, follow with all best-case stories, describe the most likely story of what happened, and take purposeful action going forward based on the facts of what most likely happened.

Trap Avoidance

Identify the thinking traps that are problems for you. Which thinking traps do you fall into—Jumping to Conclusions? Me?

Them? Mind-Reading? Catastrophic thoughts? When? Which is dominant? What will you do to stop the trap and reappraise the story the next time it appears?

The Answer Within

The way that optimism offsets pessimism and the negative set-point we have as a species is one more example of how the wherewithal to balance our lives lies within—if we can be proactive enough to bring it into our daily lives to reframe reflex emotional reactions to tough events. Seeing setbacks at temporary allows us to use our modern brain for problem-solving and not have it dumbed down by self-defeating defaults.

To take advantage of this resource, though, you must cultivate and utilize it. Put Post-It notes somewhere you will see them that say, "It's temporary" or "One time, One place." Opt out of using the language of pessimistic explanatory style—"this *always* happens to me" and "I *never* get a break." Don't fall for the knee-jerk thoughts, the real-appearing but false beliefs of thinking traps, that pop up after a stressful event.

The science of optimism gives you crucial tools to stay resilient in the face of challenges. Now it's time to dive into the active ingredient inside the skill of optimistic explanatory style: positive emotions. They keep you out of negative tailspins, outfox adversities, and lead your brain to the emotional math you need for a flourishing life.

CHAPTER 9

The Upside of Positive Emotions

Multiply Performance, Success and Happiness

Optimism can't be the supermedicine it is without the overlooked forces that animate it and give it life: positive emotions. They are central to optimism, quality of life, and what makes life worth living, yet they weren't considered important enough for serious scientific study until the 1990s. Since they didn't make you a threat to yourself or others, they seemed trifling compared to the more numerous dramas spawned by negative emotions.

Pioneering researcher Barbara Fredrickson, author of *Positivity* and a professor of psychology at the University of North Carolina, Chapel Hill, put an end to the second-class status and showed why we have to accentuate the positive. Her groundbreaking paper in 1998 asked a question science didn't have a good answer for: "What Good Are Positive Emotions?"

Thanks to the intrepid Fredrickson, we now know that positive emotions are far from trivial. Mild-mannered emotions from interest to gratitude, joy, and hope play a crucial role in reducing stress, building resilience, and driving innovation and success. Positive emotions function as a counterweight to negative emotions.

"Positive emotions help speed recovery from negative emotions," Fredrickson told me in an interview. "When people are able to self-generate a positive emotion or perspective, that enables them to bounce back. It's not just that you bounce back and then you feel good—feeling good drives the process." Positive emotions come before the rebound. They create the conditions, the outlook of a better day, and the drive to move on toward it.

Negative emotions undermine the brain's capacity to think broadly and find creative solutions. You can't see the big picture. The vise grip of fear and stress and the emotions they generate—anger, blame, panic, resentment, shame—limit thought to a rigid default that obscures options. In the work environment, for instance, negativity causes teams to lose flexibility and the ability to be curious.

Because we are so overwired for survival threats, we take negative emotions much more seriously. "Losses loom larger than gains," Fredrickson said. "Our mind is drawn into this mental time travel, and we're obsessing about something negative that happened in the past, or we're worrying about what will happen in the future."

Her work has shown that you can reframe adversity and be more effective by countering negative loops with a buried resource—the reservoir of joy, hope, amusement, love, awe and other buoyant emotions you can call on as needed. These emotional resources have the power to calm blood pressure and operate as a reset button for negative ruts.

In one of her studies, test subjects whose anxiety was driven sky-high by an impending public speech were able to reverse negative cardiovascular effects in less than a minute by viewing relaxing imagery, something you can do too to calm nerves. They were shown a tranquil film clip of ocean waves, a puppy playing, a sad film or a neutral screen saver depicting an abstract display of lines. Sensors tracking heart rate, blood pressure and artery constriction showed that those watching the positive imagery recovered the fastest. Another study, this one based on daily reports of positive and negative emotions, found that the more positive emotions people experienced, the more their resilience levels grew, enabling them to let go of negative events faster.

Positive emotions have been shown to help businesspeople negotiate better, improve decision-making, boost creativity and drive high-performance behavior.

"Positive emotions expand awareness and attention," Fredrickson explained, and that is critical for anyone looking for an opportunity or trying to solve a problem. "When you're able to take in more information, the peripheral vision field is expanded. You're able to connect the dots to the bigger picture. Instead of remembering just the most central event, you remember that and the peripheral aspects, too."

When you feel good, you pay more attention to everything, not just one perceived crisis as you do in the grip of stress and pressure. That condition leads to one of the key benefits of what Fredrickson calls the "broaden-and-build dynamic" that comes with positive emotions: more receptivity and openness. In a good mood, you open up to new ideas, people, and opportunities. You take more initiative, feel more confident, explore new things, acquire new knowledge. The power of possibility is coursing through your neurons.

Openness is also an approach crucial for resilience. By focusing thoughts on broader and more optimistic options than a single worst-case thought, it keeps the mind away from the ruminative self-destruct button. With enough positivity in the mental bank, you can crowd out the super-dire and strengthen resolve to handle the problem.

The Positivity Ratio

A thriving life is a numbers game. It's all about your emotional math. Don't worry. You don't have to do any calculus. Scientists have developed easy-to-understand ratios that spell out the prerequisites of better living. Working with the analytics of mathematician Marcial Losada, Fredrickson discovered a tipping point of positive-to-negative emotions that spells the difference between flourishing and floundering.

"It seems like we need at least three positive emotions to open and lift us up to counter every single negative emotion that drags us down," she told me. "The good news is that the positive emotions don't need to be intense or profound. They can be rather mild. They just need to be frequent."

The negative is so powerful that you have to muster more than equivalent forces to keep it in check. It's called the negativity bias. Getting that lopsided balance right is a challenge, since the negative occupies brains on autopilot, while the positive requires concerted proaction. It means you have to generate three "heartfelt emotional experiences" for every negative hit you receive.

If your positivity ratio is 3 to 1 or above, you are flourishing, able to move through challenges without being set back for very long. If you are under 3 to 1, you come under the sway of negative emotions and their replay buttons. Fredrickson found most people are at 2 to 1 positive to negative, not enough to overpower the hold of negative emotions and their ruminations and keep anxiety under control.

By the way, in relationships, John Gottman, professor emeritus at the University of Washington and owner of the Gottman Institute, a center for marital therapy, has documented that the ratio for a thriving marriage is 5 to 1 positive to negative. That may explain a few things. Divorce and depression occur at a ratio of 1 to 1. The lesson in the numbers is that success in work, life, and relationships takes effort. It doesn't happen on its own. You can't wait for someone else to do it. You have to act to increase your positive count.

The positivity ratio isn't something you need to meet every hour or day. It's a cumulative metric. Studies show that happiness is the byproduct of multiple small positive events.

If you make regular deposits to your positivity bank—your memory—you build a buffer against negative events ahead. When a withdrawal occurs after a setback, you still have enough positive deposits in the bank to avoid being overwhelmed by the negative side of the ledger.

Fredrickson concluded our talk with this final, super-important point. "There's really solid evidence that the positive emotions you feel today predict tomorrow's and next week's and next month's success, health and quality relationships, because they build your resources and resilience." If you want to know how you're going to feel next week, do something today and tomorrow to increase your positivity ratio.

High Performers Are Optimistic

Positive emotions can dramatically improve the decisions we make, the opportunities we pursue or not, the people we connect with or don't, the direction of our careers, the sales we're making, the work-life balance we feel we're achieving, and the level of performance at work.

Prior to working with Fredrickson, performance consultant Losada had analyzed hundreds of business teams in meetings, utilizing video behind a two-way mirror to examine the effect on performance of negative emotions in the work setting. He and his teams measured statements based on positive vs. negative remarks, whether comments were self-focused or other-focused, and whether participants favored inquiry or advocacy.

He found that high-performance teams have a 6 to 1 ratio of positive to negative statements, while low performing teams were under 1 to 1.

That gap makes a huge difference to the organization and the individuals in them. The best performers scored highest on profitability, customer satisfaction ratings, and evaluations by others.

High-performance teams were more flexible, resilient, and not stuck in self-absorbed defensive behavior. They also asked questions as much as they defended views and had attention directed outward as much as inward. Low performance teams had lower connectivity, asked no questions, and had almost no outward focus. Negative teams got stuck in criticism, defensiveness, and self-absorbed advocacy.

Negative emotions constrict thinking and prevent you from connecting with others. Positive emotions make you more open, curious, and receptive. A negative frame of mind puts you in "leave me alone" bunker mode. When you're irritated or pessimistic, not surprisingly, you get less interest in your ideas, cooperation, and support.

The Real Law of Attraction

The most effective weapon in the success arsenal may be something that appears to be a typo—positive affect. The word is "affect," not "effect," though it has a big one when you deploy it. Positive affect is the body language of buoyant emotions, happiness, an optimistic spirit, transmitted via facial expression, such as an easy smile and a playful demeanor. The research shows that when you have it, the world wants in. Even lab rats are attracted to playful rats.

The scientific literature brims with testaments to the power of positive affect, from success in the social arena to better health (less stress, hypertension), increased creativity, and problem-solving. Positive psychology heavyweights Sonja Lyubomirsky, Ed Diener and Laura King demonstrated in a meta-analysis of 225 research papers covering 275,000 participants that the "hallmark of well-being" of positive affect spawns "behaviors paralleling success."

They found that people with frequent positive affect are more likely to be successful in their professional lives and get more promotions. Studies show that the most cheerful people make thousands of dollars more than the least cheerful. Happy people get more raises over time and are evaluated more highly by supervisors. Those with chronic happiness have better social relationships, more support and stronger friendships.

"Chronically happy people," Lyubomirsky, Diener and King report, "are in general more successful...their success is in large part a consequence of their happiness and frequent experience of positive affect."

It turns out that a happy state leads to success, instead of the other way around. Obviously, you have to be able to do more than be upbeat to succeed in the world. But the right disposition increases the odds.

When you're in a good mood, energy soars, and you have a welcome sign out to the world that you are available for business or conversation. Visible vibrancy is contagious, thanks to the social circuitry built into our brains in the form of mirror neurons, the cells that simulate the actions of others in our minds and emotions. When a friend is depressed, your neurons follow the cues and adjust your emotions downward. When someone is visibly happy, that's contagious too.

I boarded a plane years ago for a trip to Africa to do a story on Zimbabwe. My photographer, Michael Justice, and I were so cranked up about the adventure that it showed on our faces and in our voices. A flight attendant got caught up in the excitement. Michael was a jovial guy with a booming voice and laugh. After a brief chat about the trip, the flight attendant said, "You guys have a long flight ahead. You need to be upgraded to first class." She moved us from coach to first class all the way to Johannesburg. That's positive affect, a spirit that's infectious. And that was my friend, Michael, who died in a helicopter crash a few years ago. He knew how to live to the fullest, and that spirit lit up those around him.

Research has linked positive affect with just about everything this side of lead guitar prowess—increased confidence, energy, optimism, self-efficacy, sociability, conflict resolution skills, likability, ability to cope with stress and challenges, as well as reduced cardiovascular events and improved immune function. That is an incredible payoff for just projecting a good mood.

The list goes on. Employees with a positive disposition have more autonomy and meaning in their jobs. Positive affect is such a crucial force that work performance is impacted more by well-being than the performance itself.

When you start out on the positive side of the ledger, you don't have as far to travel emotionally to connect with someone, to enjoy yourself, be spontaneous or jump into something new. It's a state that makes you prone to proaction. People animated by positive emotions are more apt "to approach than to avoid," say Lyubomirsky, Diener and King. Approaching is going to turn up more opportunities and friends than withdrawing from others.

The goal isn't nonstop grinning. That would be tough on the facial muscles. That's not how emotions work. Your mood swings back and forth in repeated cycles every day. The aim is a frequent state of positive feeling that is able to overcome the reflexes of cynicism and apathy that dog the protective realm of adulthood.

You can dramatically increase your levels of positive affect with frequent participation in experiences that boost joy, fun, and social connection. Behaviors that help you get there are physical vitality, pro-social behavior, optimism, expressive body language, playfulness, flexibility, enthusiasm, and spontaneity.

You have to be clever about it. It requires tricking the inner curmudgeon that torpedoes anything out of character. Fake it till you make it.

In one study a group of introverts asked to pretend they were extroverts in a job interview performed just as well as the extroverts in making an impression. It seems like acting at first, but once you are in the role, you find there's nothing phony about it. You are simply being friendly and overriding a mood or attitude that burrowed into your daily behavior. You are entitled to act contrary to a behavior that's counterproductive.

Push past the adult mind and let your body feel enthusiasm, excitement, and receptivity, as it did when you were young. You are not locked into an emotional code of conduct you can't break out of.

Take a Holiday Without Leaving Home

Most of us are different people when we are on vacation—lighter, more relaxed, more open. What if that was the real you, and the barricaded home version a construct of defense, stress, and impatience?

Imagine you are on vacation. Think about how relaxed you are, interested in discovering, living in the moment. You can do that at home, too, be someone livelier, friendlier.

Spend a weekend day as if you are on vacation. Your mind

is open. You're in a good mood. You don't have to rush anything. You're relaxed. You can just be wherever you are and nowhere else. Write down how that feels. Did people react to you differently? Was it calming? What did you discover?

What you mirror in your affect is what you get.

The Positive Arsenal

Unlike negative emotions—anger, envy, sadness, rage, revenge, hatred—positive emotions are less distinct and tend to get overlooked alongside the Big Positive everyone wants, happiness. Positive emotions are quieter, more subtle, and definitely shorter in duration than negative emotions, so we don't spend as much time with them. We are under-practiced. Yet they all play a role in leading to a happier life.

There are many routes to happiness, or better yet, its long-term equivalents, gratification and well-being. You can cast a wider net by hanging out more often with the rest of the positive crew. Let's get the pom-poms out for your all-star positivity team, the Big 10 Positive Emotions:

Joy

This isn't any old run-of-the-mill happy. Joy is a deeper, richer, higher plane of feeling good. It's an unconditional readiness to enjoy, let go, celebrate, appreciate. You can find it through play, affection, inspiration, and doing any activity you love—dancing, singing, biking.

Love

The kind of love here refers to the love felt toward another individual—a parent for a child, for a lover, a friend, says Fredrickson. Love radiates warmth, caring, concern, and many other behaviors that richen connection and make us and the other person feel good. More expression of love to those in your orbit is an easy way to spend more time with this emotion.

Interest

Interest and its vehicle of quest, curiosity, lead us beyond the daily fray to things that intrigue, not for any immediate external gain, but for the act of knowing itself, an intrinsic affair, which is powerful. It's a self-generating discovery device. The interest you follow up today could be your friend, career, or passion tomorrow.

Inspiration

Inspiration lifts us from the ground on which we are sometimes lying flat on our back. It makes you feel worthy, capable, powerful, and propelled toward action. Inspiration calls you to higher heights, and that feels mighty good. Harness its power in audiobooks, music, poetry, great speakers, stories of folks who have overcome obstacles, sublime music, sports performances, and spiritual sources.

Gratitude

Telling others or yourself how grateful you are is kryptonite for negative emotions, which just can't stand to be around when gratitude is in the house. Gratitude shuts down the complaint and pity-party by acknowledging that which is good and much better than the grievance of the moment. Gratitude gives you perspective, which injects positive emotions with a comparative that it could be much worse. You are fortunate to be who you are and have what you have.

Serenity

Since serenity is a sense of peace and tranquility, in a noisy world serenity aids are key. You can access this feeling by reading, meditating, watching relaxing videos, through recordings of nature—rain, birdsong—and on walks early on a Sunday morning when everyone is still sleeping. To really tune in to the serene, get outside, from your backyard to parks and forests. I love when it's quiet enough to hear wind rustling in the trees and nothing else. Take in the beauty and feel the calmness as your nerves downshift. Hike a trail where there are no humans except you and admire your world.

Hope

Hope provides strength in tough times and the fortifying will that drives persistence, purpose, and meaning. Hope isn't blind to the ugliness around us. It chooses to focus on what can be. By its nature, then, it frames the obstacles as temporary, making it the essential emotion of optimism. You hope for something better until it arrives or no longer seems viable, and then it comes time for another goal to hope and work for.

Pride

Pride in your work, your family, and your friends are all positives. It's an emotion that can be a big booster for how you react to good things. Remember, for good events, you want to take them permanently, pervasively, and personally. Pride makes sure you do exactly that and give yourself credit. Allow yourself to enjoy the fruits of your labor. Let your family and friends know how proud you are of them.

Amusement

We all once knew the power of amusement. Then we became adults. Fun and play shatter negative states with pure positivity. You do it to have the fun of doing it and not for any instrumental gain. Put fun on your calendar by choosing amusing activities—from comedy films, to clog dancing, river rafting, and croquet.

Awe

You wouldn't know it by all the time and energy we put into padding our egos, but what makes us feel really good is feeling small. That's weird. When you feel awe or wonder, its cousin, you feel the power of something bigger than yourself. The night sky, massive mountains, powerful surf—these forces allow ego to recede, making room for the uplifting state of being a tiny player in something vast, gorgeous and boggling. Awe wakes you up to the magnificence of your world and that you are lucky to be a part of it. That's a positive!

Turn Off Stress with the Undo Effect

How potent are positive emotions? They can actually stop stress in its tracks. Frederickson has shown that by simply concentrating on a powerful positive emotion such as gratitude, you can shift emotional attention so completely that it turns off the alarm of the stress response and reverses the physical symptoms of stress. Try it now.

Think of something you haven't been paying enough attention to that you should be grateful for. It could be your health, your family, your friends, your eyesight, two healthy legs.

Focus on that for two minutes. If you were in stress mode prior to the exercise, the digestion system would start up again, heart rate and blood pressure would lower, and muscles would untense. Fredrickson calls it the "undo effect." It's a remarkable example of the power of mind, attention, and directed positive emotion. You can use it anytime to restore perspective and shut down stress.

Tell Someone What You Admire About Them

There is one more positive emotion I want to mention. It's one of the least used in the positivity tool kit, but I think it's one of the most powerful: admiration. Admiration is a higher form of appreciation, which itself is an offshoot of gratitude, whose potency no doubt contributes to the power of admiration.

Most of the time admiration is used to express deep appreciation for the virtuosic skills or achievements of a well-known figure—a singer, athlete, writer, director, scientist. It encourages the emulation of good role models in society. Others we admire fall into the virtuous realm—people who help others, such as emergency room doctors and nurses, Peace Corps workers, and all the everyday essential workers who keep food on the table for us.

There is another admiration, though, one very close at hand. It's when you tell people close to you—family members and friends—what you admire about them.

Each of us wanders through life trapped behind a myopic lens. We take for granted the things that we do or miss essential elements of our own character, since we are so close to them. We get plenty of static along the way but little recognition outside performance reviews.

When admiration shows up, you are usually not around for it, since it's happening at your funeral. Why do we have to wait until someone is gone to tell them what we admired about them or how much they meant? Imagine if people could hear the praise of eulogies while they were still walking the earth. It could be so meaningful for everyone. Don't wait until it's too late to share what you find special about the people in your life.

What makes this everyday admiration pack so much positivity punch is that it carries the power of gratitude mixed with a special kind of recognition. When you say you admire someone and let them know the reason(s) why, it gratifies that person's mastery need and lets them know you respect their competence, boosting their internal validation.

Social emotions such as admiration and compassion are lodged deep in one of the oldest parts of the brain, home to fear and anger and connected to neural networks that regulate basic functions from breathing to blood pressure. This means admiration has been around a long time and is at our core for a reason, to be put into action.

Start a Mutual Admiration Society

What if we could help people see what is special about them, what they have meant to us? That could mean a lot less milk of magnesia and all-caps social media posts. You pay it forward for them to reach out to someone else they admire and do the same.

Think of someone you admire and what you admire about them. Maybe it's their kindness, persistence, how they handled something difficult, how they helped others. What attribute do you appreciate in this person? How have they impacted you and your life?

Set up a time to meet and deliver your admiration in person, if possible. Find a blank greeting card and share your admiration on it, or just tell them verbally. Pay close attention to their reaction, and afterwards write down everything that happened. The notes will serve as a reminder of how gratitude increases positive emotions for both of you. The more you can tap this state, the more you want to do things for others.

Don't wait. Tell them now about your admiration for them. They will feel amazing, and you will too.

Be There For Yourself: Flex Your Character Strengths

Admiration from the people who know you well carries extra weight and can help you see your own best attributes in a way you can't. One of my friends once said he thought I was fearless in how I'd taken on certain risks. I'm far from that. As Mark Twain put it, "Courage is resistance to fear...not absence of it." Yet my friend's comment has come to mind at times of challenge, reminding me that I had courage and that I had the capacity to keep pushing.

He had singled out a character strength, a realm that I hadn't ever thought about at the time. It turns out we all have a hidden reserve of strengths we can wield to increase resilience, positive emotions, and our motivation to overcome difficulties. Your best attributes are standing by, waiting to give you a boost when needed—if you know what they are.

Character strengths are a collection of 24 inner attributes that represent humanity at its best values across time and the globe. The University of Pennsylvania's Martin Seligman and his colleague Chris Peterson scoured children's books, religious texts, song lyrics, literature, philosophy, psychology, civic creeds, and youth development to sift out the key traits expressing character and values across cultures and history—from perseverance, to kindness, to bravery. They winnowed the list of traits that appeared the most universally important to 24 characteristics.

Since these traits are at the root of what is admired in humans, Seligman and Peterson theorized that a framework that helped promote and build these strengths could multiply these behaviors in society, particularly in young people, and they could be valuable in personal development for adults. Their work kicked off the science of character and a new style of educating that focuses on building character strengths. Teachers explain the importance of character, point out when students are using their strengths, and encourage working with the instructors to build initiative, autonomy, and self-responsibility.

Studies show that character strengths predict for everything from an optimistic outlook, to academic achievement (the strengths of perseverance and love of learning), to life satisfaction (tied to strengths such as hope, curiosity, love, vitality, and gratitude), to resilience (bravery, perseverance).

How can character strengths help? When you are facing an adversity, stress and anxiety can make you feel weary and weak. They drain emotional and physical resources needed to fight. Enter reinforcements, your strengths, to fortify you. When you reflect that you are about bravery, patience, perseverance, or hope, you can get a surge of self-belief to keep driving forward. They steel your will.

I'm not a fan of cold calls or following up potential leads. After doing the Values in Action Character Strengths test, though, I found that my top strengths are enthusiasm and bravery. Now if I have some reluctance before a call, I focus on my strengths and let enthusiasm reign. You can do the same with your top strengths. They remind you of your values and intrinsic assets. It's great to know that when you need support, you can go to someone you know will come through for you.

It's a no-brainer that character strengths can help, not just you to find more resilience, but the whole company. They improve personal well-being as well as productivity for the organization.

Which of these are your top signature character strengths?

- Gratitude
- Kindness
- Fairness
- Perseverance
- Self-Control
- Humor
- Integrity
- Bravery
- Appreciation of Beauty
- Humility
- Prudence
- Purpose

- Enthusiasm
- Leadership
- Love of learning
- Curiosity
- Social intelligence
- Love
- Enthusiasm
- Open-mindedness
- Forgiveness
- Optimism
- Creativity
- Perspective

The best way to find out the strengths you have within is to take the Character Strengths test. You can do the survey for free at the University of Pennsylvania and Seligman's website: authentichappiness.sas.upenn. edu. Take the VIA Character Strengths Test in the dropdown menu that appears under the Questionnaires tab. The survey ranks your strengths, giving you a brigade of new/old resources to bolster support when you need it. There's also an Optimism test, which I highly recommend taking.

The Mood Roller Coaster

Moods, which are driven by unconscious triggers from irritation to joy to sunlight or lack of it, lack of sleep, hunger, stress, and guilt, don't need to check in with you before doing their thing, which means it's up to you to keep them from making your day harder.

Each of us cycles in and out of positive and negative moods constantly. You're up, then moments later you're down. Positive affect is lower in the morning and rises to a peak throughout the day, then weakens at night. Mood is also better the more energy and alertness you have.

Mood also rises and falls based on your 90-minute alertness cycle, known as the ultradian rhythm. When you are at the beginning of that cycle, you are in a better mood, feel like initiating things and attack the to-do list. At the end of the period, you feel sluggish, lose focus, and the mind wanders. That's when you need to step back, recharge, and reboot the brain.

There are also mood dips and spikes based on the day of the week. Negative mood is highest on Sunday and Monday for some mysterious reason. The spirit darkens on Sunday afternoon with contemplation of the workweek ahead. Positive mood rises on Thursday as we near the freedom of the weekend and is at its highest point, you will not be surprised to learn, on Friday and Saturday.

The mood roller coaster runs you up and down the track depending on events, reactions, memories, anticipations, or being on hold for an hour with a cable company. That means you can wind up sidetracked often by negative benders. Low moods prevent you from problem-solving or getting to life activities, the natural mood elevators that can help you bounce back by infusing positive emotions.

Luckily, though, you don't have to be a bystander to mood shifts. You can take charge of mood detours by cultivating the positive and opting out of excessive negative rumination.

As we have learned, being aware of the mood when you are in it, aware of the stress response when you are in that, is how you reassert control. Bring awareness and mindfulness to your day, and you can catch yourself when a mood steps on your day or life.

You Can Rally!

Negative emotions are so potent that they can quickly divert you from where you are or what you would like to do to unproductive ruminations. Yet it is possible to opt out, since emotions aren't locked in. They are momentary, and you can exit moods as quickly as you entered them.

Whether you are hanging on to a negative mood caused by something someone said, something that didn't work out the way you wanted, or the workday is done, and you only want to veg on the couch, instead of getting together with a friend or doing a scheduled activity, that doesn't have to be the end of the story. You don't have to fall for the first mood that manifests. You can have a counterpunch by proactively shifting your mood with the exercise below.

How to Exit the Mood Trap

1. Start by recognizing the mood for what it is—a normal emotional intrusion raining on your mental parade, blocking balance, health, success, engagement with your world.
2. Ask: What do I get from clinging to this mood? Hanging on to it keeps it alive. Do I need to keep it alive?
3. Identify what you will gain by shifting mood to something more productive and positive. Less stress? More joy? A productive lesson going forward? Fun? Better rapport with others?
4. Do something positive. Put on upbeat music. Do the gratitude exercise, reflecting on something you should be grateful for, such as a healthy body that can step out the door and take a walk in a park or do an aikido, pottery, or yoga class.

Then shout out loud: *I can rally! I can rally! I can rally!*
You are the master of mood.

CHAPTER 10

The Refueling Principle

Recharge, Renew, Reset

A dvances in brain research are giving us a much better picture of when our command center has all systems firing and when it doesn't. Those who peer into the brain through magnetic resonance images say scans of fatigued brains resemble ones that are sound asleep.

I'm sure you know that feeling around 4 p.m., when you have to expend many times the effort to get something accomplished than you need when you're fresh. There's a limited amount of time that the brain can stay focused without fatiguing, spacing, or going into brownout mode.

The traditional approach to fighting mental fatigue has been to press harder and pop those blood vessels to the finish line. Like many of you, I was raised to keep on going until I needed an ambulance. But the evidence shows that brains and bodies don't respond well to the battering-ram approach. Like laptops and cell phones, minds need to be recharged on a regular basis, or they run out of juice. The brain is an energy machine, consuming 20% of the body's calories (even though it's only 2% of total body mass) and 50% of the body's sugar, according to Harvard's Neuroscience Institute.

You can keep your mental grid and body fully charged through regular application of what I call the Refueling Principle. Expended resources—energy, attention, self-regulation supplies, physical vitality, burned-up fuel chemicals in the body—need to be replaced. Your physiology is designed for this resupply mission, from the rest and digest functions of the parasympathetic nervous system to the infusion of positive emotions from a break or weekend that refreshes the mental hardware.

Brain scientists say the mind goes down from fatigue well before the body. One study found that mental fatigue took hold after three hours of continuous attention. Others point to a 90-minute threshold of alertness that comes from a cousin of the circadian rhythm, ultradian rhythms, which rise and fall throughout the day.

The CEO and founder of software giant, SAS Institute, Jim Goodnight, has said that for the first couple of hours his developers can do solid work on code, but after that the errors rise dramatically.

It takes a lot of resources to get things done, and those supplies are depleted much faster than we think. Minds and bodies run out of gas when they are not regularly recharged. This makes refueling them as crucial as any other facet of company operations, essential to health, wellness and performance.

The Fatigue Factor

Most of us wouldn't think twice about taking a breather after an hour of basketball or Zumba, but mental fatigue is another story. It seems somehow wimpy to need to take care of your mind. You're not breathing heavy. In fact, you're just sitting on your glutes.

Yet the same overuse dynamic that plays out with your body happens in your brain too. It gets spent and needs to recoup. After burning through the available energetic resources that aid clear thinking, cognitive function gets hazier the longer you go without letup. Then you find yourself straining to keep your attention focused and hit a cognitive wall. You're just going around in circles, no longer making progress.

The activation-rest dynamic is a key balancing act of the body. You are programmed for rest and body and mind maintenance to counter periods that place excess demands on resources. That comes from the parasympathetic system, which helps you restore used-up energy. The parasympathetic system slows your heart rate, reduces blood pressure, and supports digestion. Resting and digesting serve as natural tranquilizers, calming the biology and restoring homeostasis.

The refueling effort goes right down to the cellular level. Cells withdraw energy from an under-the-radar energy storage molecule called adenosine triphosphate, or ATP. It serves as a rechargeable battery pack, where, inside the bonds of its phosphates it releases energy to fuel everything from muscle contraction to synaptic signaling and the generation of neurotransmitters.

The brain depends on glucose as its main source of energy, and it gets it from ATP. The neurons in your brain need massive ongoing energy production. One study noted that "a single cortical neuron utilizes approximately 4.7 billion ATPs per second in a resting human brain." Maybe we need to take resting more seriously.

The process of how ATP releases energy through hydrolysis to become adenosine diphosphate (ADP) is as wondrous as the outer reaches of space. And if that wasn't enough, after the fueling, there's another amazing transformation. Your cells change the ADP back to ATP through the use of oxygen and glucose. You can see that the brain needs literal recharging at the cellular level to fuel the neuronal load that may be required to stay on task.

"The brain is a muscle. You can strengthen it or deplete it," Allison Gabriel, a professor of management at the University of Arizona in Tucson, told me in an interview. "If you let this muscle recharge and replenish, you'll feel better mentally and see improvements in your performance.

"There is a lot of research that says we have a limited pool of cognitive resources," said Gabriel, who studies job demands and employee well-being. "When you are constantly draining your resources, you are not being as productive as you can be. If you get depleted, we see performance decline. You're able to persist less and have trouble solving tasks."

It's a scenario brought to weary minds by the time-on-task effect. Performance steadily degrades with sustained cognitive effort, resulting in slower reaction times and increased mental fatigue. fMRI scans of fatigued brains show regions associated with attention register big declines after intensive mental focus.

There are multiple points over the course of the day when you reach a state of diminishing returns because your brain is tapped out, from demanding tasks to excess time on task, to an overly long day, or lack of food or hydration. Stress is another major factor in mental and physical fatigue, burning up energetic resources, interfering with your sleep, increasing negative mood and ruminative sidetracks, and, if it's chronic, dragging that fatigue from one day to the next.

When your attention is spinning in circles like a stuck cursor ball, mental effort becomes too much to sustain. You want to do something else, something easier than concentrating, such as trancing out to Instagram posts.

Staying disciplined and regulating your emotions is taxing. Known as ego depletion, the effort to ignore emotions and stay on task has a cost. Self-regulation demands burn up glucose, the same glucose needed to fire up resting brain neurons with 4.7 billion ATPs per second. Given that the brain has 100 billion neurons—15 billion cortical neurons—it means we all have some serious refueling to do.

The signs of physical fatigue—tiredness, drowsiness, low energy—are trying to tell you something. The same is true of mental fatigue signals, such as difficulty concentrating, self-distraction, memory problems, irritation, low motivation, and fading willpower. The message: It's time to stop, rest, and resupply.

Take a Break, Increase Productivity

In a culture in which we define ourselves by our work, the compulsion to keep at it without breaking stride is a point of pride. Endurance means you can take it. Stopping for a breather brings on the twisting nag of guilt. It's a defeat to have to give in to rest. Yet stepping away to recharge actually increases performance.

The business world has known this for nearly a century since a spate of fatigue studies in the 1920s and 1930s. One of the most famous demonstrations of the power of the pause took place at the Western Electric Hawthorne Works in Chicago from 1927 to 1932. Researchers found that when five-minute rest breaks were introduced, worker output increased. When the break increased to 10 minutes, output increased again.

Two studies in the 1990s found that performance increased even after very short pauses. Fleeting respites improved performance by allowing workers to keep the effort level consistently higher than when there were no breaks. One of the researchers involved in those tests, Ken Doerr, told me that quality went up with microbreaks measured in seconds. Even "very small breaks give you a chance to catch your breath, try a new approach."

And it's not just your mind that needs a time out, so does your body. Ergonomic experts recommend frequent brief breaks for those with intensive computer usage—at least five minutes every hour. During the breaks get up and move around, gaze out the window, do some stretches, walk down the hallway. Once your body starts aching, your concentration has already left the building.

Taking a break relieves brain and repetitive motion strain. This makes rest and renewal essential productivity and wellness agents. The recharging process heightens cognitive focus and agility and interrupts stress and negative mood. Breaks replenish energetic resources by removing demands briefly, allowing a reset to take place.

It's a mini-version of what happens from the restorative powers of sleep. In this case, the mind tires and seeks a respite from being on-task. Pioneering sleep researcher Nathaniel Kleitman called this pattern the rest-activity cycle. When we get to the end of a period of focus, alertness wanes. We self-interrupt, open a browser, look for something else that takes less effort. That's when it's time to get up and refuel.

The ultradian rhythm cycle mirrors that dynamic. Unlike the 24-hour circadian rhythm, ultradian rhythms regulate behavior in cycles of about 90 minutes. You start out at a peak of alertness, which gradually ebbs over a 90-minute to two-hour period, after which you need to take a break for 10-20 minutes to refresh, so you can return to high alertness at the top of the ultradian rhythm.

During serious mental and physical effort, the brain takes in reams of data and burns up self-regulation and cell fuels to stay focused on it all. This depletes resources that promote effective thinking. As strain develops, stress-related chemicals crash the party, gumming up the cognitive processes and leaving metabolic junk that needs to be eliminated, according to Borna Bonakdarpour, an assistant professor of neurology at Northwestern University. A break helps the mind clear out the toxic gunk and refuel the cellular and neuronal batteries.

Stepping back to recharge, so you can go forward with more vitality upgrades performance, counters fatigue, and spurs recovery, as multiple studies document.

• Researchers Mandara Savage and Darren Pipkins found that building in consistent periods for recovery reduced fatigue and "decreased the rate at which productivity declines over working periods." They concluded that as fatigue is lessened by rest time, "repetitive strain injuries will also be reduced."

• In another study, productivity increased 13% when people were given the option to determine their own rest break policies and were able to press the pause button at times when they needed it.

• A Cornell University study devised a computer program to remind certain workers to take a break throughout the day. The result: The people who got the reminders were 13% more productive than those who didn't.

• Breaks during the workday reduced fatigue significantly and also increased positive mood and reduced negative affect.

• Daily short breaks were found to be associated with increased worker engagement as well as quality sleep, an important form of break in itself.

The growth in computer time has led to a more serious look at optimal attention strategies. Productivity app Desk Time used its data to find out how much time its most productive workers spent at a stretch in front of their computer screens. The top performers logged 52 minutes before they took a break. They spent their breaktime usually away from the computer—taking a walk, talking to someone, doing physical exercises. The pause in brain strain refreshed neurons, which allowed them to work more effectively on their return.

Even 52 minutes is too long for the time management program, the Pomodoro Technique. The approach calls for 25 minutes of focused work, enforced with an alarm, followed by five-minute breaks. The rationale is that knowing you only have 25 minutes to move a task forward increases attention and motivation.

As with all breaks, the idea is to get away from mental strain and do something different, from stepping outside to stretching or walking. Removal from the source of demands is key to what happens inside the brain with a break—recovery as your neurons let go of the strain.

The Science of Work Recovery

When you start in on a task, the fresh brain is up for it. Yeah, let's do it! But the longer you spend at it and the more effort that is required, attention starts to fade and with it, the impulse control needed to stay on task.

Scientists call this struggle the effort-recovery model. Sustained effort in the form of demands and pressures creates physiological and psychological strains and reactions that drain resources—concentration, motivation, and especially energy. You get them back through strategies that refuel those resources.

There's a whole science to help you do that, known as work recovery, designed to help you manage energy, self-care, and recharging through restorative activities. The opportunities range from breaks during the workday to lunches that are restful and recuperative, and just as importantly, ways to leave work at work so you can exit stress and tension and unwind at night, on the weekends, and on vacation. The more successful you are at recovery, the better your performance, health, and attitude in the form of positive affect.

Since few of us are ever encouraged to take a break, let alone know how to take an effective one, it's nice to see that researchers are on the case and have discovered what works in the world of what I like to call the strategic pause. You don't have to worry about taking one, because it's only a pause. You will return! Let's review the conclusions of break research:

Principles of the Pause

Give Work a Rest
The first principle of recovery is you need to give the work mind a complete rest. You have to detach psychologically from work to allow the brain to rest briefly. People who use their break time for non-work-related restorative activities—relaxing, social activities, napping—get the benefit, while those who use the time for chores—other tasks and errands—don't.

To relieve brain strain, you want to do low-mental effort activities on your break. Listen to music, read about something you enjoy. Do something physical—shoulder shrugs, stretch your calves, step outside and let your eyes focus on some distant objects to give them a rest from the close-in submarine duty of staring at screens all day.

Do Something You Like
As logic would have it, break activities you enjoy doing bring more recovery. For one, you are more likely to do them. You also get more bang for your break in positive emotions, which elevate mood, calm the mind, and increase openness and patience.

Morning Is Better

Another factor in successful breaks is *when* you do them. Morning breaks are more effective, researchers say, since alertness wanes for most of us as the day wears on. We may need longer breaks in the afternoon as the swoon sets in to overcome inertia in that foggy zone (at least for morning people), as well as break activities you prefer as an incentive when you start to fade.

Lunch: Ditch the Desk

The lunch break is a recovery multiplier. You get, not only the longest time away from demands, but also the crucial nutrition needed to refuel energy and vitality. Skipping lunch or inhaling it at your desk while you work is a huge lost opportunity to reboot. Research shows that working while eating lunch does not aid recovery, while autonomy during the break does, by helping crowd out the negative effects of demands and pressures. Autonomy is also associated with less end-of-workday exhaustion, no doubt since you get an infusion of gratification from satisfying this core need.

If you do recovery activities on your lunchbreak, studies say you will have higher well-being at the end of the workday. Exercising during lunchtime is a great recovery and performance strategy. Swedish researchers found that taking two and a half hours per week for exercise, 30 minutes per day at lunch, increased productivity, even though workers were logging 6.25% fewer hours per week.

Relaxation techniques are also great afternoon recovery strategies. Stress reduction techniques we have discussed in these pages—progressive relaxation, mindfulness, and breathing exercises—have been shown to increase detachment from stressors, build concentration, and reduce fatigue in the afternoon and after work.

Get Outside

Breaks outside the office or home, if that's your office, are the most effective at yanking your mind off task. There's much more visual and sensory stimulation to help shift the mind. Take a walk, muse on the local architecture and trees, look for shapes in the clouds.

Something as simple as a 15-minute walk through a park can produce detachment and recovery by reducing stress and increasing positive affect. In one study walks at lunchtime in a park increased concentration and reduced fatigue. On days when participants in the study did lunchtime park walks, they had better focus and less strain than on days without the walks.

Natural environments attract attention without effort, giving the brain a rest from intense work focus. Pleasant outdoor scenery also is enjoyable, which increases positive emotions and creates a calming effect, which can help lower stress, increasing energy and positive mood.

Recovery Is a Two-Way Street

Turning off the stress replay machine *after* work is as critical for employees—and leaders—as it is *during* work hours. Managers can play a key role in helping employees restore well-being at home. One study found that when employees are encouraged by managers to unwind after work, they are more likely to do just that, leading to a healthier staff and workplace.

"If supervisors adopt norms supporting employees leaving work at work, employees will seek to meet these expectations," the authors, led by Andrew Bennett and Allison Gabriel, wrote.

Supervisors who are supportive of exercise, recreation, and pastimes have a big influence on the employee's ability to shift out of the work mind and get the relaxation, social interaction, or detachment they need for recovery. When managers don't signal that it's okay to step back after work, the study found that employees are more prone to take work home with them and to obsess about work.

Leaders who engage in work recovery themselves and get psychological detachment after work have even more impact on employee recovery. First, they model sustainable work behavior and give the team permission to partake in it, and second, the renewal and stress reduction they get from recovery strategies results in more positive affect and rapport with staff.

It starts with something as basic as asking what a staffer is doing to recharge and refuel. Inquire about hobbies. What do they do for exercise? If you are a manager, tell them what recreational strategies you use. Let them know that performance is the sum total of the vitality, well-being, and quality of life of the whole person. People who go home with negative affect and stress that is not alleviated come back to work with them the next day.

If you would like a leader to think this way, start a conversation about this research. How do you feel about the fact that talking about hobbies and recreation gives more permission for people to recharge? What do you like to do to unwind from work?

Leaving Work At Work

Turning off the work mind when you're not at work is a dream—and struggle—for most of us. In theory, the stress and tension are supposed to stop after work. Then we have a chance to get the unwinding under way. Nobody ever tells your mind, though. The replay button of the day's events winds over and over. It's hard to turn off, especially with work email piling up into the night. But it is doable.

The mission of work recovery is to detach yourself from work and *thoughts* of work after the end of the workday. The idea is that you need psychological distance from the concerns of the job in your free time. It's a reset that flips the switch on stowaway stress and worries.

What we're talking about are strategies to defeat rumination, the circular mental rehash that drives negative emotions, pessimism, and stress. Remember, we keep stress going by not letting go of negative events, which Rover or Fido manage to pull off expertly. We can shut down rumination by managing our thoughts and doing activities that crowd out negative emotions with positive emotions.

First, we can shoot down bogus thoughts by labeling them as the non-real neuron nags they are. When you keep worrying about all the work you have to do after work, tell yourself, "I'm having the thought that I have so much work to do. But it's just a thought. I can do the work tomorrow." If you are replaying a conversation over and over, label it. "I'm having the feeling that I won't be able to do the project, but it's just a feeling, a thought." Look at the thought, not from it. Secondly, we can create nightly and weekend recovery strategies—recreation, relaxation and mastery activities—that allow us to push out the negative self-talk loop with positive emotions.

Recovery takes place when stressors and the thoughts that drive them no longer intrude into your home life. A break from the work state of mind speeds recovery from strain and ends the pattern of negative affect that fuels pessimism and chronic stress.

"When one is not willing or able to psychologically detach from work during off-job time (when one continues to think about job-related problems and issues or even goes on with accomplishing job-related tasks) strain levels remain elevated," reported work recovery leader Sabine Sonnentag and colleagues Carmen Binnewies and Eva Mojza in a study of high job demands. They found that a lack of recovery practices after work predicted emotional exhaustion, a signal trait of burnout, one year later. Beyond that, psychological detachment reduced job strain and psychosomatic complaints.

Those who use recovery strategies come back to work the next morning without the prior day's stash of stress and with something that provides a big head-start on the day, positive affect.

Dutch researcher Jan De Jonge conducted a fascinating study measuring the effect of work detachment on health care personnel at a hospital, primarily nurses. It's highly stressful work, rife with burnout, and it lingers in the mind and arteries long after the workday. De Jonge investigated the impact of detachment on breaks and after work on emotional, cognitive, and physical health—the metrics for burnout. Survey items included: "After work, I put all thoughts of work aside" (cognitive). "After work, I put all emotions from work aside" (emotional). "After work, I shake off the physical exertion from work" (physical).

For breaks at work, participants responded to items such as, "During a work break, I focus my thoughts on other aspects than work" (cognitive), "During a work break, I emotionally distance myself from work" (emotional), and "During a work break, I physically distance myself from work" (physical).

De Jonge found that more emotional detachment contributed to less depressive feelings, less emotional exhaustion, and better sleep. More physical detachment after work predicted fewer physical problems. He writes that detaching after work was even more important than work breaks during the day.

The winning detachment strategy in the study? "Physical detachment after work acted as some sort of panacea for nearly all health outcomes," noted de Jonge.

We can't let exhaustion after the workday prevent us from doing physical exercise or activities that allow us to detach. It's easy to let the mood or obsessive thinking about work call the tune, keeping the rumination and negative affect going. But, as you have learned, you can rally! You can catch yourself and do an override.

When you do, participating in a hobby or exercise actually reduces your fatigue, as it energizes positive emotions, competence, and vitality. Have that argument ready for your brain the next time it tries to squeeze the life out of you.

Permission to Detach

When the workday is done, you have to let your brain know, or it will keep obsessing about the day's work or tomorrow's. To stop the replay, use the work recovery science to get permission to take the nights and weekends off. Their research shows you will cut stress and fatigue, be more positive and productive the next day, and put your life on the agenda.

So, the good news is: You have permission to detach from work thoughts every night and weekend. The best place to start after your stop-time alarm has gone off, marking the end of the workday, is to tell yourself:

I HAVE PERMISSION TO LIVE!

Use the statements from the de Jonge study above to inform your brain that you have switched over to the life side. Tell yourself out loud:

- "After work, I put all thoughts of work aside" (cognitive)
- "After work, I put all emotions from work aside" (emotional)
- "After work, I shake off physical exertion from work" (physical)

Then choose an activity that will help you put all the work thoughts aside, with an emphasis on something physical, since, as de Jonge showed, it's the most effective detachment strategy.

Four Routes To Recovery

The best recovery activities are those that are engaging. What is not effective at providing psychological detachment is watching too much

TV. The average state of a TV viewer is a mild depression, according to Mihaly Csikszentmihalyi, author of *Optimal Experience*. It makes you a spectator, not a participant, which is what the brain wants. Try new hobbies and mastery experiences that energize, empower and buffer job stress.

There are four main routes to recovery after work: psychological detachment, relaxation, mastery, and control. Studies show that these recovery processes can reduce fatigue, increase work engagement and improve health and well-being. One of the engines of these benefits is the affective change that relaxation and recreation sets in motion, populating the mind with positive emotions that push out the negative hangover of the day's strain. When your affect, i.e., mood, shifts upward, your energy, vitality, and spirit are buoyed.

1. Psychological detachment

This is a fancy phrase for something pretty logical. It's about finding ways to stop thinking and obsessing about work and the worries that flow from that behavior. I would also add talking about work. Try to do a lot less talking about your workday to family and friends. They will be more than happy to support you in this.

Continuing to think about work keeps you mentally at work, so find ways to change the subject. Another option is to create physical and electronic rituals to prevent the default to a desk or work email and help separate work and home. Imagine yourself flipping a light switch off as you leave work. You've switched over to what you work for, your life.

2. Relaxation

There is a false belief that you need to be near collapse before you are entitled to relax. Taking care of yourself needs no justification. Relaxation is built into the human physiology, which is why it's essential to recover and restore the body and the brain's equilibrium to pre-stressor levels.

When you are finished with work, create a transition zone of 30 minutes or more to do what you like to do to relax—listen to music, hit the gym, draw. Make it a routine.

3. Mastery

Mastery experiences are the most effective at promoting recovery and knocking out stress. These are activities done outside of work that allow for personal growth, skill-building, and learning. Mastery experiences help us gratify core needs and get us aligned with who we are.

Whether it's salsa dancing, racquetball, or learning a musical instrument or language, studies show that the mastery process can shut off stress activation even in the middle of work, such as at lunchtime, or at home. Identify things you want to learn, potential passions, and you get an infusion of the confident, positive vibe that comes from learning and skill-building.

4. Control

As you now know, the more control, or latitude, you feel you have over a stressor, the less perceived stress. There are two sides of the control issue: control at work—having the ability to make some decisions about work tasks that let you feel more choice—and leisure control, deciding how to spend your off-hours. Find ways during the day to experience more choice over how you do your work or get a dose of autonomy on a break.

Increased leisure control reduces strain by helping you feel more in charge of your life and able to put aside a bad day with something that restores capability and choice. The idea here is to identify what you, not others, like to do for fun and recreation and schedule it so you indulge in it regularly. Most of what we do outside of work is ad hoc, minus thought or planning. Put leisure ideas and activities on the calendar, and they can start happening.

What's Your Recovery Strategy?

If you don't have strategies to leave the workday behind, it lives on through rumination, and the fatigue builds. How can you step back, readjust the pressure, and restore your energy for the day's second act?

Identify activities you can do after work in each of these recovery categories:

- **Relaxation strategies**. Ideas: yoga, listening to music, reading.
- **Recreation strategies**. Ideas: walking, biking, badminton, Pilates, the gym.

- **Mastery strategies.** Ideas: aikido, bowling, tennis, playing a musical instrument.

Your Phone or Your Life

It stands to reason that it's harder to recover from the workday, if the workday keeps going after work, say, in the form of ongoing contact via your smartphone. The research shows that if you are still checking work messages, texting, and calling about business matters at home, you haven't interrupted the source of the strain and pressure.

The more of your evening you spend after work still doing job-related things, the lower your well-being by bedtime, Sabine Sonnentag, organizational psychology professor at the University of Mannheim, documented in one study. The reason is simple: You don't get the separation from stress or unwinding that relieve the day's tension.

Unbounded smartphones are an obstacle to your health and balance. If your phone is on, it makes every work message and text seem urgent and your constant vigilance seem implicitly necessary. Not having boundaries on work phone use at home doesn't just suck up time you could spend living your life, but it also keeps you in the addictive grasp of chasing constant stimuli. You're too wound up to read a book or shoot some baskets. Having a conversation with a family member or neighbor or putting on some music is too low-key. What's that compared to the excitement of a ping, ding or video on the screen?

That's how it went in a study that measured the recovery talents, or not, of smartphone users. Measured against a control group without phones, those with them had difficulty detaching. They didn't engage in leisure, relaxation, or mastery activities that could separate their brains from work and stimuli and allow them to recoup.

This underscores how unmanaged smartphones in the evenings can dominate and squeeze out everything else. We need to disconnect nightly if we're going to put recovery activities, fun, relaxation, and work-health balance on the agenda. After the workday, when can you put your device on silent, stick it in a drawer, and not check messages for the rest of the night?

There's No Success Like Recess

You may have forgotten, but there was a time when you were an ardent practitioner of the Refueling Principle—at grade school recess. It was one of the most important lessons you could learn, but you were led to believe it was only for kids. In fact, dodgeball and kickball were also part of the life curriculum, pointing the way to habits, from daily physical activity to friendship, persistence, and fun that are key to lifelong well-being and sanity.

The science shows that engaged leisure activities are the route to successful work-life balance. As the word "recreation" suggests, stepping back is a process of *re-creation* and renewal, since active leisure is a master at flushing stress out of your system and revitalizing energy. Here's what researchers say you get from stepping back to recharge.

• Recreation serves as a buffer against stress, making you more resilient. (Dennis Coleman, Seppo Iso-Ahola)

• Respites restore energy, focus, and after you've had one it takes less effort to do the job. (Dov Eden)

• Respites of two weeks help recovery from burnout. (Stevan Hobfoll)

• Active leisure boosts positive mood through self-control and social support. (David Chalip, Judith Thomas)

The Big Break: Vacations

I'd like to spend a few moments on the last, but definitely not least, of our refueling opportunities: the vacation. Though it gets very little respect, vacations are a gigantic refueling opportunity for health and performance, not to mention a crucial life activator. The annual holiday is your best chance all year to fully live your life free of duty and obligation.

Yet more than a few people skip vacations, don't use all their time off, or check work email every day of the vacay, which defeats the whole purpose of a vacation—getting complete separation from the job and interrupting the source of stress.

We are not very good vacationers for a number of reasons. First, we have the shortest annual paid vacations in the industrialized world, one or two weeks compared to four to six weeks for Western Europe and Australia. We don't have the practice that the Swiss or Germans have of enjoying ourselves on long holidays. Secondly, we are led to feel guilty about relaxing and leaving work behind. This is nonsense. What are we working for? Just to work? No, the point is in the living. Finally, some fear they will be seen as not committed enough by the organization if they take a holiday. The reality is people who don't take vacations get laid off like everyone else. I've spoken to them.

A Glassdoor survey found that half of American workers give back unused vacation time every year. Expedia's annual vacation deprivation survey reports the grim stat that Americans give back some 400 million vacation days each year. I would like to kindly plead: Please don't do this!

An Australian or German worker, manager, or CEO would find it incomprehensible to give back a single hour of their allotment of a month-plus of time off. *Wait a minute! You are actually going to voluntarily abbreviate your holiday?* No, that would be certifiable.

Not taking all your vacation time is foregoing priceless items such as life experiences, which studies show make us happier than material things. They are the living we are making for ourselves, the proof of real work-life balance, and a reminder of what's out there for us if we are.

The time you shave from your vacay or holiday that's skipped completely is never coming back again. That's not going to sit well when you look back over your life. We regret more the things we don't do than what we do. Researchers call it "the inaction effect." I think we can agree it's best to stay off the inaction list.

Holiday Insurance

One way to make sure your vacation never gets missed is to plan it early. Figure out where you want to go and start making plans at the beginning of the year. This gives you a chance to find the best time in the schedule to take time off, take advantage of advance-purchase deals, and lock the dates in for the company and yourself so they are figured into the operations and workflow for the year.

Start now. Where are you going on your next vacation?

If you have an idea ready to go, start researching it. Otherwise, make a list of three candidates, and then start whittling them down to your favorite choice.

The Healing Power of Time Off

Not taking all your time off is a lose-lose for you and the company. This is because vacations provide the biggest recuperative punch in the respite arsenal. You return to the job after a vacation refreshed in body and mind.

The concept of the vacation was actually invented by companies back in the 1920s and 1930s as a productivity tool. Fatigue studies then showed that when workers returned rejuvenated from their holiday, output increased. The same is true today. In one study by Mark Rosekind for Alertness Solutions, reaction times increased 40% after a vacation.

Some very important things happen on a vacation that boost energy and attention. The University of Tel Aviv's Dov Eden, an expert on how time off affects performance, has documented that vacations ease "the effect of stress on well-being by punctuating the otherwise constant aggravation caused by incessant job demands."

With the danger signal turned off, the stress response stops, and the body's renewal system can get to work on restorative and maintenance functions. Energy-drained cells get new sustenance.

Vacations can repair burnout by "regathering" crashed emotional resources, such as a sense of mastery or social support. But it takes two weeks of vacation for this recuperative process from burnout to occur, so you need to take all your time off and not scrimp.

The healing power of the vacation is remarkable. Vacations can substantially cut the risk of heart attack. Research shows that men who didn't take a vacation for a few years were 30% more likely to have a heart attack than those who took one every year. Women who didn't take a vacation for six years or longer were eight times more likely to have heart disease than women who took more than one vacation a year. There's no health food that can give you those benefits.

Charlotte Fritz and Sabine Sonnentag found that "health complaints and exhaustion significantly decreased during vacation" and that performance increased when employees got back to the job. Employees reported less effort needed to do their work. Vacations are at the top of the list for wellness and engagement dividends.

The medication that performs these amazing feats is distance—separation from the source of stress. With the flow of stressful events and *can't-cope* stories in the ancient brain shut off, the body can do what it is designed to—repair you.

There are a lot more benefits from time off done right. Vacations may be the best place to satisfy the core needs your mind and spirit have, such as autonomy, competence, and connection with others, which we're going to learn a lot more about in the next chapter. The holiday gives you the biggest chunk of autonomy you will have all year. Because you need to organize your trip and get from one place to another, the act of doing this is going to gratify your competence need in a big way. You'll feel like you just bench-pressed 300 pounds and can take on anything. That is valuing your life and living the worth ethic.

The shared experience of vacations also brings families and friends closer together and introduces you to a host of new folks you actually have the time of day for. You can get to know people you meet while traveling better in a few hours than people you've known for years at home. It's called "the stranger on the train effect," a face-value experience without fear of revelations coming back to haunt you. It's a powerful experience that restores your faith in humanity. The first birthday greeting I get every year is from a German couple I met in Belize years ago.

To get all these great benefits, you need time to really be somewhere else for a while, so you need to use all your vacation days. It also takes time if you want to travel to another hemisphere and see an exotic realm like the Cook Islands, way out there between Tonga and Tahiti. I visited these far-flung isles on a vacation. I found myself on Aitutaki, a series of 15 islets ringing a sunken volcano over which a lagoon has formed. The swimming-pool colored lagoon was jammed with colorful fish, a snorkeler's dream, and absolutely devoid of something that usually interrupts dreams: stress. Time urgency is an unfathomable concept here. There's a grand total of about 1700 people scattered around the islets.

You don't need a lot of money to go there. The Cook Islands are a former territory of New Zealand, a land of budget travelers. If you want to see what Hawaii might have been like 50 years ago, an Air New Zealand flight gets you there nonstop from Los Angeles to Rarotonga, the capital of the Cook Isles. *Kia orana*, or hello, turquoise waters, as they say in the Cooks. *Aere ra*, or goodbye, stress!

Resist the E-Killjoy

A Trip Advisor survey of 16,000 people in 10 countries found that 77% of Americans work on their vacations, while 40% of Europeans do. I hate to point out the obvious, but maybe it's not so obvious anymore: Vacations are supposed to be a respite from work, where you don't do what you do the other 50 or 51 weeks a year.

You have to actually be on your vacation mentally to experience your trip, and that's hard to do when you check work messages on your phone on holiday. Being absorbed in the moment is a hallmark of all optimal experience. Whether it's cycling a country road or drinking in the awe of a spectacular vista, paying attention isn't scary. It's relaxing, and that's the point of the vacay, isn't it? Your mind is relieved of overstimulation to behold the wonder of where you are.

How much will you remember about your vacation experience if you are staring at a screen the whole time? What unknown activities will you miss out on? What ideas won't pop into your head because it's being monopolized by a screen? What fascinating fellow travelers will you never meet because you are locked up with your headphones and the "leave me alone" sign?

It's time to put the devices down and let the vacation unwind a year's worth of tension. Let it unspool at its own pace and lead you to where you've never been and to things you've never done. That's where the adventures are.

How to Curb Your Checking Enthusiasm

To prevent work from intruding on holidays, arrangements on the front end make all the difference. Here's a checklist on how to set up your trip for the most stress-free enjoyment.

1. Sometimes it's not your choice to check in on vacation. Negotiate for an emergency-only arrangement for office contact, and the emergency would take place in the form of a phone call, so you don't have to check work mail on your vacay.
2. Find a colleague who your messages can be routed to while you are gone.
3. If you can, get an agreement that you don't have to check mail on vacation and permission to put up an autoresponder message that says you are out and not checking mail on your holiday— and that messages won't be read until you get back. Most people are too time-urgent to send mail they won't get a response to swiftly.
4. Do not bring your work phone with you.
5. If you are an entrepreneur, and there is no one to pick up the slack when you're on holiday, give clients an early heads-up to your vacation dates. Inform everyone several months out that you will be gone on these dates. Leave a vacation message on your autoresponder. The vast majority of clients will respect that you need time away just like everyone else. If you need to check work email, set a restriction, say, once or twice a day, and don't vary from it.

Vacation Salvation: Daimler's Brilliant Idea

German automaker Daimler, home of Mercedes-Benz, may have solved the vacation email problem. They rolled out a system that allows employees to relax without email concerns on their holidays.

Employees can set their email to auto-delete before they go on vacation. The software tells the sender the email will be deleted and not saved. The person is advised to contact someone else at the company, instead. This way employees come back to an empty in-box and have no concern about checking email on vacation.

Now that is an elegant solution, insuring continuity at the office while you're gone and enforcing cold turkey on holiday email. May it spread far and wide and put an end to the theoretical vacation.

The Fun Fuel

Signaling a sharp turn from the traditional grindstone approach to performance, companies from Google to Facebook and Uber want their employees to take breaks by playing at work. Game rooms, Foosball stations, pool tables, video game areas, and gyms have become the new model for productivity and engagement.

It turns out that one of the most powerful forces in innovation and recharging neurons is what we were once experts at: play. Playfulness at work was found by a study in Taiwan, not a place known for excess levity, to increase productivity and innovation.

The act of play is an automatic release from the straining work mind and time-urgent to-do chase. It roots your mind completely in the moment of fun, which neatly extracts you from the other tenses and their concerns. When you play, you sideline negative mood, and positive emotions take over. It broadens your attention and scope, opens up new ways of seeing things, and makes you feel good.

Play is expert at producing *aha!* moments. Most of the time the part of the brain that is associated with creative thought is drowned out by the more rational part. But when you are physically in motion, the rational part of the brain has to stay preoccupied with controlling movement, leaving the squelched creative part free to wander into the theta state, where ideas are born.

Something as simple as walking is a great tool for creativity. If I'm stuck, I'm almost always unstuck within 12 blocks of letting my mind roam as I stroll. This is also why we get ideas while driving or in the shower. With the drill sergeant of the logical brain handling vigorous soaping detail, the mind is free to wander to creative realms. Try longer vigorous soaping to reach that idea you're looking for.

The spontaneity and improvisation of play helps wake up neurons that are not usually part of the workday or forced ideation process. The way we come up with ideas is very inefficient. One thought association leads to another thought association, which leads to another. Play can skip that circuitous route and go directly to an idea that surfaces without calculation. As sociologist Alfred Kroeber once put it, "Play is responsible for all the discoveries of pure science and fine art."

You can put this elixir to work for you by taking breaks that allow you to play. The positive affect that comes from this is a mood—and performance—changer.

Angst Prevention

It's clear that breaks, recharging, and psychological detachment from work through relaxation, recreation, and play are far from things to feel guilty about. In fact, what should cause guilt is acting as if our body and mind are not subject to the laws of physics. Talk to your brain about that. Make sure it understands that whenever a pang of angst pops up when you step back, you will repeat this phrase: Not guilty as charged.

CHAPTER 11

Life's Out There, If You Are

Activate Life Skills

If there was an Olympic medal for procrastination, more than a few of us would be in the running for it. Humans have a talent for putting off just about anything—even good things. *I'll get together with Trevor next week. I'll do that weekend outing next month. My feet have an appointment with the ottoman.*

When it comes to your life, though, it's helpful to consider that there is no later, no set of moments that will come out exactly like the ones you missed and no guarantee that you will ever get to it later. The more you pass on the opportunities of life, it can become a habit hard to shake.

This is largely because the brain has an insidious default known as the law of least effort. It's one of our lesser-known drives. Call it convenience or conservation of resources, if you're generous, laziness if you're not. It's a reflex to whatever is the easiest. A bird in the hand is worth two in the bush.

It's hard to leave the comfort zone because of our wiring for safety, security, and the familiar—back again to our old, not-so-good friend, the survival equipment. The problem is that bursting out of the known and engaging with the world is exactly what the same brain that makes you want to veg wants to do. Yes, it's confusing, but the higher brain doesn't want comfort. It wants you to go beyond what you know, beyond instant gratification. It's an impulse usually squelched by the least-effort reflex, but its urgings are crucial, since they determine your self-worth, growth, sense of forward progress, and happiness.

In his book, *Satisfaction: The Science of Finding True Fulfillment*, neuroscientist Gregory Berns chronicled his journey through fMRI scans to find out what makes people satisfied. He found two drives key to a fulfilling life, both having to do with exiting the security zone: novelty and challenge. How much do we crave the new? The brain's feel-good neurotransmitter dopamine is released at the mere anticipation of something new. It's part of your incentive system to learn and grow, and the agent of exploration.

You are born to discover, take on problems and puzzles and engage with your world. Too much spectating leads to an idle, frustrated brain, and boredom, which is a bigger problem than having nothing to do. In chronic doses it's a sense of life lacking value or meaning. Researchers have found that it can lead to everything from binge eating to substance abuse, reckless driving, violence, and depression.

In 11 studies conducted for one investigation, subjects were left alone in a room with their thoughts for 6 to 15 minutes—no phones, Facebook, TV. The scientists conducting the experiment, from the University of Virginia and Harvard, wanted to highlight the pleasures of being able to think away from all the noise of life. It didn't work out that way. Being alone with thoughts was not a fun experience. So much so, that 67% of the men and 25% of the women "chose to give themselves a mild electric shock rather than be deprived of external sensory stimuli." Boredom is literally painful.

Engagement is the boredom solution. It's a big factor in fulfillment and as such is a hidden source of meaning. You feel the contentment of satisfaction after you have engaged with a challenge, not after doing something easy. Berns says that "when you are satisfied, you have found meaning." That's something billions of folks would have liked to have known over the millennia. It turns out that pushing past the default of least effort is pretty meaningful stuff.

Of all the things on the planet, humans are happiest when involved in engaging leisure activities, studies show. The buzz even extends to leisure products, Thomas Deleire of the University of Wisconsin discovered. He investigated which consumption categories (products we buy) had any effect on personal happiness. There was only one: leisure, from vacations to gear for sporting activities.

"When people engage in leisure activity, they have lower stress levels, better moods, lower heart rates and more psychological engagement — that means less boredom, which can help avoid unhealthy behaviors," U.C. Merced's Matthew Zawadzki told the school's publication, *Panora-*

ma. Zawadzki's research has shown that absorbing leisure activities lower blood pressure for participants.

There's another reason why leisure experiences are so powerful. They do what the higher brain wants. They gratify core psychological needs that make you feel you are choosing the content of your life, demonstrating competence, and connecting with others. This is not where you have been taught to go for happiness. As a result, it takes a different skillset to get there: life skills.

Yes, there is such a thing. They are an opposite toolkit that adults have a hard time fathoming. Instead of the career mode of results and rewards, life skills are about being in the experience for its own sake, for the inherent interest or fun and not for any external payoff. The skills come from a different motivational wiring altogether. Welcome to Motivation 2.0, the most potent drive on Earth and the gateway to optimal living.

The 3 Core Needs

You and I are lucky to be alive at a time when one of the biggest mysteries of life has been solved—what it is we need to be happy. For most of human history, the answer to that question has been a puzzle that peers, advertisers, and social influencers have happily claimed to solve, only for us to find out they didn't have a clue. Fortunately, some very sharp minds have deciphered the correct approach.

In the 1980s two researchers at the University of Rochester, Edward Deci and Richard Ryan, developed a framework for need gratification known as self-determination theory (SDT). They found that at the root of human aspiration we have a need to feel like we are determining the content of life. The way we do that is by satisfying three core psychological needs: **autonomy, competence, and relatedness** (the need for close social connection). Their work has since been vetted by scientists around the world and found to be applicable in cultures as different from the U.S. as that in India.

You need to feel autonomous, that you can freely choose things and are not always forced and controlled. **You also have a mandate to feel effective**, competent to take on things that are difficult and accomplish them. **And you need to have close relations with others**—we are the social animal.

The catch is you can only satisfy these needs with the right goal—intrinsic motivation, the reverse of what we are all raised on: extrinsic, or external, motivation. With intrinsic motivation, you seek no payoff, only the inherent interest in the activity itself—through inner goals such as excellence, learning, fun, service, growth. You do it just to do it, with no need for instrumental gain. Act for no payoff, though, and you get one, a whopping internal reward in the form of the lasting version of happiness, gratification.

Deci, author of *Why We Do What We Do*, a great summary of SDT, showed in one experiment how external rewards can sabotage us. Subjects were asked to solve a puzzle with an exercise for which some got paid while others didn't. The ones who received no money kept playing with the puzzle after the teacher left the room at a strategic moment, while the financially motivated had no interest playing unless they got paid for it.

"Stop the pay, stop the play," Deci summed it up later. His work and that of many others have documented that external rewards warp motivation, making the desire to do a task or an activity dependent on the payoff. If there's no external payoff, why do it? With only the finish line in mind, you also can't enjoy the experience of the moment, which is particularly self-defeating when it comes to activities beyond work. As mindfulness leader Jon Kabat-Zinn likes to put it, "We only have moments to live."

We don't know how many moments we have left, but we do know one thing: We can only live in the current moment and no other. Acting for an intrinsic goal guarantees we do that.

The three core needs tell us we can't expect other people, things, and status to make us happy. Nobody and nothing else can satisfy those needs but you since they are all an internal affair. How can anyone else satisfy your own self-determination needs? It's up to you. The brain's mandate is for you to make life better through your own choices.

The element of choice is how you express the crucial need of autonomy. You, me, and everyone on this blue orb have a need to feel as if we are putting our stamp on things. The arena that gives you the best chance of doing that, since most of us work for others, is the world beyond work. You follow curiosities, create interests, and self-direct vacations, outings, and social activities. The more effective you are at developing autonomy off the clock, the more your identity is resilient to difficulties on the work side and setbacks in life.

Competence, the second core need, is essential to self-worth. Learning a new skill is one of the best ways to gratify competence. When you find out how to make pottery, speak another language, or you take on a tough project at work and handle it, you gratify the mastery need to learn and grow. That unleashes the neurotransmitter dopamine, the signature of satisfaction in your brain, which makes you want to learn and feel that reward again.

The third core need, relatedness, is a well-documented route to increased positive mood, better health, and a longer life. Having close relationships makes you happier. A happy friend living within a mile of your house can increase your happiness 25%. That increases to 34% when you have happy next-door neighbors. A major factor in determining a person's happiness is friendship, but 70% of people don't actively seek out new friends. What is the first thing that gets cut from our lives when we're busy? The data says friends.

The key to a meaningful and fulfilling life is acting from intrinsic goals that reflect your inner compass, which, buried under all the what's-easiest reflexes, insists that you have the life you actually want. That makes sense and more than that, it makes for no doubt that your life wasn't mailed in.

Answer These Questions Before It's Too Late

Pioneering psychologist Erik Erikson studied the stages of life and their various impacts on personality. He identified eight psychosocial stages marking our passage through the years. He did a lot of work with seniors, who kept returning in their conversations with him to three themes in the sunset of their lives. Looking over their lives, they had three main questions you will have someday too.

1. **Did I get what I came here for?**
2. **Did I do what I wanted?**
3. **Was it a good time?**

What these questions are trying to tell us is that our higher brain wants to see evidence of a worth ethic, not just the work ethic. Have you lived in a way that was worthwhile? Did what you experience have value? Did you truly live?

It's stunning how closely these questions echo the work of Deci and Ryan's core-needs framework. The autonomy need screams from all three questions. Self-determination is essential to feeling that what you've done on this planet reflects a path you created. You did what you wanted, got what you came here for. And the place where you get most of that—and the good time—is from maximizing opportunities to engage with your life outside the office.

What are your answers to these questions now? Think about what you can do to have the answers you want in your later years. Act now, as they say in the infomercial business, before it's too late.

Write down what you will do to increase the likelihood that your answer will be Yes for each of these three questions.

Motivation 2.0

Until a few decades ago the consensus was that there was just one motivational dynamic: carrot and stick. We acted only for rewards and to avoid punishment. The work of Abraham Maslow and Mihaly Csikszent-mihalyi, author of *Optimal Experience* and *Flow*, showed that there was another critical goal structure—intrinsic, or internal, motivation. It's the reason why an artist spends a year crafting a sculpture that won't make him or her a penny. It's done for the internal payoff—the satisfaction and creative expression of making it.

Deci, Ryan, and others discovered that intrinsic motivation was the most potent motivation of all, because it aligns us with internal aspirations. Intrinsic goals are stronger than external approval goals since they are yours. They are about what you think, not someone else.

For instance, an intrinsic goal is what you need to overcome any difficult challenge. It drives persistence, because it's not dependent on a reward, a finish line ASAP. It's about the process, the journey. Goals such as challenge, learning and growth keep you in the middle of the action, instead of focused on the payoff. It's about acting unconditionally, something sages and creeds have encouraged for centuries.

People who go on a diet because they are being pressured by others to lose weight quit. If they diet because it's their decision, they persevere and meet their goal. Students who learn to play a musical instrument because they want to learn it and aren't doing it to pacify parents stick with it.

Intrinsic goals are key to opening up personal life, and they help you on the job too. In both places they put the emphasis on absorption in the moment. You're not trying to get somewhere else or impress anyone. People who are intrinsically motivated are continuously interested in the work they are doing, studies show.

The intrinsic approach is, of course, not second nature. We are raised on its opposite—external goals, which are based on the approval of others. You are no doubt quite familiar with the external crew below:

External Goals
Money
Success
Performance
Beauty
Status
Appearance
Fame

Though external goals seem like the way to go, they actually can make it much more difficult to be happy, if they are the only metric of your self-worth. This is because these goals are ephemeral. You get a quick bump of happiness that fades quickly, thanks to something called habituation. We are designed to get tired of things, which is a prod from the brain to learn and grow. You get used to the new status, it becomes normal, and you want more. This results in what is called a hedonic treadmill. On it, you can never catch up to your external wants. You achieve one external goal, get used to it, then need another one, and on and on.

The thrill of a job promotion is gone in two weeks. Then you need another notch to fill yourself up. Lottery winners go back to how they felt before they won the money six months later. I'm guessing, though, that you might be willing to take that risk.

Yes, money matters. No one wants to be poor. But after a certain amount of income, additional money does not equate to any more happiness. An analysis of a World Gallup Poll of 1.7 million people by University of Virginia and Purdue researchers concluded that the ideal income for individuals is $95,000 a year for life satisfaction and $60,000 to

$70,000 for emotional well-being.

External goals are fragile, not just because of habituation, but also because they are based on what other people think. The opinions of others are subject to change at any notice. They are the wrong yardstick for what produces gratification inside, so you don't really buy them. Intrinsic goals, though, are self-validating. They connect with what *you* aspire to.

Intrinsic goals aren't completely alien. It's just that we never hear about them as powerful goals in and of themselves. They're not as sexy as money and status. These mild-mannered drives aren't famous, because they don't lead to payoffs that can be seen in the outside world. The magic they work on the inside is enough, and you are too when you let them lead the way.

Learning and challenge are great intrinsic goals for life and work. You are motivated to increase your skill and grow as a person, which go to the internal bottom line. Service is another intrinsic goal to strive for in life and on the job. Helping others makes you and the people you help feel better.

The ultimate intrinsic goal is fun and the act that unleashes it, play. It's done for pure pleasure, for the participation. There are no judgments or outcomes needed. If you want to do anything with an intrinsic goal, all you have to do is find a way to make it fun—even work.

Which intrinsic goals could you use to increase the value of everything you do and motivate you to engage with the world? Choose from the lists below for life and work. Keep these goals in mind before you participate in a life opportunity or a task at work. Knowing why you are doing what you are doing helps maintain your motivation and commitment to the goal and ramps up focus on it.

Intrinsic Goals for Life	**Intrinsic Goals for Work**
Fun	Excellence
Enjoyment	Craft
Personal growth	Service
Social connection	Learning
Learning	Challenge
Challenge	Innovation
Creative expression	Social connection
Service	
Community	

Experiences Make You Happier

Fifty percent of your potential happiness is genetic, say researchers. Sorry about that. You can't do much about that. Another 10 percent comes from your circumstances (geography, family, health). Sorry again. Yet there is a chunk of what's left that doesn't have an exact percentage attached to it that you can do something about. It falls into a realm known as "intentional activities."

Unlike circumstances, which are things that tend to happen to you, you make intentional activities happen, and that makes all the difference. Intentional activities can be anything from getting together with a friend to playing soccer, helping others, going to the mountains, doing an activity on the weekend, a letter of gratitude to a friend, to positive statements you say to yourself. They are self-generated interactions with your experience.

Researchers Kennon Sheldon and Sonja Lyubomirsky say that "activity-based, well-being change" creates improved well-being. "When people change their intentional behavior—that is, doing something new that takes effort—they have a better chance of boosting their well-being and maintaining that boost than when they merely change a factual circumstance (such as moving into a new apartment, buying a car, or asking for and receiving a raise)."

An analysis of 51 studies found that people who engaged in intentional activities improved their happiness. Lyubomirsky calls the dynamic that drives the increase in satisfaction from intentional activities the Positive-Activity Model. Here's how it works:

Performance of Positive Activity leads to:
- Positive emotions
- Positive thoughts
- Positive behaviors
- Need Satisfaction
- Which all lead to Increased Well-Being

Your potential happiness, then, depends on the proactive choices you make to engage with your world in activities you choose to do. Engaged, positive leisure activities gratify the three core needs like nothing else.

The upshot is that it's not riches but living richly that makes you happy.

The key to improving happiness and sustaining the gains is "creating and maintaining a steady inflow of positive experiences, experiences that interest, inspire, connect, and uplift," report Sheldon and Lyubomirsky. The lives of people who do this "are full of deeply satisfying moments, which provide them with near-daily rewards. Importantly, such lives require a considerable investment of effort...Joyful lives involve more than mere contentment or peacefulness, requiring people to 'live large' in some way. The sum total of having many positive experiences, small and large, exerts bottom-up effects on the person's chronic well-being level, as measured and sustained over time."

This is no doubt why experiences make us happier than items you can buy at a store. Whether it's a vacation, playing chess, taking a dance class, or walking a park trail, experiences contact a deeply personal realm that makes you feel in sync with a life you have a role in creating.

Most of us spend our days caught up inside our heads, locked in perpetual analysis and imagined future threats. Direct experience gets you out of the thought factory and into the life-participant column, which fires up positive emotions from your own actions, not what someone else approves of or not. And the irony is that when you engage in experiences for your own well-being, other people like you better, research shows. They see you as a more compelling person when you have interesting experiences.

Scientists such as Leaf van Boven of the University of Colorado Boulder who have been plumbing the experiential world have found that experiences are a goldmine of satisfaction because of their uniquely personalized nature. Experiences can't be compared to anyone else's experience, so they don't lose their value through social comparison like objects do. They are your personal event. Each is singular, so you don't get sick of them through habituation. Experiences also embody the self-determination mandate, as they are directed at your command.

The interactive nature of experiences sets off multiple brain neuron firings. The neurons that fire together wire together, so they form memories that stick with you and provide a long run of positive emotions, available at any recall. And finally, experiences are fulfilling because they tend to be done with others, satisfying your core need for social connection.

When you are in an activity in which your skills meet a challenge, you have the chance to tap in to a higher realm known as optimal experience, or flow, a state of absorption so complete that your thoughts and deeds are one. This is a place you can visit on a regular basis by matching your wits and abilities with an equal or just a little bit lower level of challenge—whether it's coding a big digital project, playing a new song on the piano, or volleyball.

If the test is too great, your skill level won't be up to it, and you'll quit or fail. It's a delicate balance. If the activity is too easy, you're bored. This is the dance of life for all of us, avoiding boredom and ennui on one side and pushing aside the fear and safety reflex to seek out manageable engagement on the other.

In the flow experience you lose self-consciousness, sense of time, the wandering mind and all intrusions from the outside and inside that are usually barraging your brain. You are riding the moment like a surfer on a wave. I've experienced it in various forms through the years, from running, to surfing, backcountry hiking, travel, and salsa and samba dancing—when I get into a synchronous rhythm between my body, mind, and environment. It's an immersion into the whole around me. On the samba and salsa front, it's like I am inside the music and the rhythm itself.

Flow experiences are the times when people report they are at their happiest and life is at its most satisfying. Research subjects who have been through a flow experience have described it in these terms:

- I am so involved in what I am doing, I don't see myself as separate from what I'm doing.
- My mind isn't wandering.
- During the activity, there were times when things were going so well, I felt as if I could do almost anything.
- I forgot my worries during the activity I was involved in.

I always feel flow when I travel, particularly on foreign trips, as I negotiate unknown realms, local transportation, a potpourri of interesting fellow travelers and locals, and detour off track to a place I didn't intend to go to that turns out to be a highlight. The movement of travel leads to a literal feeling of flow, of moving through an experience I created, solving challenges on the fly. It provides a sense of mastery that comes from pulling off all the various pieces of the trip, while at the same time surrendering to what happens along the way.

I'm making it happen, but at the same time the world is moving me along on a scenic ride. I feel that power of discovery in motion even on some business trips, such as journeys I've taken to rural Michigan; the backroads of woodsy Maine; Mumbai, India during the monsoon; or a super-scenic journey with lots of connections and stops, including a car ferry, that took me to the end of the North American continent on the Cabot Trail of Cape Breton Island, Nova Scotia for the United Association Canada trade union. Travel makes you feel you can direct your path and that your journey in life has forward movement.

Go Where You've Never Been Before

You can get an instant dose of core-need gratification as well as novelty and challenge that brain scientist Gregory Berns says are crucial for fulfillment anytime you head out your front door to somewhere new. Make a point of visiting places in your city or area you haven't been to before. The stream of new visual and sensory data will give your brain neurons the novelty they crave and you the opportunity to navigate the unknown, which feeds your mastery need.

Try to discover one or two new places per month. Where could you go that's new for you? A nearby small town? A trail you have never walked? A neighborhood you have overlooked? A place off the beaten path from all your usual trips? A garden or maybe a roadside fruit stand with straight-from-the-harvest treats? Research online, talk to friends for tips, and consult local guidebooks for leads.

Expand from there to weekend trips that can give you more lasting immersion. Where would you like to go? What would you like to experience? A music festival? A park campground? A fish market at a port? Horseback riding? A wine-tasting? A historical site? A museum you've never seen? A city you've been meaning to go to for years? A sporting event? Travel is the brain's tonic for keeping life new.

The Work of Sustainable Happiness

The hidden caveat about happiness is that it takes work. Intentional activities, positive emotions, and happiness all require effort in the form of initiative, motivation, and willpower. They don't happen without putting in the time, energy, and persistence. Are you going to let that stand between you and your fulfillment on this planet? The higher brain hopes not.

To get to the good stuff, you need to make time to do the activities, learn how to do them, and then keep at them. Sheldon and Lyubomirsky say the two biggest keys to sustainable happiness are initiating intentional activities and then sustaining them.

It takes discipline and motivation to do an hour of yoga, go for a hike, take an online history course, or try anything new. No one is there to make you do it. It's hard in the beginning. There are so many other easier things to do. The temptation to not budge from the couch is enticing, but you must unglue yourself from the furniture, because participation is your prime directive.

You have the discipline and motivation for this assignment. Just look at what you do at work. Each day you muster the self-discipline needed to get your work done. You just need to break out the self-regulation and willpower for your life too. That's worth it, isn't it? An intrinsic goal will help. You act to learn, grow, get healthy, have fun, be social, or just show up—and to not have regrets in your later years.

Intentional activities that have been shown to increase well-being and mood range from reflective exercises to activities and hobbies that require physical effort. Thinking about things you should be grateful for, mindfulness, acts of kindness and notes of appreciation to others all have boosted well-being in the research, as have a regular exercise program, rafting, hiking the Appalachian Trail, and cycling.

Intentional Activities Checklist

1. Make sure the activity fits with your interests and personality, that it's concordant, as Sheldon puts it, with your values

and goals.
2. Extroverts may prefer more social activities with others.
3. Check your affinities: Do you prefer indoor or outdoor activities, mental or physical?
4. The activity should increase positive emotions, thoughts, and behaviors. If it's not doing that after you've gotten over the learning curve of the activity, look for something else.
5. Find ways to vary the activity (a different running route, distance) to overcome habituation.
6. By all means, stick with it.

Pleasures vs. Gratifications

The battle between the higher brain and its impulsive default to instant payoff boils down to two very different styles of feeling good. The dominant one by far, and the one that keeps us chasing external desires, is the body's idea of happiness—pleasures. These are quick hits, from a hot fudge sundae to new clothes.

The sensations of pleasure mode have only a fleeting effect on well-being, like scratching an itch. There's nothing wrong with passive leisure activities, say, a glass of wine or watching a movie, but they don't provide the lasting kick that active leisure does.

Feeling good means something entirely different to the deeper recesses of your mind, where your self-determination needs reside. They require a higher standard for long-term satisfaction and fulfillment. The University of Pennsylvania's Martin Seligman calls these "gratifications."

Pleasures are easy, but it takes initiative to put gratifications into action. Active hobbies, recreational pursuits, and volunteering are primo gratifications, satisfying your mind, not just your senses. Participant activities such as singing in a choir or softball deliver experiences that stick with you through the competence and relationships they build and the fun experiences that linger in memory.

The University of Maryland's Seppo Iso-Ahola, who specializes in the psychology and motivation behind exercise and health behaviors, says that a seeking mindset delivers the best recreational and leisure experiences. People who are driven by personal and interpersonal goals are less bored, more fulfilled, and healthier than those who are motivated by pleasure or escapist goals.

The takeaway is you are not here to watch—or you may have the wrong answers in your senior years to those three questions of Erik Erikson we touched on earlier in this chapter.

Higher Recreation

The local community college is a great place to go for potential recreational activities. They usually offer a variety of pursuits for a very affordable price. My local college offers table tennis and badminton in the gym on weekends ($6 per day). Great workouts, fun, and camaraderie are on tap there every weekend day, with vigorous participants in their seventies not unusual. Check out the potential offerings at a college near you.

You Can't Play Hopscotch With a Flow Chart

Years ago, I had a conversation with Mark Cullen, former senior associate dean of research at Stanford Medical School, and he told me something that nailed a hidden truth about our culture of overperformance. He had done research on retired Wall Street executives who had been very successful in their careers. Shortly after they retired, though, many felt worthless.

"The minute they stop, 20 or 25 years of accomplishments all leak out," said Cullen. "In this moment they're not accomplishing anything, so they feel they are nothing."

Their identity had been so tied up in output, they didn't know what to do with themselves beyond performance. "They had no leisure skills," said Cullen. No what? Leisure skills. They didn't know how to derive pleasure from life's input, how to entertain themselves. They hadn't developed hobbies and interests along the way.

In one of the not-so-great ironies of the modern world, we are well-trained to make a living but not how to do the living we're making. We wind up without the ability and mindset to step back from the scramble for daily bread and partake in enthusiasms and recreational activities for no other reason than our own enjoyment.

A lot of us could use some leisure skills. What are they? There are two kinds. First, there's a participant and experiential skillset that prompts you to seek out interests, try new things, get absorbed in them, and stick with them that uses a different part of your wiring than the work mind— the play mind. They are tools of curiosity and exploration, life participant skills.

Secondly, there are the skills needed to participate in the various hobbies and recreational activities. Once you learn the rules of badminton, for instance, and play it for a while, you can continue to get better at it, and it can become a lifelong outlet. I know one badminton fan who plays it on the road on business trips. He finds local gyms or colleges nearby his business meeting and drops in for pickup games. It's a great way to stay in shape, do what he loves, and meet new people.

Without life-participant skills, though, you can't get to the starting line of a new pastime. There's a big roadblock to these skills in the form of the usual work mindset, which wants an external payoff for everything. What am I going to get out of learning backgammon, mandolin, or archery? It's the wrong question.

You can't play hopscotch with a flow chart. The goal for leisure experiences, for instance, is simply being in the experience for its own sake. It's a different mindset and skillset. At the office, the premium is on control and micromanaging; on the life side, risk-taking is crucial. At work, it's about the familiar; in your free time, it's novelty and challenge that lead to the good stuff. At the office, you don't want to stray from the task at hand; on the life side, though, tangents and detours turn into highlights.

It's a lot easier to upgrade your quality of life when you are using the right life-participant tools, like the ones below.

The 7 Skills You Can't Live Without

1. **Intrinsic motivation**. The goal is to partake unconditionally. You do it for the inherent interest, fun, learning, or challenge. It doesn't matter what others think about it. You are going to enjoy yourself for your own internal reasons and interests.

2. **Curiosity.** This is the gateway to interests, passions, and keeping life new. Follow the glimmers of curiosity and see where they lead. When you are curious about something, the mind is trying to tell you: Learn about this. Thoughts such as "I wonder if I could do that," "That looks like fun," and "I've always wanted to try that" are signs to follow up on.

3. **Initiating.** Initiating intentional activities is one of the keys of sustainable happiness. Be proactive, go online for ideas and opportunities, plan activities, seek out and try new things, invite others to get out and participate—and if they don't reciprocate, go alone.

4. **Risk-taking.** There is no progress without risk. Play is a great realm for risk-taking, since there's nothing important at stake. You have to try new activities to acquire the skills to do them. You risk looking like you don't know what you're doing when trying something new, but so what? You don't know what you're doing. The only way to learn it is to plunge in and try. Humor and humility will get you over the learning curve and the ego's fear of you being seen as anything but total master of the adult world.

5. **Pursuit of competence.** Since competence is one of your core needs, it's a handy thing to build and sublime to feel. The idea here is that you want to take on a challenge or get better at something for your own knowledge or growth. Pursuing competence leads you to build your skills at an activity to the point where it can become a passion. It's a fabulous gratification-building skill.

6. **Going for the experience.** The key to optimal experiences is being 100 percent engaged in what you're doing. That means losing the electronic devices and distractions and putting all your concentration into the activity at hand. The more absorbed you are in your experience, the fewer outside nags and the more moments just this side of catnip for felines.

7. **Sustaining the activity.** You need to deploy persistence to stick with a new activity until your skill level is at a point where you can do it well enough to really enjoy yourself. It's self-sustaining after that.

These skills lead you inside the participant dynamic essential for a healthy and extraordinary life. The good life doesn't depend on any external elements—a certain car, designer gear, station in life—but only on the willingness that comes from within to immerse in your world.

Don't Have Shame

There are some places where switching over to the life side is as easy as breathing. Brazil would have to be near the top of that list. I'm a big fan of Brazilian culture and music. Some of the best music ever composed comes out of the bossa nova, Musica Popular Brasileira, or MPB, and samba traditions. It all started with an interest in bossa nova, then grew deeper to other rhythms, styles, dances, and travel around Brazil.

It's a good example of how a simple curiosity or interest can lead to a passion and an entire universe of discoveries. On one trip to Brazil, I found myself at a funky dance hall in Rio de Janeiro that dated back to the 19th century. Inside, a crowd of working-class Brazilians was enjoying dollar beers and slide-stepping their way through classic samba. I noticed an older fellow dancing by himself nonstop for an hour and twenty minutes. The stamina was impressive, so at a break in the action, I went up to talk to him.

Reynaldo dos Santos was 70 years old. The retired businessman was here every Friday night getting down on the dance floor. Not surprisingly, samba is his passion. If he hears it coming out of a shop downtown, he'll dance right on the sidewalk. When he hears the sound of the cavaquinho, the mandolin-like instrument at the core of samba, he gets goosebumps. I asked him how I could become a good samba dancer. "Don't have shame!" he told me instantly.

One of the biggest obstacles to the life that's out there for us is worrying about what others think. We worry about looking like a fool, when foolishness is just the state of not knowing something on the way to knowing it, as any kid knows.

Reynaldo pinpointed the problem succinctly. The only thing we have to fear is being an onlooker. You can't let the gaze of complete strangers prevent you from ratcheting up life to the highest levels of gratification, because here's the truth: They are not the audience. *You are the audience.* Only you can satisfy the core needs at the heart of your gratification equipment, no one else.

Don't be mortified if you are learning to paint or are bowling for the first time in two decades. Forget the performance metric of how good you are at it—that's the external trap trying to trip you up. See yourself as a lifelong learner. How harshly would you judge someone who was just starting to learn something? Be patient, have no expectations, and try to be less bad than you were the prior week. Enjoy the feeling of not having to be perfect or have everything controlled. It's like a vacation from your regimented adult self. How good does that feel?

Put a Bounce in Your Step

My favorite part of the *Work Smarter, Live Better* training comes when I ask everyone to stand up and see if they can walk in a circle. I take them through the paces of three simple steps. Then they find out they are dancing, doing the box step of samba, and I put on the samba music.

It's always a hit and 100% fun. You can hear the energy come up in the room, accompanied by laughter and smiles. In an instant, the room is transformed. The samba step illustrates the power of experience and attention in the moment and how we can energize ourselves in seconds through play. As some get good at the step, they feel in sync with the rhythm, even cocky, and that's great, because that stokes their mastery need.

This is a superb exercise to do every day to reset the brain and body with pure fun. Get up from your chair and take a walk in a circle several times a day to shake off brain strain, smile, get the blood moving, walk a few blocks without leaving the building, and put a bounce in your step.

How to Do the Box Step of Samba

1. Stand with your feet hip-width apart.
2. Step your left foot forward.
3. Swing your right leg and foot around the left until the right foot is standing on the left side of your left foot.
4. Now move only your left foot a couple inches behind your

right foot.
5. Then move only your right foot to the starting position, hip-width apart from the left.
6. Now repeat steps 1 to 5.
7. As you do this a few times and get the step down, bounce on the balls of your feet and swing your arms upward like you're running.
8. You are now a sambista!

Samba Dance Tunes

Here are a few samba tunes you can find on YouTube to inspire your moves. The first couple of songs ease you into the rhythm, and then you can speed it up for the last number. Start with Thais Macedo's live version of "Já é". The title reads: Já é—Thais Macedo (Sambabook Jorge Aragao). The Sambabook series of DVDs and albums is a great way to explore samba through tributes to the samba masters by the top performers in the realm.

Then check out Maria Rita's "Ta Perdoado" and Joao Nogueira doing the great samba classic, "Poder da Criacao." Next move: Find a samba class to explore a new potential passion.

Home of the True Self

Play may feel unimportant and childish, yet it happens to be the place where you live, along with your real identity that it helps you discover. It gives you the opportunity to step away from duty and be an individual. Play scholar Michael Ellis had a great description of play. "You commit to be yourself."

I love that. By stepping back, letting your hair down, rediscovering the still-enthused kid within, you wind up committing to yourself, instead of just adult responsibilities. You value your time and yourself when you play. The authentic self can emerge, revel, connect with others doing the same, and find life satisfaction on the spot. No one has a need to look for happiness when they are in the middle of it.

"A human is most human when at play," wrote psychologist Daniel

Berlyne, who studied the influence on behavior of curiosity, arousal, and exploration.

All those things and much more are on display when you play. You are completely free since the choice to do so is entirely up to you. This places you in control of your time, the way your autonomy-seeking neurons like it. Play is also the ultimate intrinsic activity because the whole point of it is being in the experience itself.

Amy Doran was a recently divorced mother of a son with epilepsy. She had relocated from Michigan to Oregon to start a new life and was feeling alone and fearful about her future. One day she was driving along the coast of Oregon, and she stumbled upon a kite festival. She got out and joined the festivities, flying a two-handled stunt kite that can do dips and tricks—and didn't put it down for hours. Local fliers came up to her, excited and impressed. They told her that she was a natural and should join their flying group.

She took them up on the offer, and in time she was performing on the kite festival and competition circuit around the country and the world. If you haven't been to one before, I recommend checking online to see where there is a kite festival near you. Kites have come a long way from the old paper-and-string diamond model. Today, the skies are dancing with everything from giant inflatables in the shape of dragons, frogs, or dolphins, to parafoils that tow other shapes, to multi-box kites and novelty characters in the spirit of the Macy's Thanksgiving parade. Performers do choreographed routines to music like ice skaters. At a kite festival in Oregon, I watched Amy, dressed as Charlie Chaplin, mimic his famed silly walks and pratfalls while putting her kite through a series of aerobatics. The crowd loved it.

Her son, Connor, got bullied in high school because of his epilepsy. He told me he felt worthless, like he "couldn't do anything" because of his condition. He learned how to fly a stunt kite and got skilled enough to win competitions, and things changed radically. He wound up on *America's Got Talent*, and almost made it to the quarterfinals. Today he is a spokesperson for the cause of epilepsy and has thousands of friends and supporters, as does Amy. Lives transformed.

What do we say to people we want to get rid of? Go fly a kite. That's how much value we place on an activity that has re-created these two lives. It shows how much we know, or don't, about the life under our noses.

The Rules of Recess

Kids have a lot to learn, but one thing they have mastered is play. Of course, that's your job when you are a child, so you get to be very good at it. Unfortunately, adults regress to a calcified state and lose the ability to do what they once did without thinking. Maybe thinking is the problem? Let's do more participating by relearning what we once knew as the rules of recess.

Be eager and enthused.

One kid I know has a mantra that is ideal for bringing back the old recess spirit. "I wanna try! I wanna try! I wanna try!" The phrase comes in triplets, and that's good, because it helps underscore the enthusiasm and purpose needed to fling us into the new.

You don't need to know how to do it.

Not knowing how to do something was never an obstacle when we were young. It would all come together by doing the new activity. There was no embarrassment that someone might see you doing something not perfectly. There was a first time for any skill you ever learned. There are still no prerequisites for fun.

Don't wait for an invite.

No formal invitation was needed back in the day. You walked up and joined in or, if there was no one else, you were perfectly capable of playing by yourself. Life is too short to leave to others. Be bold and do the inviting or choose activities you can do yourself.

Be spontaneous, be ready.

You used to be ready at any moment to have fun. Those moments of spontaneity get fewer and fewer over the years. The magic of life is in the surprises and improvisations off the usual script that spark joy and discovery.

Interests Make Life Interesting

If I could do two things to make the world a better, more humane, safer, more friendly, less unhealthy, and much happier place, Number 1 would be stress management skills for all and Number 2 would be multiple healthy interests for all. Number 2 would help the cause on Number

1, since pastimes slay stress.

Show me someone with a lot of interests, and I'll show you someone who finds life interesting, and whose life satisfaction is high as a result. I met a guy a few years ago who is a role model for the possibilities when you explore new interests. He had two seemingly opposite hobbies going: playing in a 50-piece marching band and orienteering, a race with a topographical map to find control stations hidden along an outdoor trail. They satisfied two different needs. Orienteering got him outdoors and competing on mountain trails, while the band lifted his social life. His life was full. He loved the challenges and the people he met.

Start looking for areas and activities that are intriguing. Experts say it's the range of leisure activities you are exposed to that gives you the best chance of finding interests that lead to a thriving life outside work, so spread your net wide.

Ask yourself: What can I learn? What can I try? What do I really want to experience? Where can I discover something?

Think about sampling potential hobbies or interests as you might with various wines at a tasting. Consider it life-tasting, which can produce a much more lasting high. To start, look at the genres of activities and recreation below. Which fit your interests? Which are you curious about? Which offer the most potential fun, challenge, or expression?

- Creative arts
- Games
- Sports, fitness
- Dance
- Outdoors
- Music
- Science, mind play
- Volunteering, service
- Travel
- Social connection
- Languages

Once you have identified genres you like, then open your Internet browser and start digging into the activities within them to sample. What would you really like to learn or just take a stab at?

Find a Hobby, Discover a Passion

One of the best places to look for a new interest and for a regular dose of intentional activity is a hobby. The concept almost seems archaic these days. The image comes to mind of train sets, stamp collecting, or gluing model ships together, something a child, not an adult, would do. This insidious belief makes the idea of having a hobby seem trivial, or maybe that you have too much time on your hands, or you aren't a seriously productive person.

Hobbies are simply concentrated doses of living, activities we engage in for the pure enjoyment to discover, have fun or build a skill or knowledge. What's great about hobbies is that they commit you to participate every week. They provide structured work recovery, so you can't bail as easily. You remove the least-effort excuses that pile up when the activity is not scheduled and blocked out.

That's what Wesley Nelson, director of operations at Hepper.com, a pet products website, likes about his hobby, taking a language learning course for fun. He's learning Mandarin Chinese. "I loved the fact that the grammar is very simple, so once you have the tones and the vocab cracked, you're 90% of the way there," he says.

Nelson pinpoints three upsides of his hobby that build in an ongoing commitment to his life: 1) "It's an in-person group, which means I feel social pressure to attend, 2) It is paid for, which means I feel a wallet pressure to attend, and 3) There are two sessions a week, which means I get four hours of guaranteed work-free time."

Hobbies are a refuge where you can reinvent yourself, often before a new circle of potential friends, and engage with others on the basis of a shared interest. It's a face-value world, where no one cares what you do for a living. You are accepted for who you are on a field of fun and growth.

A hobby can be something you do on your own, say, painting or learning a language, or with others in the form of hiking, birding, photography, or table tennis. It's an outlet to express other parts of your personality—creativity, physical or interpersonal skills—that you don't use on the job. Hobbies, then, expand human potential, no matter your age.

Start with something that looks like fun or that you would like to learn or have admired from afar. If the activity is the right fit, the pull of experiencing more and more of it grows with your skill level. You will see then that finding a hobby can also turn into a lifelong passion.

Richard Weinberg is a Chicago businessman who went out with his wife one night for a Mexican dinner. After a fine meal the tables and chairs disappeared, a dance floor opened up, and the salsa music commenced. His wife was excited, "C'mon, let's dance!" But Richard, being an adult American male, was having none of it. He didn't want to make a fool out of himself and flap his appendages around. So, his wife danced with the waiters all night long.

The next day, Richard thought about how much fun his wife had dancing with the waiters and decided to take a salsa lesson at a local dance studio. He was intrigued so he took another class. Then another one and another one. Five years later he was dancing professionally in 14 different dance categories and had won a national dance competition. He was 49 when he started.

A very successful entrepreneur, Richard has what we would consider the American Dream—wealth, a successful career, the house, the spouse, the family he loves. He told me something, though, that shreds the perception most have of success, along with the adult taboo against play. "I didn't realize I wasn't really living until I discovered dancing," he said. "Now that I have dancing in my life, I feel like I have a purpose."

A purpose? From play? That's right. When you are engaged in activities of "personal expressiveness," ones that are self-chosen and that reflect intrinsic goals, you are operating from the "true self," Alan Waterman of the College of New Jersey has written. This leads to optimal psychological functioning (happiness). We're talking about something far from tangential to your existence. Play scholar John Neulinger called passionate play pursuits none other than the "central life interest."

When you skate, draw, birdwatch, or get your telescope out to watch the stars, you are in a creative improvisation that lets you express yourself through your interests. In its low-key, humble way, play yanks grownups out of their purposeful sleepwalk to reveal the animating spirit within. You are alive, and play proves it to you.

Do a Free-Time Log

Contrary to the conventional wisdom, we do have spare time.

It's just not organized, according to the time experts. Or it occurs at odd times that we can't take advantage of because of our lack of discipline over our schedules outside work.

One way to pinpoint the times you have available is by keeping track of all your time beyond work hours for a week. Find the slots that you might have available. Maybe it's thirty minutes on a Wednesday night, an hour on Saturday morning. Once you find the openings, slot in potential hobby activities you have identified.

Then put those activities on a separate calendar from your work calendar. Give these times the importance they're due and stick to your appointments with yourself.

Discover a New Identity

When you are young, time seems to creep at the pace of geologic time. I could swear the clock on the schoolroom wall appeared to stop for long stretches in math class. Days and weeks still appear long in our 20s, years filled with so many experiences that the time between 20 and 30 seems the length of two decades. Then in the 30s, the passage of time picks up speed and seems to get faster after that.

We can slow that perception down by living fully as many moments as we can. That is hard to do, though, when the performance mind and its need for validation through output is in charge of your identity outside the office. This is why it's critically important to find a life identity beyond job, career, or profession.

I do an activity in my work-life balance trainings whose goal is to help participants find an identity beyond livelihood and see themselves in a different way, as a life participant. I have everyone create a business card for their life, since life is your real business. The life card can be very revealing for those who struggle to come up with a self-definition beyond what's on the business card. Having an identity not related to productive endeavor seems strange at first, since our self-definitions are so externally based.

Are you up for the challenge? It's time to create your life card.

What's on Your Life Card?

To put engaging leisure activities on the calendar, it helps to have an identity apart from the job. Start by creating a business card for your life. What would your Life I.D. consist of? Identify yourself by a hobby, interest, or something you'd like to do or always wanted to. The main stipulation: Your Life I.D. can't be about anything productive. We used to refer to someone who had interests and pastimes as a well-rounded person. It's the essence of work-life balance.

For example: John Smith|Cyclist, Laurie Collins|Travel Enthusiast, Jay Ellsworth|Guitarist.

- Create your Life Card
- Name:
- Life I.D.:

If you had difficulty with this exercise, don't worry. Use it to motivate yourself to find outlets outside work to explore.

Put It on the Calendar

Imagine that a thriving life was your job, or better yet, your mission and that it depended on your diligent efforts to put it into action. How much more attention would you give it, or put into the planning of it? It turns out it is your mission. Given that, how can you get ideas out of your head and onto a schedule, so they became real?

You could start a separate life calendar. You could use a white board posted in a place where everyone in the household can see it that details the week's activities and a wish list of things to move up the board to the live list. Everyone can add items to the board. Have a section for weekends and your next vacation.

Choose a couple of activities to try out. When can you slot them in? For this, do your Free Time Log to find available times in your non-work hours.

Now let's fill in some blanks in your life by returning to the Life Balance Sheet from Chapter 2. We've covered a lot of ground since then, so I'd like you to jot down two specific actions you can take to increase the level of attention you give to any of these personal life categories that you aren't satisfied with now. What are you going to do to activate the undernourished categories of your life?

- Family Time
- Significant Other
- Friends
- Me-Time
- Exercise
- Health
- Recreation/Hobbies
- Social Outlets
- Learning
- Entertainment
- Travel
- Personal Growth

Life Assurance

There is no shortage of industries that are here for you when it comes to bad things happening to you, your car, house, pet, or health. We spend a lot of money on insurance, in case the worst occurs, which, of course, does happen. While it's wise to be protected from things that may befall you, it's also smart to ensure you have the life you are being insured for.

To help with that, I introduce Life Assurance. It's a lot more fun than life insurance, because you are actually around to get the benefits. Life Assurance is the focused creativity and diligence to map out a path to the big experiences you want to have on this planet. What do you want to do just for the sake of the experience? In other words, what's on your bucket list?

Life has a way of eluding us unless we proactively take actions to get into the thick of it while the getting is still possible. There are few better indicators of determining the content of your life—and the gratification that comes from them—than planning and pulling off bucket projects. You are the director. What do you want to do?

When we do this exercise in my programs, participants get to give voice to something that usually they have never thought about or that has never made its way from the mind to the realm of speech or writing, their dreams. Here's what they want to do in their time on this planet:

- Visit all the U.S. national parks
- See the Northern Lights
- Learn piano
- Skydive
- Travel to Italy
- Hike the Appalachian Trail
- Run a marathon
- Go to Alaska
- Learn Spanish
- Sail the South Seas
- Write a book
- Go on a safari

Now it's your turn to make a list of your big life aspirations, your bucket list. See if you can come up with five items to put on your list. Pick one to focus on, then identify a couple of action steps to start getting the wheels in motion. As you accomplish one of your items, add another one to keep a rotating top five list. Your best life is out there, as long as you are proactively doing the planning and thinking to make it happen.

Give Your Brain a Souvenir To Remember

In the last few days of the year, we often look back over the prior twelve months to review what notable things have happened. Sometimes, though, you think and think and can't come up with anything. Unfortunately, the brain is wired to notice new things. When it gets the same data over and over, it literally stops registering it.

It's like when you commute to the office, and you don't even remember the last five exits on your route. You have been coasting on memory, while the mind has shifted to autopilot. It's kind of passive-aggressive, but your brain is trying to tell you something.

If you want a memorable life, you have to live a life worth remembering.

Let's get to it.

Notes

Introduction

4   *A fabulous study*...Sheldon, Kennon and Sonja Lyubomirsky. "Is It Possible to Become Happier? (And If So, How?)." *Social and Personality Psychology Compass* 1, 2007.

Chapter 1—You Are Not a Hard Drive with Hair

8   *As work overlaps*...Halkos, George and Dimitrios Bousinakis. "The Effect of Stress and Satisfaction on Productivity." *International Journal of Productivity and Performance Management*, Vol. 59, 2010.

8   *Longer hours multiply*...Demke, Allard E. and Xiaoxi Yao. "Chronic Disease from Exposure to Long-Hour Work Schedules Over a 32-Year Period." *Journal of Occupational and Environmental Medicine*, Vol. 58, No. 9, 2016.

8   *Working more than 55 hours*...Kivimaki, Mika, Markus Jokela, Solja T. Nyberg, Archana Singh-Manoux, Eleonor I. Fransson, Lars Alfredsson, Jakob B. Bjorner, Marianne Borritz, Hermann Burr, Annalisa Casini, Els Clays, Dirk De Bacquer, Nico Dragano, Raimund Erbel, Goedele A. Geuskens, Mark Hamer, Wendela E. Hooftman, Irene L. Houtman, Karl-Heinz Jockel, France Kittel, Anders Knutsson, Markku Koskenvuo, Thorsten Lunau, Ida E. H. Madsen, Martin L. Nielsen, Maria Nordin, Tuula Oksanen, Jan H. Pejtersen, Jaana Pentti, Reiner Rugulies, Paula Salo, Martin J. Shipley, Johannes Siegrist, Andrew Steptoe, Sakari B. Suominen, Tores Theorell, Jussi Vahtera, Peter J. M. Westerholm, Hugo Westerlund, Dermot O'Reilly, Meena Kumari, G. David Batty, Jane E. Ferrie, Marianna Virtanen, IPD Work Consortium. "Long Working Hours and Risk of Coronary Heart Disease and Stroke: A Systematic Review and Meta-Analysis of Published and Unpublished Data for 603,838 Individuals." *The Lancet*. Published Aug. 19, 2015.

9   *Some researchers say*...Gailliot, Matthew T., Roy F. Baumeister, C. Nathan DeWall, Jon K. Maner, E. Ashby Plant, Dianne M. Tice, Lauren E. Brewer, Brandon J. Schmeichel. "Self-Control Relies on Glucose as a Limited Energy Source: Willpower Is More Than a Metaphor." *Journal of Personal Social Psychology*, Feb. 2007.

9   *One study documented...*Arthur, Michelle M. "Share Price Reactions to Work-Family Human Resource Decisions: An Institutional Perspective," 2003.

9   *Contrast that with...*Anderson, Stella E., Betty S. Coffey, Robin T. Byerly. "Formal Organizational Initiatives and Informal Workplace Practices: Links to Work-Family Conflict and Job-Related Outcomes," 2002.

9   *Employees with high strain...*Azagba, Sunday and Mesbah F. Sharaf. "Psychosocial Working Conditions and the Utilization of Health Care Services." BMC Public Health, 2011.

Chapter 2—What Is Work-Life Balance, Anyway?

13   *It's called the time-on-task effect...*Lim, Julian, Wen-chau Wu, Jiongjiong Wang, John A. Detre, David F. Dinges, Hengyi Rao. "Imaging Brain Fatigue from Sustained Mental Workload: An ASL Perfusion Study of the Time-on-Task Effect." *NeuroImage* 49, 2010.

16   *The study found that our ears...*Cousineau, Marion, Josh H. McDermott, and Isabelle Peretz. "The Basis of Musical Consonance as Revealed by Congenital Amusia." PNAS November 27, 2012.

16   *Other researchers measured...*Brown, William M., Lee Cronk, Keith Grochow, Amy Jacobson, C. Karen Liu, Zoran Popovic, Robert Trivers. "Dance Reveals Symmetry, Especially in Young Men." *Nature*, Dec. 22, 2005.

26   *As one study put it...*Thiede Thomas, Linda and Daniel C. Ganster. "Impact of Family-Supportive Work Variables on Work-Family Conflict and Strain: A Control Perspective." *Journal of Applied Psychology*, 1995.

33   *An analysis of 36 pharmaceutical companies...*Shepard III, Edward, Thomas Clifton, Douglas Kruse. "Flexible Work Hours and Productivity: Some Evidence from the Pharmaceutical Industry," 1996.

34   *Researchers who looked at...*Perry-Smith, Jill, Terry Blum. "Work-Life Human Resources Bundles and Perceived Organizational Performance." *The Academy of Management Journal*, 2000.

34   *One study documented...*Shin, Duckjung and Jackson Enoh. "Availability and Use of Work-Life Balance Programs: Relationship with Organizational Profitability." MDPI.com, 2020.

34   *A researcher who looked...*Sheppard, George. "Work-Life Balance Programs to Improve Employee Performance." Walden University, 2016

Chapter 3—You Can't Control the Wind, But You Can Adjust the Sails

44   *A report from the World Health Organization...*Pega, Frank, Balint Nafradi, Natalie C. Momen, Yuka Ujita, Kai N. Streicher, Annette M. Pruss-Ustun, Technical Advisory Group, Alexis Descatha, Tim Driscoll, Frida M. Fischer, Lode Godderis, Hannah M. Kiiver, Jian Li, Linda L. Magnusson Hanson, Reiner Rugulies, Kathrine Sorensen, Tracy J. Woodruff. "Global, Regional and National Burdens from Ischemic Heart Disease and Stroke Attributable to Exposure to Long Working Hours for 194 Countries, 2000-2016: A Systematic Analysis from the WHO/ILO Joint Estimates of the Work-Related Burden of Disease and Injury." *Science Direct*, May 17, 2021.

45 *Stanford economist*...Pencavel, John. "The Productivity of Working Hours." Stanford Institute for Economic Policy Research, 2013.

45 *Overtime shrank productivity*... Shepard III, Edward M., Thomas J. Clifton, Douglas Kruse. "Flexible Work Hours and Productivity: Some Evidence from the Pharmaceutical Industry," 1996.

45 *People who work chronically long hours*...Yang, Haiou, Peter L. Schnall, Maritza Jauregui, Ta-Chen Su, Dean Baker. "Work Hours and Self-Reported Hypertension Among Working People in California." *Hypertension*, 2006.

46 *Long working hours*... Virtanen, Marianna and Mika Kivimaki. "Long Working Hours and Risk of Cardiovascular Disease." *Current Cardiology Reports*, 2018.

46 *The nation of Iceland*...Haraldsson, Gudmundur D., Jack Kellam. "Going Public: Iceland's Journey to a Shorter Workweek," June 2021.

48 *Harvard Business School's*...Nash, Laura and Howard Stevenson. *Just Enough: Tools for Creating Success in Your Work and Life*. Harvard Business School Publishing, 2004.

50 *Melissa Clark of the University of Georgia*...Clark, Melissa A., Jesse S. Michel, Gregory W. Stevens, Julia W. Howell, Ross S. Scruggs. "Workaholism, Work Engagement and Work-Home Outcomes: Exploring the Mediating Role of Positive and Negative Emotions." *Stress Health*, Oct. 30, 2014.

52 *A report in*...Detert, James and Amy Edmondson. "Why Employees Are Afraid to Speak," *Harvard Business Review*, 2007.

Chapter 4—Stay Calm in the Storm

69 *Mental strain that leads to*...Karasek, Jr., Robert A. "Job Demands, Job Decision Latitude, and Mental Strain: Implications for Job Design." *Administrative Science Quarterly*, Vol. 24 No. 2, 1979.

69 *Workplaces with high demands*...Ninaus, Katharina, Sandra Diehl, Ralf Terlutter, Kara Chan, Anqi Huang. "Benefits and Stressors: Perceived Effect of ICT Use on Employee Health and Work Stress: An Exploratory Study from Austria and Hong Kong." *International Journal of Qualitative Studies on Health and Well-Being*," October 2015.

72 *This was confirmed in research by Penn State's*...Borkovec, Thomas D., Michelle G. Newman, Aaron L. Pincus, Richard Lytle. "A Component Analysis of Cognitive-Behavioral Therapy for Generalized Anxiety Disorder and the Role of Interpersonal Problems." *Journal of Consulting*, 2002.

77 *Harvard researchers*...Killingworth, Matthew A., and Daniel T. Gilbert. "A Wandering Mind Is an Unhappy Mind." *Science*, 2010.

84 *We vastly overestimate*...Gilbert, Daniel T., Elizabeth C. Pinel, Timothy D. Wilson, Stephen J. Blumberg. "Immune Neglect: A Source of Durability Bias in Affective Forecasting." *Journal of Personality and Social Psychology*, No. 3, 1998.

85 *One fascinating study by*... Johnson, Eric J. and Amos Tversky. "Affect, Generalization, and the Perception of Risk." *Journal of Personality and Social Psychology*, July 1983.

88 *Stress contagion comes from…* Dimitroff, Stephanie J., Omid Kardan, Elizabeth A. Necka, Jean Decety, Marc G. Berman, Greg J. Norman. "Physiological Dynamics of Stress Contagion." Open access. July 2017.

Chapter 5 — The Hidden Blowback of Stress and Burnout

98 *One massive meta-study…*Kivimaki, Mika, Jaana Pentti, Jane E. Ferrie, G. David Batty, Solja T. Nyberg, Marcus Jokela, Marianna Virtanen, Lars Alfredsson, Nico Dragano, Eleonor I. Fransson, Marcel Goldberg, Anders Knutsson, Markku Koskenvuo, Aki Koskinen, Anne Kouvonen, Ritva Luukkonen, Tuula Oksanen, Reiner Rugulies, Johannes Siegrist, Archana Singh-Manoux, Sakari Suominen, Tores Theorell, Ari Vaananen, Jussi Vahtera, Peter J. M. Westerholm, Hugo Westerlund, Marie Zins, Timo Strandberg, Andrew Steptoe, John Deanfield, for the IPD Work Consortium. "Work Stress and Risk of Death in Men and Women with and without Cardiometabolic Disease: a Multicohort Study." *The Lancet Diabetes and Endocrinology*, 2018.

99 *The risk is higher…*Huang, Yuli, Shuxian Xu, Jinghai Hua, Dingji Zhu, Changhua Liu, Yunzhao Hu, Tiebang Liu, Dingli Xu. "Association Between Job Strain and Risk of Incident Stroke: A Meta-Analysis." *Neurology*, Nov. 10, 2015.

99 *Women with moderate to high stress…* Harris, Melissa L., Christopher Oldmeadow, Alexis Hure, Judy Luu, Deborah Loxton, John Attia. "Stress Increases the Risk of Type 2 Diabetes Onset in Women: A 12-Year Longitudinal Study Using Causal Modeling." PLos One. Feb. 21, 2017.

101 *A whopping 78%…* Bastiem, Celyne H., Annie Vallieres, Charles M. Morin. "Precipitating Factors of Insomnia." *Behavioral Sleep Medicine*, 2004.

101 *Acute and chronic stress…*Meerlo, Peter, Bertrand J. Pragt, Serge Daan. "Social Stress Induces High Intensity Sleep in Rats." *Neuroscience Letters*, April 1997.

102 *Without these elements, sleep is interrupted…*Han, Kuem Sun, Lin Kim, Insop Shim. "Stress and Sleep Disorder." *Experimental Neurobiology* Vol. 21, Dec. 2012.

103 *"Acute stress impairs"…*Sanger, Jessica, Laura Bechtold, Daniela Schoofs, Meinolf Blaszkewiz, Edmund Wascher. "The Influence of Acute Stress on Attention Mechanisms and Its Electrophysiological Correlates," 2014.

104 *One study that examined…*Echouffo-Tcheugui, Sara C. Conner, Jayandra J. Himali, Pauline Maillard, Charles S. DeCarli, Alexa S. Beiser, Ramachandran S. Vasan, Sudha Seshadri. "Circulating Cortisol and Cognitive and Structural Brain Measures. The Framingham Heart Study." 2018

104 *Stress also makes us…*Mather, Mara and Nichole R. Lighthall. "Both Risk and Reward Are Processed Differently in Decisions Made Under Stress." *Current Directions in Psychological Science*, March 26, 2012.

106 *Researchers Katherine…*Richardson, Katherine M. and Hannah R. Rothstein. "Effects of Occupational Stress Management Intervention Programs: A Meta-Analysis," 2008.

109 *A study at Stockholm University*...Ost, L. G. and B. E. Westling. "Applied Relaxation vs. Cognitive Behavior Therapy in the Treatment of Panic Disorder." *Behavioral Research Therapy*, Feb. 1995.

115 *Leisure activities cut stress*...Zawadzki, Matthew, Joshua M. Smyth, Heather A. Costigan. "Real-Time Associations Between Engaging in Leisure and Daily Health and Well-Being." *Annals of Behavioral Medicine*, 2015.

115 *Gardening, doing puzzles*...Zawadzki, Matthew, Joshua M. Smyth, Marcellus M. Merritt, William Gerin. "Absorption in Self-Selected Activities Is Associated with Lower Ambulatory Blood Pressure But Not for High Trait Ruminators." *American Journal of Hypertension*, 2013.

117 *This is bad news*...Hu, Qiao, Wilmar B. Schaufeli, Toon W. Taris. "The Job Demands-Resources Model: An Analysis of Additive and Joint Effects of Demands and Resources." APA PsycNet, 2011.

118 *The cost of depression*...Greenberg, Paul, Andree-Anne Fournier, Tammy Sisitsky, Crystal T. Pike, Ronald C. Kessler. "The Economic Burden of Adults with Depressive Disorder." *Journal of Clinical Psychology*, 2015

118 *Burnout is a relentless demotivating tool*...Duplooy, J. and G. Roodt. "Work Engagement, Burnout and Related Constructs as Predictors of Turnover Intentions." *SA Journal of Industrial Psychology* 36, 2010.

118 *Swiss, French, and American researchers*...Bianchi, Renzo, Eric Laurent, Irvin Sam Shonfeld. "Is the Burnout Process a Process of Depression? A Categorical Approach," 2014.

118 *Burnout scholar Christina Maslach*...Maslach, Christina, Michael P. Leiter. "Understanding the Burnout Experience: Recent Research and Its Implications for Psychiatry." *World Psychiatry*, 2016.

120 *Burnout has been shown*...Alexandrova-Karamanova, Anna, Irine Todorova, Anthony Montgomery, Efharis Panagopoulou, Patricia Costa, Adriana Baban, Asli Davas, Milan Milosevic, Dragan Mijakowski. "Burnout and Health Behaviors in Health Professionals from Seven European Countries." *International Archives of Occupational and Environmental Health*, 2016.

120 *Since the effects of burnout*...Salvagioni, Denise Albieri Jodas, Francine Nesello Melanda, Arthur Eumann Mesas, Alberto Duran Gonzalez, Flavia Lopes Gabani, Selma Maffei de Andrade. "Physical, Psychological, and Occupational Consequences of Job Burnout: A Systematic Review of Prospective Studies." PLos One. Oct 4, 2017.

123 *A huge study of 90,164 workers*... Dragano, Nico, Johannes Siegrist, Solja T. Nyberg, Thorsten Lunau, Eleonor I. Fransson, Lars Alfredsson, Jakob B. Bjorner, Marianne Borritz, Hermann Burr, Raimund Erbel, Göran Fahlén, Marcel Goldberg, Mark Hamer, Katriina Heikkilä, Karl-Heinz Jöckel, Anders Knutsson, Ida E. H. Madsen, Martin L. Nielsen, Maria Nordin, Tuula Oksanen, Jan H. Pejtersen, Jaana Pentti, Reiner Rugulies, Paula Salo, Jürgen Schupp, Archana Singh-Manoux, Andrew Steptoe, Töres Theorell, Jussi Vahtera, Peter J. M. Westerholm, Hugo Westerlund, Marianna Virtanen,

Marie Zins, G. David Batty, Mika Kivimäki, IPD-Work Consortium. "Effort-Reward Imbalance at Work and Incident Coronary Heart Disease: A Multicohort Study of 90,164 Individuals." *Epidemiology*, July, 2017.

124 *Yet there aren't...*Shirom, Arie and Samuel Melamed. "Burnout and Health Review: Current Knowledge and Future Research Directions." Chapter from *International Review of Industrial and Organizational Psychology*, Vol. 20, 2005.

124 *A stress management program for teachers...*Zolniercyk-Zreda, D. "An Intervention to Reduce Work-Related Burnout in Teachers." *International Journal of Occupational Safety and Ergonomics*, 2005.

124 *Meta-studies on burnout among physicians...*West, Colin P., Liselotte N. Dyrbye, Patricia J. Erwin, Tait D. Shanafelt. "Interventions to Prevent and Reduce Physician Burnout: A Systematic Review and Meta-Analysis." *The Lancet, 388, 2016.*

124 *Meta-studies on burnout among physicians...* Panagioti, Maria, Efharis Panagopoulou, Peter Bower, George Lewith, Evangelos Kontopantelis, Carolyn Chew-Graham, Shoba Dawson, Harm van Marwijk, Keith Geraghty, Aneez Esmail. "Controlled Interventions to Reduce Burnout in Physicians: A Systematic Review and Meta-Analysis." *JAMA Internal Medicine*, 2017.

125 *Arnold Bakker, a prolific Dutch researcher...*Bakker, Arnold, Evangelia Demerouti, Martin C. Euwema. "Job Resources Buffer the Impact of Job Demands on Burnout." *Journal of Occupational Health Psychology*, 2005.

128 *Vacations, for instance...*Hobfoll, Stevan E. "Conservation of Resources Theory: Applications to Stress and Management in the Workplace," 2001.

Chapter 6—Be Quick, But Don't Hurry

132 *Real or perceived time pressure...*Syrek, Christine, Ella Apostel, Conny H. Antoni. "Stress in Highly Demanding IT Jobs: Transformational Leadership Moderates the Impact of Time Pressure on Exhaustion and Work-Life Balance." *Journal of Occupational Health Psychology*. July 2013.

133 *As a study led by...*Kowalski-Trakofler, Kathleen M., Charles Vaught, Ted Scharf. "Judgment and Decision Making Under Stress: An Overview for Emergency Managers." *International Journal of Emergency Management*. January 2003.

135 *This is why...*Streufert, Siegfried, Susan C. Streufert, David Gorson. "Time Urgency and Coronary-Prone Behavior: The Effectiveness of a Behavior Pattern," 1981. APA PsycNet.

136 *Decision-making during stressful emergencies...*Kontogiannis, Tom and Zoe Kossiavelou. "Stress and Team Performance: Principles and Strategies for Intelligent Decision Aids." *Safety Science*, Dec. 1999.

136 *Just the perception of time urgency...*de Dreu, Carsten K. W. "Time Pressure and Closing of the Mind in Negotiation," 2003.

138 *It's such a red flag...*Niaura, Raymond, John F. Todaro, Avron Spiro III, Kenneth D. Ward, Scott Weiss. "Hostility, the Metabolic Syndrome, and Inci-

dent Coronary Heart Disease." *Health Psychology*, 2002.

138 *It's no surprise then*...Cole, Stephen R., Ichiro Kawachi, Simin Liu, J. Michael Gaziano, Joanne E. Manson, Julie E. Buring, Charles H. Hennekens. "Time Urgency and Risk of Non-Fatal Myocardial Infarction." *International Journal of Epidemiology*, Apr. 30, 2001.

138 *On top of that*...Conte, Jeffrey M., Kathleen L. Ringenbach, Stacey K. Moran, Frank J. Landy. "Criterion-Validity Evidence for Time Urgency: Associations with Burnout, Organizational Commitment, and Job Involvement in Travel Agents." *Applied H. R. M. Research*, 2001, Vol. 6.

138 *Anger can triple the risk*...Kawachi, Ichiro, D. Sparrow, P. S. Vokonas, S. T. Weiss. "Symptoms of Anxiety and Risk of Coronary Heart Disease: The Normative Aging Study," Nov. 1994.

138 *A huge meta-study*...Mostofsky, Elizabeth, Elizabeth Anne Penner, Murray A. Mittleman. "Outbursts of Anger as a Trigger of Acute Cardiovascular Events: A Systematic Review and Meta-Analysis." *European Heart Journal*, Vol. 35, June 1, 2014.

Chapter 7—Set the Terms of Engagement

151 *"Addiction to technology"*... Kakabadse, Nada, Gayle Porter, David Vance. "Addicted to Technology." 2007

151 *An interruption averaging 2.8 seconds*...Altmann, Erik M., J. Gregory Trafton, David Z. Hambrick. "Momentary Interruptions Can Derail the Train of Thought." *Journal of Experimental Psychology*, Feb. 2014.

153 *Nope*...Mark, Gloria, Daniel Gudith, Ulrich Klocke. "The Cost of Interrupted Work: More Speed and Stress." *Proceedings of the SIGCHI Conference on Human Factors in Computing Systems*, 2008.

154 *Studies show that the better you are*...Hasher, Lynn, Cindy Lustig, Rose Zacks. "Inhibitory Mechanisms and the Control of Attention." APA PsycNet, 2007.

154 *One thing shown*...Jha, Amism P., Jason Krompinger, Michael J. Baime. "Mindfulness Training Modifies Subsystems of Attention." *Cognitive, Affective & Behavioral Neuroscience*, Jun 7, 2007.

155 *Not surprisingly*...Bailey, Brian P., Joseph A. Konstan, John V. Carlis. "Measuring the Effects of Interruptions on Task Performance in the User Interface." *Proceedings of the IEEE International Conference on Systems, Man and Cybernetics*, 2000.

155 *Then-University of Michigan*...Perlow, Leslie. "Finding Time, Stopping the Frenzy." *Business Health*, Aug. 16, 1998.

160 *Temple University researchers*...Wilmer, Henry H. and Jason M. Chein. "Mobile Technology Habits—Patterns of Association Among Device Usage, Intertemporal Preference, Impulse Control, and Reward Sensitivity." *Psychonomic Bulletin & Review*, 2016.

161 *Researchers were puzzled*...Twenge, Jean M., Jonathan Haidt, Andrew B. Blake, Cooper McAllister, Hannah Lemon, Astrid Le Roy. "Worldwide Increases in Adolescent Loneliness." *Journal of Adolescence*, July 2021.

165 *He investigated...*Meyer, David and David Kieras. "Effective Control of Cognitive Processes in Task-Switching," 2001.

167 *In her research...*Mark, Gloria, Shamsi T. Iqbal, Mary Czerwinski, Paul Johns, Akane Sano. "Email Duration, Batching, and Self-Interruption: Patterns of Email Use on Productivity and Stress," 2016.

167 *One study identified...*Ninaus, Katharina, Sandra Diehl, Ralf Terlutter, Kara Chan, Anqi Huang. "Benefits and Stressors: Perceived Effect of ICT Use on Employee Health and Work Stress: An Exploratory Study from Austria and Hong Kong." *International Journal of Qualitative Studies on Health and Well-Being,*" October 2015.

173 *However, if you turn off...*Jackson, Thomas, Ray Dawson, Darren Wilson. "Understanding Email Interaction Increases Organizational Productivity." *Communications of the ACM,* 2003.

173 *People who choose...*Mark, Gloria, Shamsi T. Iqbal, Mary Czerwinski, Paul Johns, Akane Sano. "Email Duration, Batching, and Self-Interruption: Patterns of Email Use on Productivity and Stress," 2016.

177 *Eight music...*Ruthsatz, Joanne and Jourdan B. Urbach. "Child Prodigy: A Novel Cognitive Profile Places Elevated General Intelligence, Exceptional Working Memory, and Attention to Detail at the Root of Prodigiousness," 2012.

179 *A study that examined the attention prowess...*McLean, Katherine A., Emilio Ferrer, Stephen R. Aichele, David A. Bridwell, Anthony Zanesco, Tonya L. Jacobs, Brandon G. King, Erika L. Rosenberg, Baljinder K. Sahdra, Phillip R. Shaver, B. Alan Wallace, George R. Mangun, Clifford D. Saron. "Intensive Meditation Training Improves Perceptual Discrimination and Sustained Attention." *Psychological Science*, June 21, 2010.

Chapter 8—The Power of Possibility

184 *Optimistic people live...*Lee, Lewina O., Peter James, Emily S. Zevon, Eric S. Kim, Claudia Trudel-Fitzgerald, Avron S. Spiro III, Francine Grodstein, Laura D. Kubzansky. "Optimism Is Associated with Exceptional Longevity in 2 Epidemiologic Cohorts of Men and Women." PNAS, Sept. 10, 2019.

184 *Optimists manage stress...*Rozanski, Alan, Chirag Bavashi, Laura D. Kubzansky, Randy Cohen. "Association of Optimism with Cardiovascular Events and All-Cause Mortality: A Systematic Review and Meta-Analysis." JAMA Netw Open, 2019

185 *In a Dutch study,* Giltay, Erik J., Johanna Geleijnse, Frans G. Zitman, Tiny Hoekstra, Evert G. Schouten. "Dispositional Optimism and All-Cause Cardiovascular Mortality in a Prospective Cohort of Elderly Dutch Men and Women." *Archives of General Psychiatry,* 2004.

187 *It turns out...* Moser, Jason S., Rachel Hartwig, Tim P. Moran, Alexander A. Jendrusina, Ethan Kross. "Neural Markers of Positive Reappraisal and Their Associations with Trait Reappraisal." *Journal of Abnormal Psychology,* 2014.

191 *For one...*Gilbert, Daniel T. and Timothy D. Wilson. "Prospection: Experiencing the Future." *Science*, Oct. 2007.

192 *"People profoundly misestimate"...*Gilbert, Daniel T., Elizabeth C. Pinel, Timothy D. Wilson, Stephen J. Blumberg, Thalia P. Wheatley. "Immune Neglect: A Source of Durability Bias in Affective Forecasting." *Journal of Personality and Social Psychology*, 75, 1998.

Chapter 9—The Upside of Positive Emotions

209 *Her ground-breaking paper...* Fredrickson, Barbara. "What Good Are Positive Emotions?" *Review of General Psychology*, Vol. 2 No 3, 1998.

213 *Positive psychology heavyweights...*Lyubomirksy, Sonja, Laura King, Ed Diener. "The Benefits of Frequent Positive Affect: Does Happiness Lead to Success?" *Psychological Bulletin* 131, No. 6, 2005.

213 *Happy people get more raises...*Wright, Thomas A., Russell Cropanzano, Douglas G. Bonett. "The Moderating Role of Employee Well-Being on the Relationship Between Job Satisfaction and Job Performance." *Journal of Occupational Health Psychology*, May 2007.

221 *Character strengths are...*Peterson, Christopher and Martin Seligman. *Character Strengths and Virtues*. American Psychological Assoc., Oxford University Press, 2004.

Chapter 10 —The Refueling Principle

226 *Brain scientists say...* Boksem, Maarten A. S., Theo F. Meijman, Monique M. Lorist. "The Effects of Mental Fatigue on Attention: An ERP Study," 2005.

226 *It serves as...*Dunn, Jacob and Michael H. Grider. *Physiology, Adenosine Triphosphate*. StatPearls, 2021.

227 *One study noted...* Zhu, Xiao-Hong, Hongyan Qiao, Fei Du, Qiang Xiong, Xiao Liu, Xiaoliang Zhang, Kamil Ugurbil, Wei Chen. "Quantitative Imaging of Energy Expenditure in the Human Brain." *Neuroimage*, May 1, 2012.

227 *It's a scenario...* Lim, Julian, Wen-chau Wu, Jiongjiong Wang, John A. Detre, David F. Dinges, Hengyi Rao. "Imaging Brain Fatigue from Sustained Mental Workload: An ASL Perfusion Study of the Time-on-Task Effect." *NeuroImage* 49, 2010.

228 *Staying disciplined...*Gailliot, Matthew T., Roy F. Baumeister, C. Nathan DeWall, Jon K. Maner, E. Ashby Plant, Dianne M. Tice, Lauren E. Brewer, Brandon J. Schmeichel. "Self-Control Relies on Glucose as a Limited Energy Source: Willpower Is More Than a Metaphor." *Journal of Personal Social Psychology*, Feb. 2007.

229 *Researchers Mandara Savage...*Savage, Mandara and Darren Pipkins. "The Effect of Rest Periods on Hand Fatigue and Productivity," 2006.

229 *Productivity increased 13%...*Janaro, Ralph E. and Stephen E. Bechtold. "A Study of the Reduction of Fatigue Impact on Productivity Through Optimal Rest Break Scheduling." Aug. 1985.

230 *A Cornell University study...*Hedge, Alan. "Effects of Ergonomic Management Software on Employee Performance," 1999.

230 *Breaks during the workday*...Zhu, Ze, Lauren Kuykendall, Xichao Zhang. "The Impact of Within-Day Work Breaks on Daily Recovery Processes: An Event-Based Pre-/Post-Experience Sampling Study," 2018.

230 *Daily short breaks*...Kuhnel, Jana, Hannes Zacher, Jessica De Bloom, Ronald Bledow. "Take a Break! Benefits of Sleep and Short Breaks for Work Engagement." *European Journal of Work and Organizational Psychology*, Vol. 26, Issue 4, 2017.

231 *As logic would have it*...Hunter, Emily and Cindy Wu. "Give Me a Better Break: Choosing Workday Break Activities to Maximize Resource Recovery." *Journal of Applied Psychology*, Feb. 2016.

232 *Research shows that working while eating lunch doesn't aid recovery*...Trougakos, John P., Ivona Hideg, Bonnie Hayden Cheng, Daniel J. Beal. "Lunch Breaks Unpacked: The Role of Autonomy as a Moderator of Recovery During Lunch." *The Academy of Management Journal*, Apr. 2014.

232 *Something as simple as*...Sianoja, Marjaana, Christine J. Syrek, Jessica De Bloom, Kalevi Korpela, Ulla Kinnunen. "Enhancing Daily Well-Being at Work Through Lunchtime Park Walks and Relaxing Exercises: Recovery Experiences as Mediators." *Journal of Occupational Health Psychology*, 23(3) 2018.

233 *When employees are encouraged*...Bennett, Andrew A., Allison S. Gabriel, Charles Calderwood, Jason J. Dahling, John P. Trougakos. "Better Together? Examining Profiles of Employee Recovery Experiences." *Journal of Applied Psychology, 101*(12), 2016.

234 *A break from the work state of mind*...Sonnentag, Sabine and Charlotte Fritz. "Recovery from Job Stress: The Stressor-Detachment Model as an Integrative Framework." *Journal of Organizational Behavior*, Apr. 2014.

234 *"When one is not willing"*...Sonnentag, Sabine, Carmen Binnewies, Eva Mojza. "Staying Well and Engaged When Demands Are High." *Journal of Applied Psychology*, 2010.

235 *Dutch researcher*...De Jonge, Jan. "What Makes a Good Work Break? Off-Job and On-Job Recovery as Predictors of Employee Heath." *Industrial Health*, Mar. 2020.

237 *Studies show that these recovery processes*...Ten Brummelhuis, Lieke L. and Arnold B. Bakker. "Staying Engaged During the Week: The Effect of Off-Job Activities on Next Day Work Engagement." APA PsycNet. 2012.

237 *Improve health and well-being*...Sonnentag, Sabine, Carmen Binnewies, Eva J. Mojza. "Did You Have a Nice Evening? A Day-Level Study on Recovery Experiences, Sleep, and Affect." *Journal of Applied Psychology*, May 2008.

239 *The more of your evening*... Sonnentag, Sabine and F.R. H. Zijlstra. "Job Characteristics and Off-Job Activities as Predictors of Need for Recovery, Well-Being, and Fatigue." *Journal of Applied Psychology*, 9, 2006.

239 *That's how it went*...Derks, Daantje, Lieke L. ten Brummelhuis, Dino Zecic, Arnold Bakker. "Switching On and Off...Does Smartphone Use Obstruct the Possibility to Engage in Recovery Activities?" *European Journal of Work*

and Organizational Psychology," Dec. 2012.

240 *Recreation buffers stress...*Coleman, Dennis and Seppo E. Iso-Ahola. "Leisure and Health: The Role of Social Support and Self-Determination." *Journal of Leisure Research*, Vol. 25, 1993.

240 *Respites restore energy...*Eden, Dov. "Vacations and Other Respites: Studying Stress On and Off the Job." *International Review of Industrial and Organizational Psychology*, 16, 2001.

240 *Respites of two weeks...*Hobfoll, Stevan. E. and Arie Shirom. "Stress and Burnout in the Workplace: Conservation of Resources." *Handbook of Organizational Behavior*, 1993.

240 *Active leisure boosts positive mood...*Chalip, L., David R. Thomas, Judith Voyle. "Enhancing Well-Being Through Sport and Recreation," March 1996.

242 *Vacations can substantially cut the risk...*Gump, Brooks and Karen A. Matthews. "Are Vacations Good for Your Health? The 9-Year Mortality Experience After the Multiple Risk Factor Intervention Trial." *Psychosomatic Medicine*, Sept.- Oct. 2000.

243 *Charlotte Fritz and Sabine Sonnentag found...*Fritz, Charlotte and Sabine Sonnentag. "Recovery, Well-Being, and Performance-Related Outcomes: The Role of Workload and Vacation Experiences." *Journal of Applied Psychology*, Jul. 2006.

246 *Playfulness at work...*Lin, Liang-Hung, Wei-Hsin Lin, Ching-Yueh Chen, Ya-Feng Teng. "Playfulness and Innovation—A Multilevel Study in Individuals and Organizations," 2010.

Chapter 11—Life's Out There, If You Are

249 *Researchers have found that it can lead...* Kim, Meeri. "Boredom's Link to Mental Illnesses, Injuries, and Dysfunctional Behaviors," *Washington Post*, July 17, 2021.

249 *In 11 studies conducted...*Wilson, Timothy D., David A. Reinhard, Erin C. Westgate, Daniel T. Gilbert, Nicole Ellerbeck, Cheryl Hahn, Casey L. Brown, Adi Shaked. "Just Think: The Challenges of the Disengaged Mind." *Science*, July 4, 2014.

249 *Of all things...*Krueger Alan B., Daniel Kahneman, David Schkade, Norbert Schwarz, Arthur Stone. "National Time Accounting: The Currency of Life." Working Papers, Princeton University, 2008.

249 *The buzz even extends...*DeLeire, Thomas, and Ariel Kalil. "Does Consumption Buy Happiness? Evidence from the United States." *International Review of Economics*, Vol. 57, 2010.

252 *A happy friend...*Fowler, James H. and Nicholas A. Christakis. "Dynamic Spread of Happiness in a Large Social Network: Longitudinal Analysis Over 20 Years in the Framingham Heart Study." *The BMJ*, Dec. 5, 2008.

254 *People who are...* Elliot, Andrew and Judith Harackiewicz. "Goal Setting, Achievement Orientation, and Intrinsic Motivation: A Mediational Analysis." *Journal of Personality and Social Psychology*, 1994.

256 *Researchers Kennon Sheldon*...Sheldon, Kennon M. and Sonja Lyubomirsky. "Revisiting the Sustainable Happiness Model: Can Happiness Be Pursued?" *Journal of Positive Psychology*, 2019.

256 *An analysis*...Sin, Nancy L. and Sonja Lyubomirsky. "Enhancing Well-Being and Alleviating Depressive Symptoms with Positive Psychology Interventions: A Practice-Friendly Meta-Analysis. *Journal of Clinical Psychology*, 65, 2009.

256 *Fifty percent of your potential happiness*...Sheldon, Kennon M. and Sonja Lyubomirsky. "Is It Possible to Become Happier? (And If So How?)." *Social and Personal Psychology Compass* I, 2007.

256 *Lyubomirsky calls*...Lyubomirsky, Sonja and Kristin Layous. "How Do Simple Positive Activities Increase Well-Being?" *Current Directions in Psychological Science*, 2013.

257 *This is no doubt*...Van Boven, Leaf. "Experientialism, Materialism, and the Pursuit of Happiness." *Review of General Psychology* 9, No. 2, 2005.

257 *The key to*...Lyubomirsky, Sonja, Kennon M. Sheldon, David Schkade. "Pursuing Happiness: The Architecture of Sustainable Change." *Review of General Psychology*, Vol. 9, 2005.

Bibliography

Alexandrova-Karamanova, Anna, Irina Todorova, Anthony Montgomery, Efharis Panagopoulou, Patricia Costa, Adriana Baban, Asli Davas, Milan Milosevic, Dragan Mijakowski. "Burnout and Health Behaviors in Health Professionals from Seven European Countries." *International Archives of Occupational and Environmental Health*, 2016.

Allen, David. *Getting Things Done*. Viking, 2001.

Altmann, Erik M., J. Gregory Trafton, David Z. Hambrick. "Momentary Interruptions Can Derail the Train of Thought." *Journal of Experimental Psychology*, Feb. 2014.

Anderson, Stella E., Betty S. Coffey, Robin T. Byerly. "Formal Organizational Initiatives and Informal Workplace Practices: Links to Work-Family Conflict and Job-Related Outcomes," 2002.

Arthur, Michelle M. "Share Price Reactions to Work-Family Human Resource Decisions: An Institutional Perspective," 2003.

Azagba, Sunday and Mesbah F. Sharaf. "Psychosocial Working Conditions and the Utilization of Health Care Services." BMC Public Health, 2011.

Bailey, Brian P., Joseph A. Konstan, John V. Carlis. "Measuring the Effects of Interruptions on Task Performance in the User Interface." *Proceedings of the IEEE International Conference on Systems, Man and Cybernetics*, 2000.

Bakker, Arnold, Evangelia Demerouti, Martin C. Euwema. "Job Resources Buffer the Impact of Job Demands on Burnout." *Journal of Occupational Health Psychology*, 2005.

Bastiem, Celyne H., Annie Vallieres, Charles M. Morin. "Precipitating Factors of Insomnia." *Behavioral Sleep Medicine*, 2004.

Baumeister, Roy F. and Kathleen D. Vohs. "Self-Regulation, Ego Depletion, and Motivation. *Social and Personality Psychology Compass* 1/1, 2007.

Bennett, Andrew A., Allison S. Gabriel, Charles Calderwood, Jason J. Dahling, John P. Trougakos. "Better Together? Examining Profiles of Employee Recovery Experiences." *Journal of Applied Psychology, 101*(12), 2016.

Bianchi, Renzo, Eric Laurent, Irvin Sam Shonfeld. "Is the Burnout Process a Process of Depression? A Categorical Approach," 2014.

Boksem, Maarten A. S., Theo F. Meijman, Monique M. Lorist. "The Effects of Mental Fatigue on Attention: An ERP Study," 2005.

Borkovec, Thomas D., Michelle G. Newman, Aaron L. Pincus, Richard Lytle. "A Component Analysis of Cognitive-Behavioral Therapy for Generalized Anxiety Disorder and the Role of Interpersonal Problems." *Journal of Consulting*, 2002.

Brown, William M., Lee Cronk, Keith Grochow, Amy Jacobson, C. Karen Liu, Zoran Popovich, Robert Trivers. "Dance Reveals Symmetry, Especially in Young Men." *Nature*. Dec. 22, 2005.

Chalip, L., David R. Thomas, Judith Voyle. "Enhancing Well-Being Through Sport and Recreation," March 1996.

Clark, Melissa A., Jesse S. Michel, Gregory W. Stevens, Julia W. Howell, Ross S. Scruggs. "Workaholism, Work Engagement and Work-Home Outcomes: Exploring the Mediating Role of Positive and Negative Emotions." *Stress Health*, Oct. 30, 2014.

Cole, Stephen R., Ichiro Kawachi, Simin Liu, J. Michael Gaziano, Joanne E. Manson, Julie E. Buring, Charles H. Hennekens. "Time Urgency and Risk of Non-Fatal Myocardial Infarction." *International Journal of Epidemiology*, Apr. 30, 2001.

Coleman, Dennis and Seppo E. Iso-Ahola. "Leisure and Health: The Role of Social Support and Self-Determination." *Journal of Leisure Research*, Vol. 25, 1993.

Conte, Jeffrey M., Kathleen L. Ringenbach, Stacey K. Moran, Frank J. Landy. "Criterion-Validity Evidence for Time Urgency: Associations with Burnout, Organizational Commitment, and Job Involvement in Travel Agents." *Applied H. R. M. Research*, 2001, Vol. 6.

Cousineau, Marion, Josh H. McDermott, and Isabelle Peretz. "The Basis of Musical Consonance as Revealed by Congenital Amusia." PNAS November 27, 2012.

Csikszentmihalyi, Mihaly. *Flow*, 1990.

Csikszentmihalyi, Mihaly. *Optimal Experience*. Cambridge University Press, 1992.

Deci, Edward. *Why We Do What We Do*. Penguin Books, 1991.

De Dreu, Carsten K. W. "Time Pressure and Closing of the Mind in Negotiation," 2003.

De Jonge, Jan. "What Makes a Good Work Break? Off-Job and On-Job Recovery as Predictors of Employee Heath." *Industrial Health*, Mar. 2020.

DeLeire, Thomas and Ariel Kalil. "Does Consumption Buy Happiness? Evidence from the United States." *International Review of Economics*, Vol. 57, 2010.

Demke, Allard E. and Xiaoxi Yao. "Chronic Disease from Exposure to Long-Hour Work Schedules Over a 32-Year Period." *Journal of Occupational and Environmental Medicine*, Vol. 58, No. 9, 2016.

Derks, Daantje, Lieke L. ten Brummelhuis, Dino Zecic, Arnold Bakker. "Switching On and Off…Does Smartphone Use Obstruct the Possibility to Engage in Recovery Activities?" *European Journal of Work and Organizational Psychology*," Dec. 2012.

Detert, James and Amy Edmondson. "Why Employees Are Afraid to Speak," *Harvard Business Review*, 2007.

Diener, Ed. "Subjective Well-Being." *Psychological Bulletin*, 95, 1984.

Dimitroff, Stephanie J., Omid Kardan, Elizabeth A. Necka, Jean Decety, Marc G. Berman, Greg J. Norman. "Physiological Dynamics of Stress Contagion." Open access. July 2017.

Dragano, Nico, Johannes Siegrist, Solja T. Nyberg, Thorsten Lunau, Eleonor I. Fransson, Lars Alfredsson, Jakob B. Bjorner, Marianne Borritz, Hermann Burr, Raimund Erbel, Göran Fahlén, Marcel Goldberg, Mark Hamer, Katriina Heikkilä, Karl-Heinz Jöckel, Anders Knutsson, Ida E. H. Madsen, Martin L. Nielsen, Maria Nordin, Tuula Oksanen, Jan H. Pejtersen, Jaana Pentti, Reiner Rugulies, Paula Salo, Jürgen Schupp, Archana Singh-Manoux, Andrew Steptoe, Töres Theorell, Jussi Vahtera, Peter J. M. Westerholm, Hugo Westerlund, Marianna Virtanen, Marie Zins, G. David Batty, Mika Kivimäki, IPD-Work Consortium. "Effort-Reward Imbalance at Work and Incident Coronary Heart Disease: A Multicohort Study of 90,164 Individuals." *Epidemiology*, July, 2017.

Dunn, Jacob and Michael H. Grider. *Physiology, Adenosine Triphosphate*. StatPearls, 2021.

Duplooy, Janine D. and Gert Roodt. "Work Engagement, Burnout and Related Constructs as Predictors of Turnover Intentions." *SA Journal of Industrial Psychology* 36, 2010.

Echouffo-Tcheugui, Sara C. Conner, Jayandra J. Himali, Pauline Maillard, Charles S. DeCarli, Alexa S. Beiser, Ramachandran S. Vasan, Sudha Seshadri. "Circulating Cortisol and Cognitive and Structural Brain Measures. The Framingham Heart Study." 2018

Eden, Dov. "Vacations and Other Respites: Studying Stress On and Off the Job." *International Review of Industrial and Organizational Psychology*, 16, 2001.

Elliot, Andrew and Judith Harackiewicz. "Goal Setting, Achievement Orientation, and Intrinsic Motivation: A Mediational Analysis." *Journal of Personality and Social Psychology*, 1994.

Ellis, Michael J. *Why People Play*. Prentice-Hall, 1973.

Filbey, Francesca M. and Uma S. Yezhuvath. "A Multimodal Study of Impulsivity and Body Weight: Integrating Behavioral, Cognitive, and Neuroimaging Approaches." *Obesity*, Jan. 25, 2017.

Finney, Montenique, Catherine M. Stoney, Tilmer O. Engebretson. "Hostility and Anger Expression in African American and European American Men Is Associated with Cardiovascular and Lipid Reactivity." March 12, 2003.

Fowler, James H. and Nicholas A. Christakis. "Dynamic Spread of Happiness in a Large Social Network: Longitudinal Analysis Over 20 Years in the Framingham Heart Study." *The BMJ*, Dec. 5, 2008.

Fredrickson, Barbara. *Positivity*. Crown, 2009.

Fredrickson, Barbara. "What Good Are Positive Emotions?" *Review of General Psychology*, Vol. 2 No 3, 1998.

Fritz, Charlotte and Sabine Sonnentag. "Recovery, Well-Being, and Performance-Related Outcomes: The Role of Workload and Vacation Experiences." *Journal of Applied Psychology*, Jul. 2006.

Frone, Michael. *Handbook of Occupational Health Psychology*. American Psychological Association, 2003.

Frone, Michael R., Marcia Russell, Grace M. Barnes. "Work-Family Conflict, Gender, and Health-Related Outcomes: A Study of Employed Parents in Two Community Samples." APA PsycArticles, 1996.

Gailliot, Matthew T., Roy F. Baumeister, C. Nathan DeWall, Jon K. Maner, E. Ashby Plant, Dianne M. Tice, Lauren E. Brewer, Brandon J. Schmeichel. "Self-Control Relies on Glucose as a Limited Energy Source: Willpower Is More Than a Metaphor." *Journal of Personal Social Psychology*, Feb. 2007.

Gallagher, Winifred. *Rapt: Attention and the Focused Life*. The Penguin Press, 2009.

Gilbert, Daniel T., Elizabeth C. Pinel, Timothy D. Wilson, Stephen J. Blumberg. "Immune Neglect: A Source of Durability Bias in Affective Forecasting." *Journal of Personality and Social Psychology*, No. 3 1998.

Gilbert, Daniel T. and Timothy D. Wilson. "Prospection: Experiencing the Future." *Science*, Oct. 2007.

Giltay, Erik J., Johanna Geleijnse, Frans G. Zitman. "Dispositional Optimism and All-Cause Cardiovascular Mortality in a Prospective Cohort of Elderly Dutch Men and Women." *Archives of General Psychiatry*, 2004.

Gollwitzer, Peter M. "Implementation Intentions: Strong Effects of Simple Plans." *American Psychologist*, 1999.

Gordon, Gil. *Turn It Off!* Three Rivers Books, 2001.

Greenberg, Paul, Andree-Anne Fournier, Tammy Sisitsky, Crystal T. Pike, Ronald C. Kessler. "The Economic Burden of Adults with Depressive Disorder." *Journal of Clinical Psychology*, 2015.

Gump, Brooks and Karen A. Matthews. "Are Vacations Good for Your Health? The 9-Year Mortality Experience After the Multiple Risk Factor Intervention Trial." *Psychosomatic Medicine*, Sept.- Oct. 2000.

Halkos, George and Dimitrios Bousinakis. "The Effect of Stress and Satisfaction on Productivity." *International Journal of Productivity and Performance Management*, Vol. 59, 2010.

Hallowell, Edward. *Driven to Distraction*. Anchor, 2011.

Han, Kuem Sun, Lin Kim, Insop Shim. "Stress and Sleep Disorder." *Experimental Neurobiology* Vol. 21, Dec. 2012.

Haraldsson, Gudmundur D. and Jack Kellam. "Going Public: Iceland's Journey to a Shorter Workweek," June 2021.

Harris, Melissa L., Christopher Oldmeadow, Alexis Hure, Judy Luu, Deborah Loxton, John Attia. "Stress Increases the Risk of Type 2 Diabetes Onset in Women: A 12-Year Longitudinal Study Using Causal Modeling." PLos One. Feb. 21, 2017.

Hasher, Lynn, Cindy Lustig, Rose Zacks. "Inhibitory Mechanisms and the Control of Attention." APA PsycNet, 2007.

Hayes, Steven. *Get Out of Your Mind and into Your Life*. New Harbinger Publications, 2005.

Hedge, Alan. "Effects of Ergonomic Management Software on Employee Performance." Cornell University, 1999.

Hill, Edward, Brent C. Miller, Sara P. Weiner, and Joe Colihan. "Influences of the Virtual Office on Aspects of Work and Work/Life Balance." *Personnel Psychology*, 2006.

Hobfoll, Stevan E. "Conservation of Resources Theory: Applications to Stress and Management in the Workplace," 2001.

Hobfoll, Stevan E. and Arie Shirom. "Stress and Burnout in the Workplace: Conservation of Resources." *Handbook of Organizational Behavior*, 1993.

Hu, Qiao, Wilmar B. Schaufeli, Toon W. Taris. "The Job Demands-Resources Model: An Analysis of Additive and Joint Effects of Demands and Resources." APA PsycNet, 2011.

Huang, Yuli, Shuxian Xu, Jinghai Hua, Dingji Zhu, Changhua Liu, Yunzhao Hu, Tiebang Liu, Dingli Xu. "Association Between Job Strain and Risk of Incident Stroke: A Meta-Analysis." *Neurology*, Nov. 10, 2015.

Hunter, Emily and Cindy Wu. "Give Me a Better Break: Choosing Workday Break Activities to Maximize Resource Recovery." *Journal of Applied Psychology*, Feb. 2016.

Jackson, Maggie. *Distracted*. Prometheus Books, 2008.

Jackson, Thomas, Ray Dawson, Darren Wilson. "Understanding Email Interaction Increases Organizational Productivity." *Communications of the ACM*, 2003.

Janaro, Ralph E. and Stephen E. Bechtold. "A Study of the Reduction of Fatigue Impact on Productivity Through Optimal Rest Break Scheduling," Aug. 1985.

Jensen, Bill. *The Simplicity Survival Handbook*. Basic Books, 2007.

Jha, Amism P., Jason Krompinger, Michael J. Baime. "Mindfulness Training Modifies Subsystems of Attention." *Cognitive, Affective & Behavioral Neuroscience*, June 7, 2007.

Johnson, Eric J. and Amos Tversky. "Affect, Generalization, and the Perception of Risk." *Journal of Personality and Social Psychology*, July 1983.

Kabat-Zinn, Jon. *Full Catastrophe Living*. Bantam Books, 2013.

Kahneman, Daniel. *Thinking, Fast and Slow*. Farrar, Strauss, and Giroux, 2013.

Kakabadse, Nada, Gayle Porter, David Vance. "Addicted to Technology," 2007.

Karasek, Jr., Robert A. "Job Demands, Job Decision Latitude, and Mental Strain: Implications for Job Design." *Administrative Science Quarterly*, Vol. 24 No. 2, 1979.

Kawachi, Ichiro, D. Sparrow, P. S. Vokonas, S. T. Weiss. "Symptoms of Anxiety and Risk of Coronary Heart Disease: The Normative Aging Study," Nov. 1994.

Killingworth, Matthew A. and Daniel T. Gilbert. "A Wandering Mind Is an Unhappy Mind." *Science*, 2010.

Kim, Meeri. "Boredom's Link to Mental Illnesses, Injuries, and Dysfunctional Behaviors," *Washington Post*, July 17, 2021.

Kivimaki, Mika, Markus Jokela, Solja T. Nyberg, Archana Singh-Manoux, Eleonor I. Fransson, Lars Alfredsson, Jakob B. Bjorner, Marianne Borritz, Hermann Burr, Annalisa Casini, Els Clays, Dirk De Bacquer, Nico Dragano, Raimund Erbel, Goedele A. Geuskens, Mark Hamer, Wendela E. Hooftman, Irene L. Houtman, Karl-Heinz Jockel, France Kittel, Anders Knutsson, Markku Koskenvuo, Thorsten Lunau, Ida E. H. Madsen, Martin L. Nielsen, Maria Nordin, Tuula Oksanen, Jan H. Pejtersen, Jaana Pentti, Reiner Rugulies, Paula Salo, Martin J. Shipley, Johannes Siegrist, Andrew Steptoe, Sakari B. Suominen, Tores Theorell, Jussi Vahtera, Peter J. M. Westerholm, Hugo Westerlund, Dermot O'Reilly, Meena Kumari, G. David Batty, Jane E. Ferrie, Marianna Virtanen, IPD Work Consortium. "Long Working Hours and Risk of Coronary Heart Disease and Stroke: A Systematic Review and Meta-Analysis of Published and Unpublished Data for 603,838 Individuals." *The Lancet*. Published Aug. 19, 2015.

Kivimaki, Mika, Jaana Pentti, Jane E. Ferrie, G. David Batty, Solja T. Nyberg, Marcus Jokela, Marianna Virtanen, Lars Alfredsson, Nico Dragano, Eleonor I. Fransson, Marcel Goldberg, Anders Knutsson, Markku Koskenvuo, Aki Koskinen, Anne Kouvonen, Ritva Luukkonen, Tuula Oksanen, Reiner Rugulies, Johannes Siegrist, Archana Singh-Manoux, Sakari Suominen, Tores Theorell, Ari Vaananen, Jussi Vahtera, Peter J. M. Westerholm, Hugo Westerlund, Marie Zins, Timo Strandberg, Andrew Steptoe, John Deanfield, for the IPD Work Consortium. "Work Stress and Risk of Death in Men and Women with and without Cardiometabolic Disease: a Multicohort Study." *The Lancet Diabetes and Endocrinology*, 2018.

Kontogiannis, Tom and Z. Kossiavelou. "Stress and Team Performance: Principles and Strategies for Intelligent Decision Aids." *Safety Science*, Dec. 1999.

Kowalski-Trakofler, Kathleen M., Charles Vaught, Ted Scharf. "Judgment and Decision Making Under Stress: An Overview for Emergency Managers." *International Journal of Emergency Management*, January 2003.

Krueger Alan B., Daniel Kahneman, David Schkade, Norbert Schwarz, Arthur Stone. "National Time Accounting: The Currency of Life." Working Papers, Princeton University, 2008.

Kuhnel, Jana, Hannes Zacher, Jessica de Bloom, Ronald Bledow. "Take a Break! Benefits of Sleep and Short Breaks for Work Engagement." *European Journal of Work and Organizational Psychology*, Vol. 26, Issue 4, 2017.

Lee, Lewina O., Peter James, Emily S. Zevon, Eric S. Kim, Claudia Trudel-Fitzgerald, Avron S. Spiro III, Francine Grodstein, Laura D. Kubzansky. "Optimism Is Associated with Exceptional Longevity in 2 Epidemiologic Cohorts of Men and Women." PNAS, Sept. 10, 2019.

Lim, Julian, Wen-chau Wu, Jiongjiong Wang, John A. Detre, David F. Dinges, Hengyi Rao. "Imaging Brain Fatigue from Sustained Mental Workload: An ASL Perfusion Study of the Time-on-Task Effect." *NeuroImage* 49, 2010.

Lin, Liang-Hung, Wei-Hsin Lin, Ching-Yueh Chen, Ya-Feng Teng. "Playfulness and Innovation—A Multilevel Study in Individuals and Organizations," 2010.

Lyubomirksy, Sonja, Laura King, Ed Diener. "The Benefits of Frequent Positive Affect: Does Happiness Lead to Success?" *Psychological Bulletin* 131, No. 6, 2005.

Lyubomirsky, Sonja and Kristin Layous. "How Do Simple Positive Activities Increase Well-Being?" *Current Directions in Psychological Science*, 2013.

Lyubomirsky, Sonja, Kennon M. Sheldon, David Schkade. "Pursuing Happiness:

The Architecture of Sustainable Change." *Review of General Psychology*, Vol. 9, 2005.

Mark, Gloria, Daniel Gudith, Ulrich Klocke. "The Cost of Interrupted Work: More Speed and Stress." *Proceedings of the SIGCHI Conference on Human Factors in Computing Systems*, 2008.

Mark, Gloria, Shamsi T. Iqbal, Mary Czerwinski, Paul Johns, Akane Sano. "Email Duration, Batching, and Self-Interruption: Patterns of Email Use on Productivity and Stress," 2016.

Maslach, Christina and Michael Leiter. *The Truth About Burnout*. Jossey-Bass, 2000.

Maslach, Christina, Michael P. Leiter. "Understanding the Burnout Experience: Recent Research and Its Implications for Psychiatry." *World Psychiatry*, 2016.

Mather, Mara and Nichole R. Lighthall. "Both Risk and Reward Are Processed Differently in Decisions Made Under Stress." *Current Directions in Psychological Science*, March 26, 2012.

McLean, Katherine A., Emilio Ferrer, Stephen R. Aichele, David A. Bridwell, Anthony Zanesco, Tonya L. Jacobs, Brandon G. King, Erika L. Rosenberg, Baljinder K. Sahdra, Phillip R. Shaver, B. Alan Wallace, George R. Mangun, Clifford D. Saron. "Intensive Meditation Training Improves Perceptual Discrimination and Sustained Attention." *Psychological Science*, June 21, 2010.

Meerlo, Peter, Bertrand Pragt, Serge Daan. "Social Stress Induces High Intensity Sleep in Rats." *Neuroscience Letters*, April 1997.

Mergenthaler, Philipp, Ute Lindauer, Gerald A. Dienel, Andreas Meisel. "Sugar for the Brain: The Role of Glucose in Physiological and Pathological Brain Function." *Trends in Neuroscience*, Oct. 2013.

Meyer, David and David Kieras. "Effective Control of Cognitive Processes in Task-Switching," 2001.

Moser, Jason S., Rachel Hartwig, Tim P. Moran, Alexander A. Jendrusina, Ethan Kross. "Neural Markers of Positive Reappraisal and Their Associations with Trait Reappraisal." *Journal of Abnormal Psychology*, 2014.

Mostofsky, Elizabeth, Elizabeth Anne Penner, Murray A. Mittleman. "Outbursts of Anger as a Trigger of Acute Cardiovascular Events: A Systematic Review and Meta-Analysis." *European Heart Journal*, Vol. 35, June 1, 2014.

Nash, Laura and Howard Stevenson. *Just Enough: Tools for Creating Success in Your Work and Life*. Harvard Business School Publishing, 2004.

Niaura, Raymond, John F. Todaro, Avron Spiro III, Kenneth D. Ward, Scott Weiss. "Hostility, the Metabolic Syndrome, and Incident Coronary Heart Disease." *Health Psychology*, 2002.

Ninaus, Katharina, Sandra Diehl, Ralf Terlutter, Kara Chan, Anqi Huang. "Benefits and Stressors: Perceived Effect of ICT Use on Employee Health and Work Stress: An Exploratory Study from Austria and Hong Kong." *International Journal of Qualitative Studies on Health and Well-Being*," October 2015.

Nolen-Hoeksema, Susan. *Women Who Think Too Much: How to Break Free of Overthinking and Reclaim Your Life*. Holt, 2003.

Ost, L. G. and B. E. Westling. "Applied Relaxation vs. Cognitive Behavior Therapy in the Treatment of Panic Disorder." *Behavioral Research Therapy*, Feb. 1995.

Panagioti, Maria, Efharis Panagopoulou, Peter Bower, George Lewith, Evangelos Kontopantelis, Carolyn Chew-Graham, Shoba Dawson, Harm van Marwijk, Keith Geraghty, Aneez Esmail. "Controlled Interventions to Reduce Burnout in Physicians: A Systematic Review and Meta-Analysis." *JAMA Internal Medicine*, 2017.

Pega, Frank, Balint Nafradi, Natalie C. Momen, Yuka Ujita, Kai N. Streicher, Annette M. Pruss-Ustun, Technical Advisory Group, Alexis Descatha, Tim Driscoll, Frida M. Fischer, Lode Godderis, Hannah M. Kiiver, Jian Li, Linda L. Magnusson Hanson, Reiner Rugulies, Kathrine Sorensen, Tracy J. Woodruff. "Global, Regional and National Burdens from Ischemic Heart Disease and Stroke Attributable to Exposure to Long Working Hours for 194 Countries, 2000-2016: A Systematic Analysis from the WHO/ILO Joint Estimates of the Work-Related Burden of Disease and Injury." *Science Direct*, May 17, 2021.

Pencavel, John. "The Productivity of Working Hours." Stanford Institute for Economic Policy Research, 2013.

Perlow, Leslie. "Finding Time, Stopping the Frenzy." *Business Health*, Aug. 16, 1998.

Perlow, Leslie. *Sleeping with Your Smartphone*. Harvard Business School Publishing, 2012.

Peterson, Christopher and Martin Seligman. *Character Strengths and Virtues*. American Psychological Assoc., Oxford University Press, 2004.

Reivich, Karen and Andrew W. Shatte. *The Resilience Factor*. Broadway Books, 2003.

Richardson, Katherine M. and Hannah R. Rothstein. "Effects of Occupational Stress Management Intervention Programs: A Meta-Analysis," 2008.

Rozanski, Alan, Chirag Bavashi, Laura D. Kubzansky, Randy Cohen. "Association of Optimism with Cardiovascular Events and All-Cause Mortality: A Systematic Review and Meta-Analysis." JAMA Network Open, 2019.

Ruthsatz, Joanne and Jourdan B. Urbach. "Child Prodigy: A Novel Cognitive Profile Places Elevated General Intelligence, Exceptional Working Memory, and Attention to Detail at the Root of Prodigiousness," 2012.

Salvagioni, Denise Albieri Jodas, Francine Nesello Melanda, Arthur Eumann Mesas, Alberto Duran Gonzalez, Flavia Lopes Gabani, Selma Maffei de Andrade. "Physical, Psychological, and Occupational Consequences of Job Burnout: A Systematic Review of Prospective Studies." PLos One. Oct 4, 2017.

Sanger, Jessica, Laura Bechtold, Daniela Schoofs, Meinolf Blaszkewiz, Edmund Wascher. "The Influence of Acute Stress on Attention Mechanisms and Its Electrophysiological Correlates," 2014.

Sapolsky, Robert. *Behave*. Penguin Books, 2017.

Sapolsky, Robert. *Why Zebras Don't Get Ulcers*. St. Martin's Griffin, 2004.

Savage, Mandara and Darren Pipkins. "The Effect of Rest Periods on Hand Fatigue and Productivity," 2006.

Seligman, Martin. *Flourish*. Free Press, 2011.

Seligman, Martin. *Learned Optimism*. Vintage Books, 2006.

Sheldon, Kennon M. and Sonja Lyubomirsky. "Is It Possible to Become Happier?

(And If So, How?)." *Social and Personality Psychology Compass* 1, 2007.

Sheldon, Kennon M. and Sonja Lyubomirsky. "Revisiting the Sustainable Happiness Model: Can Happiness Be Pursued?" *Journal of Positive Psychology*, 2019.

Shepard III, Edward M., Thomas J. Clifton, Douglas Kruse. "Flexible Work Hours and Productivity: Some Evidence from the Pharmaceutical Industry," 1996.

Sheppard, George. "Work-Life Balance Programs to Improve Employee Performance." Walden University, 2016.

Shin, Duckjung and Jackson Enoh. "Availability and Use of Work-Life Balance Programs: Relationship with Organizational Profitability." MDPI.com, 2020.

Shirom, Arie and Samuel Melamed. "Burnout and Health Review: Current Knowledge and Future Research Directions." Chapter from *International Review of Industrial and Organizational Psychology, Vol. 20*, 2005.

Sianoja, Marjaana, Christine J. Syrek, Jessica de Bloom, Kalevi Korpela, Ulla Kinnunen. "Enhancing Daily Well-Being at Work Through Lunchtime Park Walks and Relaxing Exercises: Recovery Experiences as Mediators." *Journal of Occupational Health Psychology*, 23(3) 2018.

Sin, Nancy L. and Sonja Lyubomirsky. "Enhancing Well-Being and Alleviating Depressive Symptoms with Positive Psychology Interventions: A Practice-Friendly Meta-Analysis." *Journal of Clinical Psychology*, 65, 2009.

Sonnentag, Sabine. "Work, Recovery Activities, and Individual Well-Being: A Diary Study." *Journal of Occupational Health Psychology*, 6, 2001.

Sonnentag, Sabine, Carmen Binnewies, Eva J. Mojza. "Did You Have a Nice Evening? A Day-Level Study on Recovery Experiences, Sleep, and Affect." *Journal of Applied Psychology*, May 2008.

Sonnentag, Sabine, Carmen Binnewies, Eva J. Mojza. "Staying Well and Engaged When Demands Are High." *Journal of Applied Psychology*, 2010.

Sonnentag, Sabine, and Caterina Schiffner. "Psychological Detachment from Work During Nonwork Time and Employee Well-Being: The Role of Leader's Detachment." *The Spanish Journal of Psychology*, 2019.

Sonnentag, Sabine and Charlotte Fritz. "Recovery from Job Stress: The Stressor-Detachment Model as an Integrative Framework." *Journal of Organizational Behavior*, Apr. 2014.

Sonnentag, Sabine and Fred R. H. Zijlstra. "Job Characteristics and Off-Job Activities as Predictors of Need for Recovery, Well-Being, and Fatigue." *Journal of Applied Psychology*, 9, 2006.

Streufert, Siegfried, Susan C. Streufert, David Gorson. "Time Urgency and Coronary-Prone Behavior: The Effectiveness of a Behavior Pattern," 1981. APA PsycNet.

Syrek, Christine, Ella Apostel, Conny H. Antoni. "Stress in Highly Demanding IT Jobs: Transformational Leadership Moderates the Impact of Time Pressure on Exhaustion and Work-Life Balance." *Journal of Occupational Health Psychology*, July 2013.

Ten Brummelhuis, Lieke L. and Arnold B. Bakker. "Staying Engaged During the Week: The Effect of Off-Job Activities on Next Day Work Engagement." APA

PsycNet. 2012.

Thiede Thomas, Linda and Daniel C. Ganster. "Impact of Family-Supportive Work Variables on Work-Family Conflict and Strain: A Control Perspective." *Journal of Applied Psychology*, 1995.

Tracy, David. *Eat That Frog*. Berrett-Koehler Publishers, *2017*.

Trougakos, John P., Ivona Hideg, Bonnie Hayden Cheng, Daniel J. Beal. "Lunch Breaks Unpacked: The Role of Autonomy as a Moderator of Recovery During Lunch." *The Academy of Management Journal*, Apr. 2014.

Twenge, Jean M., Jonathan Haidt, Andrew B. Blake, Cooper McAllister, Hannah Lemon, Astrid Le Roy. "Worldwide Increases in Adolescent Loneliness." *Journal of Adolescence*, July 2021.

Van Boven, Leaf. "Experientialism, Materialism, and the Pursuit of Happiness." *Review of General Psychology* 9, No. 2, 2005.

Van Boven, Leaf, Margaret C. Campbell, Thomas Gilovich. "Stigmatizing Materialism: On Stereotypes and Impressions of Materialistic and Experiential Pursuits." *Personality and Social Psychology Bulletin* 85, No. 4, 2010.

Virtanen, Marianna and Mika Kivimaki. "Long Working Hours and Risk of Cardiovascular Disease." *Current Cardiology Reports*, 2018.

Von Thiele Schwarz, Ulrica and Henna Hasson. "Employee Self-Rated Productivity and Objective Organizational Production Levels." *Journal of Occupational and Environmental Medicine*, 2011.

Ware, Bronnie. *The Top Five Regrets of the Dying*. Hay House Inc., 2019.

West, Colin P., Liselotte N. Dyrbye, Patricia J. Erwin, Tait D. Shanafelt. "Interventions to Prevent and Reduce Physician Burnout: A Systematic Review and Meta-Analysis." *The Lancet, 388, 2016.*

Wiginton, Keri. "Your Ability to Stay Focused May Be Limited to 4 or 5 Hours a Day." *Washington Post*, June 1, 2021.

Wilmer, Henry H. and Jason M. Chein. "Mobile Technology Habits—Patterns of Association Among Device Usage, Intertemporal Preference, Impulse Control, and Reward Sensitivity." *Psychonomic Bulletin & Review*, 2016.

Wilson, Timothy D., David A. Reinhard, Erin C. Westgate, Daniel T. Gilbert, Nicole Ellerbeck, Cheryl Hahn, Casey L. Brown, Adi Shaked. "Just Think: The Challenges of the Disengaged Mind." *Science*, July 4, 2014.

Wright, Thomas A., Russell Cropanzano, Douglas G. Bonett. "The Moderating Role of Employee Well-Being on the Relationship Between Job Satisfaction and Job Performance." *Journal of Occupational Health Psychology*, May 2007.

Yang, Haiou, Peter L. Schnall, Maritza Jauregui, Ta-Chen Su, Dean Baker. "Work Hours and Self-Reported Hypertension Among Working People in California." *Hypertension*, 2006.

Zawadzki, Matthew, Joshua M. Smyth, Heather A. Costigan. "Real-Time Associations Between Engaging in Leisure and Daily Health and Well-Being." *Annals of Behavioral Medicine*, 2015.

Zawadzki, Matthew, Joshua M. Smyth, Marcellus M. Merritt, William Gerin. "Absorption in Self-Selected Activities Is Associated with Lower Ambulatory Blood

Pressure But Not for High Trait Ruminators." *American Journal of Hypertension*, 2013.

Zhu, Xiao-Hong, Hongyan Qiao, Fei Du, Qiang Xiong, Xiao Liu, Xiaoliang Zhang, Kamil Ugurbil, Wei Chen. "Quantitative Imaging of Energy Expenditure in the Human Brain." *Neuroimage*, May 1, 2012.

Zhu, Ze, Lauren Kuykendall, Xichao Zhang. "The Impact of Within-Day Work Breaks on Daily Recovery Processes: An Event-Based Pre-/Post-Experience Sampling Study," 2018.

Zolnierczyk-Zreda, D. "An Intervention to Reduce Work-Related Burnout in Teachers." *International Journal of Occupational Safety and Ergonomics*, 2005.

Index

A

ABC Model 106-109, 130, 201
Activation-rest dynamic 226
Adenosine triphosphate (ATP) 226-228
Admiration 219, 220
Adrenal glands 75
Agile mind 3, 189, 203
Allen, David 142, 145
Amygdala 65-67, 69, 73, 75, 80
Ancient brain 55, 66, 68, 72, 75, 79, 84, 99
Attention 2-5, 9-11, 18, 39, 41, 42, 56, 78, 103, 110-113, 134-136, 151, 153, 154, 158, 159, 160-165, 177-182, 210, 218, 227, 230, 244
  and control 135, 154, 159, 160, 164
  and happiness 2, 10, 110-116, 258, 265, 273
  and interruptions 151, 152, 160, 162
  and multitasking 164, 165
  and self-regulation 154, 158, 160, 162, 163
  and stress 77, 110, 111, 133, 135, 136, 141, 155, 159, 163, 164, 167, 173, 178
  alertness 181, 182, 229
  attention tools 179, 180
  bottom-up attention 11, 159
  focusing on a target 110, 177, 178
  focus zones 180, 182
  increasing attention 177-182
  limits 8, 9, 159, 160, 163, 164
  top-down attention 158, 179
  working memory 8, 39, 153, 154
Attention Deficit Trait 163
Autonomy 2, 3, 11, 13, 26, 58, 69, 70, 78, 112, 125, 141, 179, 192, 221, 232, 243, 250-253, 268
Awareness 2, 3, 11, 13, 16, 78, 112, 141, 148, 179

B

Balance Blockers 23
  obstacles at home 23
  obstacles at work 22, 23
Berlyne, Daniel 266
Berns, Gregory 248, 259
Benson, Herbert 110, 111
Bonakdarpour, Borna 180, 229
Boredom 249
Borkovec, Thomas 72, 77
Boston Consulting Group 43
Boundaries 2, 8, 12, 19, 23, 28, 32, 39-64, 128, 150, 152, 156, 157, 163, 167, 168, 170, 171, 175, 239
  aligning expectations 59
  boundary language 62, 63, 64
  email and messaging 166-176
  identifying boundaries 41, 54, 54-60
  negotiating for 61, 63, 64
  remote office boundaries 55-57
  saying No 52, 59, 62
  saying Yes too often 40, 55, 59

speaking up 12, 27, 41, 52, 53, 55, 58, 59, 61, 62, 105
Brain 8, 9, 65-87, 97-100, 105-113, 116-119, 135-141, 153-160, 163-165, 184-207, 209-218, 226-239
  amygdala 55, 65, 66, 67, 73, 75
  ancient 55, 66, 68, 72, 75, 79, 84, 99
  dopamine 115, 249, 252
  endorphins 114
  energy 225, 226-229
  limbic system 11, 66, 103
  limitations 8, 9, 12, 39, 163, 164
  self-regulation 9, 160, 163, 228, 229
  working memory 8, 39, 153-154, 177
Breaks 43, 57, 162, 180, 228-233
Burnout 1, 2, 9, 40, 43, 52, 57, 58, 69, 74, 92, 96, 116-129, 138, 150, 167, 168, 235, 242
  and depression 92, 118, 119, 121
  and engagement 50, 117, 118, 121
  and exhaustion 116, 117, 118
  and long hours 50, 116, 119, 125, 126, 167, 168
  and productivity 50, 116, 117, 119
  definition of 116
  effect on performance 2, 50, 116, 117, 119, 124
  health conditions caused by 121
  main dimensions 121
  speaking up 41, 58, 59, 125-128
  threat to employment 40
  work overload 116, 117, 119, 122, 126
Burnout recovery 124-129
Burnout symptoms 121
Burnout test 129
Burnout triggers 122, 123, 126
Busyness 4, 134, 140, 141

C

Catastrophic thoughts 67, 84-87, 191
  challenging them 87, 107, 108, 202
  circling 86
  downward spiral 85
  scattershot 85

thinking traps 201, 204-208
triggers 86, 87
Character strengths 220-222
Chein, Jason 160
Clark, Melissa 50
Clifton, Thomas 33
Cognitive Behavioral Therapy 106
Cognitive defusion 11, 82, 83, 130
Competence 26, 69, 115, 116, 118, 192, 250, 252
Control 10, 34, 41, 54, 68, 69, 70, 71-72, 112, 123, 151, 158, 187, 193, 194, 238
Cortisol 75, 92, 93, 100, 101, 103, 104, 185
Csikszentmihalyi, Mihaly 237
Cullen, Mark 48, 262

D

Dancing 16, 265-267, 272, 273
Deci, Edward 69, 250, 251, 253
De Jonge, Jan 235, 236
Depression 46, 72, 92, 100, 118, 119, 121, 161, 184, 188, 192, 200, 212, 235
Devices 39, 146, 150, 151, 166
  and control of 156-159, 165, 168-176
  and distractions 11, 150-155
  and impulse control 11, 160-162
Diabetes 19, 74, 92, 98, 99
  and stress 74, 92, 98, 99
Dimitroff, Stephanie 89
Doerr, Ken 228
Doran, Amy 268

E

Eden, Dov 240, 242
Edmonson, Amy 52
Ellis, Albert 106
Ellis, Michael 266
Email and messaging 12, 23, 54-55, 59-60, 150-153, 165-176, 244-246
  and addiction 151
  and boundaries 170-176
  and mental health 150-155, 160-162
  and stress 151, 153, 164-169

aligning expectations 59, 60, 157, 168
checking schedules 54, 172-174
disconnecting 160, 161-163, 168
email management tips 170-176
email rules and norms 176
email on vacation 175, 244-246
emergencies 60, 174
messaging apps 146, 172
overload 23, 80, 81, 157, 161, 163, 169-176
response times 54, 59, 60, 166-172
volume of 168, 169-176
work email at home 23, 54, 166-168, 174, 175
Employee Engagement 69, 117, 237
Engagement 33, 34, 47, 50, 124, 249, 250, 253
and core needs 69, 250, 253
and happiness 243, 250
and leisure activities 238, 243
Erikson, Erik 252
Expectations 59, 60, 157
aligning with after-hours work 55, 57, 60
aligning with clients 60
aligning with email response times 54, 59, 60, 157, 168
Experiences 4, 5, 256-258, 262, 265
Explanatory style 5, 185, 187, 188, 190-199, 202
optimistic explanatory style 188, 189, 194-199, 202
pessimistic explanatory style 188, 190, 191, 193, 196-198

F

False beliefs 2, 5, 13, 42, 65, 75, 82, 84, 86, 87, 99, 106-108, 140, 157, 187-199, 201-204
and catastrophic thoughts 67, 84-87, 191, 207
and rigid thinking 201
and stress 65, 74, 84-87, 191, 207
icebergs 76, 201, 203, 204

surface beliefs 201, 202
thinking traps 201, 204-208
Family 17, 24, 28, 29-31, 34-36, 54
and life balance 17-24, 29-31, 34-36
and scheduling 19, 29
Fatigue 8, 13, 45, 112, 113, 117, 119, 120, 225-229, 242
and attention 13, 45, 46, 112, 113, 226, 227
and breaks 46, 228-233
effort-recovery model 230
recharging 225-226, 227-249
strain and stress 45, 46, 227, 229
studies 45, 46, 233-240, 242
ultradian rhythm 229
Fight-or-flight response 66, 67, 73, 74, 80, 84, 98
Five Principles of Smarter Work 10
Flexible work 13, 25, 26, 33-38
remote work 13, 34-36, 56, 57
Work-Life Policy Menu 35
Focus on a target 177
counting exercise 178
mindfulness 111-113, 131
relaxation response 110, 111, 131
Fredrickson, Barbara 115, 209, 211, 212, 218
gratitude 116, 217, 218
positive emotions 209-213, 216-218
positivity ratio 211, 212
undo effect 116, 218
Friendship 22, 240, 252
Fritz, Charlotte 243

G

Gabriel, Allison 227, 233
Gallagher, Winifred 159
Gilbert, Daniel 77, 192
Gollwitzer, Peter 97
implementation intention 97, 204
mental contrasting 97
Gratification 4, 13, 216, 248, 251, 255, 262, 266
Gratitude 116, 217-219

Guilt 3, 12, 18, 22, 50, 52, 228, 241, 242
and stress 18, 50

H

Haidt, Jonathan 162
Happiness 4, 5, 22, 23, 46, 77, 213, 214,
   241, 248, 249-258, 260, 261, 269
and experiences 256-258, 262
and intrinsic motivation 251, 252, 256,
   257
and friendship 22, 252
and gratifications 262
and life engagement 256, 257
and money 254, 255
Hayes, Steven 82, 83
thought labeling 82, 83, 202
Health 8, 9, 16, 17, 19, 22, 27, 28, 34, 40,
   49, 52, 58, 61, 71, 74, 82-84, 90-92,
   95-108, 109-116, 116-130, 132, 152,
   160, 161, 163, 167, 184-185, 187-198,
   210-211, 218, 225-226, 228-233, 235,
   237-238, 242-243, 250-252, 256-257
and long hours 17, 40, 44, 45, 46, 50,
   52, 116-128
and stress 8, 44, 46, 47, 61, 71, 74, 84,
   95-131, 132-138
and time urgency 132, 136, 138
diabetes 19, 74, 92, 99
exercise 115, 232, 236
hobbies 20, 29, 57, 115, 180, 233, 238,
   239 256-259, 260-263
sleep 92, 101, 102, 180, 227
stroke 8, 98, 99
Heart disease 8, 19, 44, 74, 92, 94-96,
   121, 132, 138
cardiovascular disease 96, 207
coronary artery disease 44, 138, 181,
   189
heart attack 44, 50, 98, 132, 138, 189,
   207
high blood pressure 45, 74, 96 105, 138
hypertension 46, 47, 74
Hobbies 29, 57, 115, 128, 180, 233, 234,
   252, 262, 263, 270-273

Huang, Yuli 98

I

IBM Research 47
Icebergs 3, 76, 201, 203, 204
Identity 6, 49, 57, 274
Life I.D. 274
overwork 49, 50, 51
performance identity 49
Impatience 138-141, 148, 155, 163
Implementation Intention 96, 97, 141
Impulse control 104, 136, 150, 151 159,
   160, 161, 163, 177
and attention 134-136
and devices 160-163, 166-168
and instant gratification 159-163
Attention Deficit Trait 163
damaged by interruptions 159, 160
effortful control 136, 160
Information management 40, 150-176
checking email on a set schedule
   172-174
creating rules 169, 170-176
email management 150, 153-155, 157,
   166-176
managing volume 169-172
no-interruption zones 156, 157, 182
response expectations 59, 60, 168, 174,
   175
Information overload 42, 151, 152, 153,
   154-157, 163, 164-176
Instant gratification 134, 159, 160
and impulse control 154, 160, 161, 162
and messaging 159, 160, 169, 175
Intentional activities 256, 260
Interruptions 9, 150, 151, 153-155, 157,
   159, 160
and attention 9, 151-177
and email 166-176
and IQ 153
and mistakes 151
and multitasking 164-166
and productivity 152, 153, 155, 156
eroding impulse control 136, 150-151,

160-163
no-interruption zones 156, 157, 182
working memory 9, 153, 154, 158, 165
Interruption management 27, 154, 155,
   156, 157-177
Intrinsic motivation 4, 29, 251-256, 264
   and attention 251, 254, 266
   and choice 264, 268
   and happiness 4, 237, 238, 250, 251,
      252, 256-264
   and resilience 253
   going for the experience 29, 265
   intrinsic goals 29, 252-256, 260
   life skills 263, 264
Iso-Ahola, Seppo 262

J

Jensen, Bill 61
Job-Demands Resources Model 69, 125
Job/work satisfaction 4, 8, 9, 19, 33, 34,
   38, 48, 50, 213, 214
Job/work stress 8, 9, 18, 19, 34, 44-46,
   50, 58, 68-71, 104-105, 116-119, 132,
   136, 137-138, 151, 155, 163, 164, 167,
   169, 194, 196-198, 205, 207, 227,
   233, 234-240
   cardiovascular disease 96, 207
   coronary artery disease 44, 138, 181,
      189
   diabetes 19, 74, 92, 99
   heart attack 44, 50, 98, 132, 138, 189,
      207
   high blood pressure 45, 74, 96 105, 138
   hypertension 46, 47, 74
   stroke 8, 98, 99
   time urgency 132-142
Justice, Michael 214

K

Kabat-Zinn, Jon 111, 112, 251
Kahneman, Daniel 3, 135, 186
   System 1 and 2 thinking 11, 135, 136,
      163, 205
Karasek, Robert 68, 69

Demand-Control Model 69, 124
Killingworth, Matthew 77
Kivimaki, Mika 8, 98
Kleitman, Nathaniel 229

L

Learned helplessness 188, 191
Leaving work at work 234-239
Lee, Lewina 186
LEGO 44
Leisure activities 4, 29, 57, 114, 115, 128,
   180, 249, 250, 257, 261, 263, 264,
   270
Leisure skills 263-265
Leiter, Michael 122
Life adjustments for balance 28, 29, 39
Life Assurance 276
Life Balance Sheet 21, 275
Life satisfaction 4, 20, 26-27, 33, 48,
   49, 248-249, 250, 253, 256, 257-261,
   263-273
Life skills 4, 5, 20, 29, 250, 253-256,
   263-265
   and intrinsic motivation 29, 253-256,
      260, 264
   going for the experience 256-259
Long work hours 7, 8, 17, 36, 40, 44, 45,
   46, 50, 116, 119, 123
   and depression 46
   and productivity 40, 45, 46, 50, 98
   and stress 8, 28, 40, 41, 44, 45, 46, 50,
      98, 116-129
   coronary artery disease 44
   coronary heart disease 46
   death 44
   fatigue 40, 41, 44, 45, 116-129, 226-
      229, 234-236, 239
   heart attack 44, 45
   hypertension 45, 46
Lytle, Richard 72
Lyubomirsky, Sonja 4, 213, 214, 215, 256,
   257
   intentional activities 256
   positive affect 213, 215

Positive-Activity Model 256, 257
sustainable happiness 260

M

Mark, Gloria 153, 154, 167, 173
email batching 173
email and stress 167
interruptions 155
task-switching 154, 155
Maslach, Christina 118, 122
burnout 118
burnout triggers 122
Maslow, Abraham 253
Mastery activities 29, 57, 115, 238, 239,
252, 253, 258-265, 270-273
Mental health 3, 10, 11, 19, 34, 50-52, 66,
75-87, 103-106, 116-129, 150, 167,
184-187, 188-200, 209-212, 229-239,
256-264
Meyer, David 9, 164, 165, 166
Mind 2, 3, 10, 11, 13, 19, 26, 49-52, 66,
69-70, 75-78, 79-87, 97, 102-104,
105-113, 116-120, 135-136, 138-141,
147-148, 153, 163, 187-208, 216-218,
220, 224, 226-239, 243-245, 249-274
and attention 3, 9, 19, 78, 79, 103,
104, 159-164, 177-180
and burnout 116-129
and catastrophic thoughts 67, 82-87,
191
and overwork 40, 41, 45, 46, 117, 118,
119, 121
and stress 19, 66, 75-87, 103, 104, 105,
116-229, 184-208, 210-213, 216-218
managing thoughts 68-70, 72-75, 76-
78, 79, 81-87, 91, 96, 105-113, 130,
131, 187-208
recharging of 225-233
self-awareness 3, 78, 82, 83, 111, 112,
134, 158-160
thinking traps 200-208
Mind-wandering 77
Mindfulness 111, 112, 152, 154
Mirror neurons 89, 214

Mood 91, 115, 214, 215, 222-224, 246, 261
Moser, Jason 187
Motivation 4, 20, 69, 221, 250-253, 260
autonomy support 69
external motivation 252, 254
intrinsic motivation 29, 252-256, 264
self-determination theory 250, 251
Multitasking 9, 54, 152, 164-166
and attention 158, 159, 165
and productivity 152
neural channels 164
the myth of 164

N

Nash, Laura 48
Negative emotions 3, 8, 50, 91, 108, 115,
120, 128, 185, 196, 209-213, 216-217,
223, 234
Neulinger, John 272
Newman, Michelle 72
Nolen-Hoeksema, Susan 86

O

Optimal experience 2, 237, 244, 258, 259
and flow 253, 257-259
Optimism 5, 184-209, 214, 215
and cardiovascular disease 184
and coronary deaths 185
and health 184
and positive emotions 196
and resilience 185-187, 193, 196
increasing daily optimism 199, 200
optimistic explanatory style 188-189,
194-195, 196-198, 201, 202
Overload 6, 7, 17, 23, 28, 40, 44-46, 80,
116-119, 122, 123, 142, 144, 145, 151-
153, 155, 156, 163-165, 166-176
Overwhelm 4, 10, 25, 39, 40, 42, 163,
169
Overwork 28, 49, 50, 51, 98, 99, 116-121,
124-128 155, 156, 163-165, 166-176
burnout 116-129
productivity of 45, 46, 50

P

Parasympathetic nervous system 3, 15, 75, 226
Parker, Sophie 25
Patience 147, 148
Pelow, Leslie 156
Pencavel, John 45
Pessimism 50, 72, 120, 185-191, 193, 196-198, 234-235
  and depression 188, 189, 191
  and negative emotions 50, 185, 190-194, 209, 210, 213
  and rumination 185, 190, 211
Pincus, Aaron 72
Pipkins, Darren 229
Play 240, 246-247, 252, 255, 262-263, 268-275
  hobbies 29, 57, 115, 128, 180, 233, 238, 239, 255-263, 270-272
  intrinsic experience 255, 260, 268
  Rules of Recess 269
Positive affect 213, 214, 215, 222, 231
Positive emotions 3, 23, 50, 108, 115, 116, 120, 125, 128, 180, 196, 199, 209-220, 232, 234, 236, 237, 260, 261
  and attention 210, 211
  and health 184, 185, 209, 211, 214, 218, 223
  and mood 209, 211, 213-215
  and performance 210, 212-214
  and resilience 209, 210
  and stress reduction 116, 218, 233, 240, 242-244
  and success 210, 213, 214
  list of 216-218
  positivity ratio 211, 212
  the undo effect 116, 218
Productivity 2, 4, 7, 8, 9, 44-46, 48, 50, 54, 63, 103, 104, 124, 127, 132, 134, 136, 142, 152-157, 163, 164, 167, 170, 173, 174, 179-183, 212-214, 228, 229, 230, 232, 242
  and attention 7, 103, 104, 134, 136, 152-154, 156, 163, 164, 167, 178, 199, 229

  and burnout 2, 40, 41, 44-46, 50, 117, 119, 124
  and long hours 44-46, 50, 98, 116-121
  and stress 8, 9, 44-46, 50, 98, 103, 104, 127, 134, 136, 140, 152, 156, 157, 163, 164, 167, 178, 228-233, 234-239, 242-243
Progressive relaxation 109, 110

Q

Quiet Time 156, 157

R

Recharging 9, 12, 13, 28, 57, 115, 226, 227, 229, 234, 237, 238, 242-244, 256-260
  hobbies 15, 29, 57, 115, 180, 233, 238, 239, 256-259, 260-263, 270-273
  increasing positive mood 29, 115, 237, 240
  mastery activities 115, 234, 237-239
  relaxation strategies 109-114, 234-238, 239
  the Refueling Principle 12, 225, 240
  vacations 34, 37, 240-246
Recreation 13, 237, 238, 240, 242-244, 256-260, 262, 270, 271
  and autonomy 69, 243, 250, 253
  and competence 69, 236, 238, 243, 250, 264
  and stress reduction 29, 115, 240, 242, 243
Red Zone 43
Reflex reactions 1, 2, 3, 11, 27, 67, 106, 152, 187-208, 190, 194, 201, 210, 211
Regrets 22, 23, 253, 260
Reivich, Karen 85, 87, 107
  catastrophic thoughts 84-87, 107
Relaxation response 110, 111
Relaxation strategies 108-116, 132, 231, 232, 237-239, 241-244, 252, 257-259, 263-265
Remote work 35, 36, 56, 57
Resilience 5, 185-187, 193, 195, 200-208

and optimism 185, 186, 187, 211
and positive emotions 210-212
bouncing back 209-211
reframing negative events 201-208
resilience strategies 76, 79, 87, 107,
    108, 195-198, 201-208
Rigid mind 3, 27, 201, 203, 204
Rosekind, Mark 242
Rumination 71, 72, 74, 77, 86, 99, 115,
    120, 185, 204, 223, 234
Ruthsatz, Judith 177
Ryan, Richard 250, 253

S

Samba 265-267
Sanchez, Jose 25
Sanchez, Oz 192
Sanger, Jessica 103
Sapolsky, Robert 101
Savage, Mandara 229
Schor, Juliet 45
Secondhand stress 88-91
Self-awareness 78, 81-83, 110-112
Self-control 9, 136, 151, 159, 160, 163
    and digital devices 160, 161, 162, 167
    impulse control 9, 136, 150, 151, 159,
        160, 163
Self-talk 81, 83, 84, 140, 185-208
    and explanatory style 186, 187
    and false beliefs 81-83, 84-87, 108,
        201-208
Self-worth 4, 49, 141, 252, 254
Seligman, Martin 188, 191, 221, 262
    character strengths 221, 222
    explanatory style 185, 187, 188
Shatte, Andrew 87
Sheldon Kennon 4, 256, 257, 260
    intentional activities 256, 257
    sustainable happiness 260
Shepard, Edward 33
Shorter workweek 46, 47
Smartphones 160, 161, 166, 167, 168
    and attention 159-163
    and impulse control 160, 161

and loneliness 162
and stress 166, 167, 168
Sonnentag, Sabine 235, 239, 240, 243
Stress 6, 8, 9, 10, 12, 15, 18, 23-25, 26,
    28, 34, 41, 44-46, 55, 61-94, 95-131,
    132, 133, 136, 142, 151, 154, 155, 164,
    165, 167, 173, 184, 185, 189, 202, 210,
    227, 234, 242
and boundaries 23, 39, 42, 44, 45, 46,
    70
and burnout 70, 74, 116-123, 124-128
and high blood pressure 45, 74, 93,
    96, 105, 120, 138, 184
and long hours 8, 28, 44-46, 50, 117-
    119, 227
and productivity 9, 44-46, 50, 98,
    103, 104, 123, 134, 136, 140, 142, 152,
    155, 156, 163, 164, 167, 178
and sleep 101, 102, 227
amygdala 65-67, 69, 73, 75, 80
Demand-Control Model 69, 125
false beliefs from 75-80, 81-87, 106,
    107
fight-or-flight response 65-68, 71, 74,
    105
identifying stressors 71
Job Demands-Resources Model 69,
    125
rumination 71, 72, 74, 77, 86, 99, 115,
    120, 185, 204, 223, 234
Stress, impact on body 8, 19, 44-46, 50,
    58, 69, 74, 75, 92, 93, 95-121, 132,
    135, 138, 184, 185, 189, 201, 207, 228,
    229
cardiovascular disease 96, 138, 184, 185,
    207
chronic stress 2, 44-46, 58, 69, 74, 75,
    95-104, 116-129, 135
coronary heart disease 8, 19, 92, 96,
    116, 121, 132, 184
diabetes 19, 74, 92, 98, 99
digestion 74, 99
heart attack 44, 50, 74, 98, 132, 138,
    189, 201

high blood pressure 45, 74, 93, 96,
    105, 120, 138, 184
immune function 74, 100, 101
insomnia 101, 102
stroke 8, 98, 99
symptoms 100
Stress, impact on mind 66, 67, 77, 82,
    83, 84-87, 103, 104, 105-108, 116-121,
    187-198, 200-208, 235, 239, 240, 243
    and aggression 104, 133, 138, 155
    and anger 67, 104, 138, 155
    and decision-making 66, 103, 134-136
    and discipline 103, 104, 159, 160
    and sleep 101, 102
    amygdala hijack 67
    impulsive behavior 103, 104, 159, 160,
    163
Stress reduction exercises 72, 73, 76, 79,
    102, 106-109, 110-113, 114, 115, 116,
    130, 131, 218
    ABC Model 106-109, 130
    attitude breathing 79, 130
    challenging catastrophic thoughts
    84-87, 130
    deliberate breathing 72, 73, 130
    exercise and recreation 114, 115
    meditation 110-113
    mindfulness 111-113, 131
    positive emotions, 115, 218
    progressive muscle relaxation 111
    the reality response 76, 108, 109, 130
    the relaxation response 110, 111, 131
    the stress audit 102, 130
    the undo effect 116, 218
Stress response 9, 66, 69, 73, 74, 78, 80,
    95, 99, 100, 103, 114, 132, 138, 242
    activation phase 75
    adrenaline 75
    amygdala 65-67, 69, 73, 75, 80
    cortisol 93, 95, 100, 101, 103, 104, 185
    glucocorticoids 75, 100, 101
Stress symptoms 71, 74, 99-102, 121
Stress tests 92
Sustainable happiness 260

Sustainable performance 2, 3, 4, 9, 10 13,
    33, 59, 60, 69, 142, 147, 233
System 1 thinking 135, 136, 163, 205
System 2 thinking 135, 136

T
Taking things personally 189, 193, 194,
    197
    challenging ego 90, 139, 149
Technology addiction 151, 160
Thinking traps 3, 200-208
Thought labeling 82, 83
Thoughts 2, 9, 11, 18, 22, 28, 29, 33, 75-
    87, 97, 106, 111, 112, 156, 157, 160,
    161, 185-207, 218, 234-236, 257
    and anxiety 66, 67, 72, 77, 82, 83, 84-
    87, 200-208, 234, 247
    and false beliefs 2, 13, 64, 65, 76, 82,
    ·   83, 84-87, 106-108, 140, 157, 187-
    189, 200-208, 234, 235, 236
    and rumination 71, 72, 74, 86, 99, 115,
    120, 204, 223, 234
    and stress 66, 67, 71-87, 97, 98, 103,
    104, 105-113, 118, 185-208, 210, 218
    catastrophic 84-87
    predicting 77, 84-87
Time management 141-147
    and email 153, 163-176
    and prioritization 146
Time urgency 23, 132-149, 244
    and anger 132, 138
    and decision-making 135, 136
    and false urgency 141, 148
    and heart attacks 132, 138
    and impatience 137-140, 148, 149
    and impulsive behavior 133, 135, 136
    and irritability 132, 137, 138, 139
    and mistakes 133
    and productivity 132, 134
    and rushing 134, 135, 141
    and work-life balance 133, 138
    busyness 140, 141
    the speed trap 134, 141
    traits of 137

Travel 240-245, 258, 259, 260, 265
 and autonomy 243, 259, 250
 and flow 258, 259, 260
Twenge, Jean 162

U

Ultradian rhythm 223, 226-229
Urbach, Jourdan 177

V

Vacations 13, 36, 37, 128, 240-246, 249,
 257-260
Van Boven, Leaf 257

W

Ware, Bronnie 22
Waterman, Alan 272
Weinberg, Richard 272
Wellness 19, 33, 34, 38, 229, 243
Willpower 9, 150, 151, 160, 228
Wilmer, Henry 160
Work adjustments for balance 26-28
Workaholism 23, 49, 50, 51, 52, 98
 and heart attacks 44, 50, 98
 and negative emotions 50, 98
 and performance 50, 98
 and stress 45, 50, 98
Work ethic 5, 6, 49, 117, 253
Work-health balance 10, 19, 239
Working memory 8, 39, 151-154, 158, 165,
 177, 181

and attention 153, 154, 158
and interruptions 9, 154, 155, 165
Worth ethic 18, 243, 253
Work-life balance 3, 4, 5, 8, 10, 13, 15, 16,
 17, 20, 21, 24, 25, 26-31, 32, 34, 40,
 42, 43, 46, 47, 51, 52, 54-55, 59, 78,
 128, 133, 139, 146, 151, 155, 156, 166-
 168, 174-175, 185, 199-200, 234-243,
 275-276
 and commitment 33, 34
 and engagement 33, 34
 and family 17, 18, 19, 20, 29, 34, 35
 and friendship 22, 240, 252
 and job satisfaction 9, 19, 33
 and increased profitability 34, 35
 and productivity 10, 30, 33, 34
 identifying work-life targets 20, 22
 negotiating for 37, 38
 work-life balance policies 36
Work-life conflict 10, 18, 27, 33, 34
Work recovery 12, 28, 115, 230-239
 breaks during the workday 231, 232
 detachment from demands at night
 235, 237, 238
 strategies of work recovery 237
Work style 1, 3, 13, 26, 30, 41, 42, 61,
 69, 125

Z

Zawadski, Matthew 115, 249, 250

About the Author

Work-life balance and stress management leader Joe Robinson is one of the country's most quoted experts on the art and science of effective work. He has appeared on *Today*, CNN, *All Things Considered* and in *Time*, *Fortune*, the *Los Angeles Times*, and dozens of other media outlets to discuss how to work smarter, break out of the burnout cycle, and refuel brains and bodies.

His commentaries on the workplace have been featured on the public radio program, *Marketplace*. His articles have appeared in *Entrepreneur*, *Fast Company*, the *New York Times*, the *Los Angeles Times*, CNN.com and in many other outlets on a range of issues, from work-life balance to switching off stress to travel and activating the fullest life.

As a keynote speaker and trainer, Joe has led conferences and workshop programs for organizations from IBM to Ocean Spray, Kellogg's, Nestle, Amazon, Siemens, Imagine Entertainment, Pfizer, Anheuser-Busch, LEGO, the Reserve Bank of India, the National Council for Mental Wellbeing, the University of Texas Medical Branch and many more.

He coaches individuals around the country and world on how to manage stress and the mind that creates it, recover from burnout, build optimism and resilience, and live the most gratifying life.

Joe is author of *Work to Live*, and on the other side of the work-life hyphen, *Don't Miss Your Life*, which shows through the science how to put active leisure experiences and intrinsic goals on the calendar.

Based in Los Angeles, Joe is an avid photographer, hiker, salsa and samba aficionado, adventure traveler and music fan. You can connect with him at www.worktolive.info.

Made in the USA
Middletown, DE
06 May 2022

65361727R00179